▶ **David Baker**
The Anthony Gell School, Wirksworth

▶ **Jim Griffith**
The Bishop of Hereford's Bluecoat School, Hereford

▶ **Paul Hogan**
St. Wilfrid's Church of England High School, Blackburn

▶ **Chris Humble**
Gillotts School, Henley-on-Thames

▶ **Barbara Job**
Christleton County High School, Chester

▶ **Peter Sherran**
Weston Road High School, Stafford

Series Editor: **Paul Hogan**

ÐloÞ

First published in 1998 by
Stanley Thornes (Publishers) Ltd
Second edition published in 2001 by
Nelson Thornes Ltd
Delta Place
27 Bath Road
CHELTENHAM
GL53 7TH
United Kingdom

02 03 04 05 / 10 9 8 7 6 5 4

A catalogue record for this book is available from the British Library.

ISBN 0-7487-6204-3

Illustrations by Maltings Partnership, Peters and Zabransky, Oxford Illustrators, Clinton Banbury
Page make-up by Tech Set Ltd

Printed and bound in China by Midas Printing International Ltd

Acknowledgements
The publishers thank the following for permission to reproduce copyright material:
Britstock-IFA: 235 (Walsh), 246 (Walsh); Colorsport: 183 (top), 193; Getty Images: 1 (Tony Stone Images/Will and Deni McIntyre), 17 (left – Will and Deni McIntyre); Image Bank: 137 (Colin Molyneux), 311 (Pete Turner); Martyn Chillmaid: 41, 42, 77, 78, 120, 121, 141, 144, 152, 159, 221, 322, 327, 360, 373 (top left); Rex Features: 204 (Charles Ommanney), 342 (Michael Dunn), 361 (Roy Garner); Science Photolibrary: 17 (right – John Sanford); Skyscan Balloon Photography: 25, 39, 359, 373 (top right – Skyscan/Unichrome (Batti) Ltd); Sporting Pictures: 183 (bottom), 205; Stockmarket: 337, 338, 340; Sue Sharp: 217; Topham Picturepoint: 202 (bottom – Associated Press), 215 (Press Association), 223 (Press Association); All other photographs Nelson Thornes Archive.

The publishers have made every effort to contact copyright holders but apologise if any have been overlooked.

Contents

1 Transformations

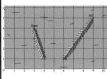

1 Co-ordinates
Using co-ordinates to locate a point
Finding equations of horizontal and vertical
lines

2 Single transformations
Describing translations
Drawing reflections
Drawing rotations
Drawing enlargements

CORE

3 Combined transformations
Showing the effect of two successive
transformations
Replacing two transformations by a single
transformation

QUESTIONS

EXTENSION

TEST YOURSELF

1 Co-ordinates

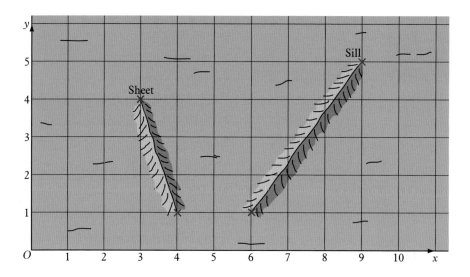

The diagram shows some features found on the surface of the Earth.

Wasim is studying geology.
He has to write a report on what can be seen in the diagrams.
He needs to describe the position of special features in his report.

He decides to use co-ordinates to do this.

This is part of his report:

'I will use co-ordinates to identify features on the diagrams.
The first number is the x co-ordinate. It gives the **horizontal** distance.
The second number is the y co-ordinate. It gives the **vertical** distance.

Both the sheet and the sill are bodies of rock.
The sheet starts at (3, 4) and stops at (4, 1).
The sill starts at (6, 1) and stops at (9, 5).'

Exercise 1:1

1 This is a page of another report.
There are some mistakes with the co-ordinates.
a Write down the features that have the wrong co-ordinates.
b Write down the correct co-ordinates for these features.

'The diagram shows part of the ocean bed.'

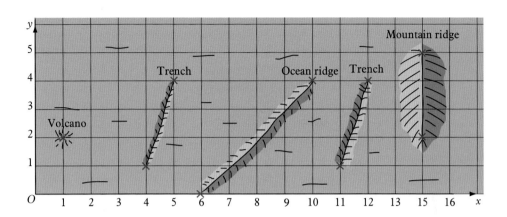

'The left-hand trench goes from (4, 0) to (5, 4).
The right-hand trench goes from (1, 11) to (12, 7).
The ridge of mountains goes from (15, 2) to (15, 5).
The ocean ridge goes from (7, 1) to (4, 10).
There is a volcano at (7, 2).'

2 Use the diagram to write down the co-ordinates of each of these:

a left-hand tuft
b right-hand tuft
c country rock
d crater sediment
e top of blind intrusion
f base of dyke

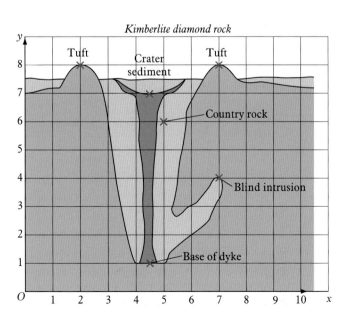

The picture shows the cross section of a mine.

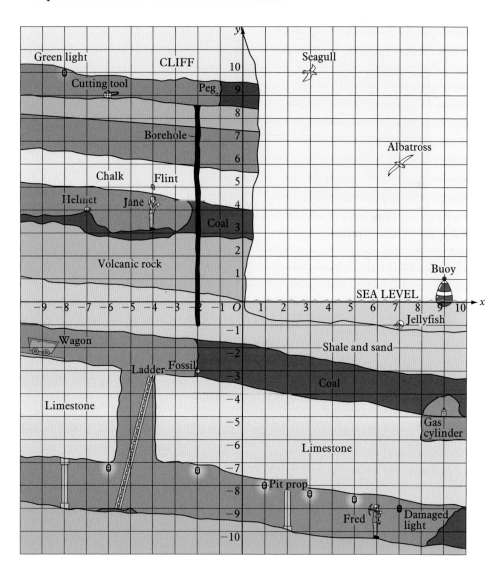

3   What is at each of these co-ordinates?
    a (9, 1)   **d** (−4, 4)   **g** (−4, −3)
    b (3, 10)   **e** (2, −8)   **h** (−9, −2)
    c (−1, 9)   **f** (6, −9)   **i** (7, −9)

4   Write down the co-ordinates of each of these:
    a albatross   **d** green light   **g** jelly fish
    b cutting tool   **e** gas cylinder   **h** flint
    c helmet   **f** fossil

Wasim wants to describe the position of the layers (strata) in the diagram.

These points all lie on the black line:
(0, 10)   (1, 10)   (2, 10),   (5, 10)
The y co-ordinate is always 10.
This tells you that the equation of the line is $y = 10$.

This is what Wasim has written:

'The wall rock lies between 2 lines.
Both lines are horizontal.
The top horizontal line crosses the y axis at 10. This line is called $y = 10$.
The bottom horizontal line crosses the y axis at 9.
This line is called $y = 9$.
The wall rock lies between $y = 10$ and $y = 9$.'

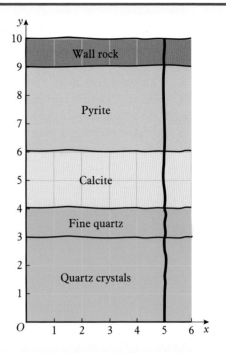

Exercise 1:2

1   Write down the equation of the line between:
   a   calcite and pyrite
   b   fine quartz and calcite
   c   quartz crystals and fine quartz

2   Each unit of the grid represents 1 m.
   Write down the thickness of each layer (stratum).

3   There is a vertical crack in the diagram.
   a   Write down the co-ordinates of 5 points on this crack.
   b   What do you notice about the x co-ordinates of these points?
   c   Copy and fill in:
      The crack lies on a vertical line.
      The equation of this line is $x = ...$

4   These lines have been drawn on a set of axes.

   Write down the equation of each line.

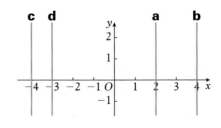

5 The diagram shows the strata under the sea bed.

Write down the equation of the line between:
a sediments and lavas
b primitive mantle and mantle
c lavas and layer of dykes
d gabbroic rocks and mantle

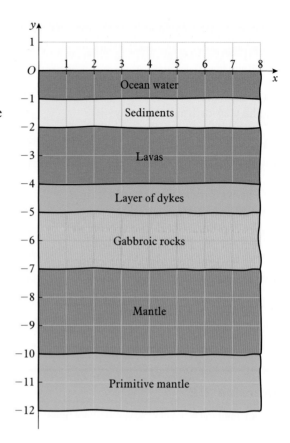

6 These lines have been drawn on a set of axes.
Write down the equation of each line.

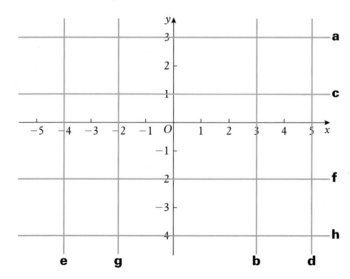

2 Single transformations

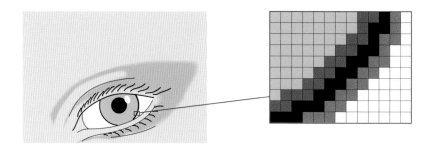

Pictures shown on a computer screen are made up of tiny squares.
Each tiny square is called a **pixel**. Storage of pictures based on single
pixels can use too much memory.
Patterns of pixels are often repeated in a picture.
Details of how these patterns relate to each other are stored as
transformations. This saves memory.

Transformation   A transformation can change the size, shape or position of an
object.

Translation   A **translation** is a movement in a straight line.

The movement shown is a
translation of 3 places to the
right and 2 places down.

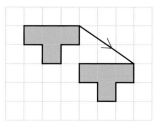

The arrow represents the
movement.

The translation can be written as $\begin{pmatrix} 3 \\ -2 \end{pmatrix}$

This is called a **column vector**.

The sign of each number in a
column vector gives the *direction*
of movement.
This matches the way that axes
are labelled.

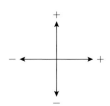

Exercise 1:3

1 Copy and fill in the column vectors for these translations.

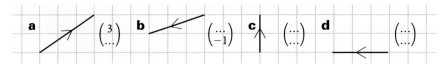

2 Use column vectors to describe these translations.

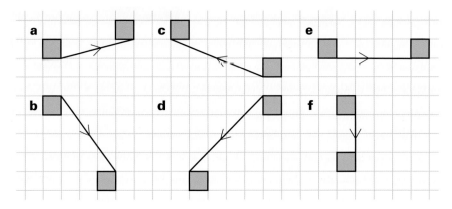

You can describe the translations of single points in the same way as translations of shapes.

---

3 Give the translations from **P** to each of the other points in turn.
Use column vectors.

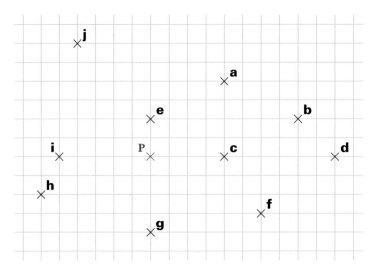

Inverse	A transformation that *undoes* the effect of another is called its **inverse**.

The inverse of 'move 5 places up' is 'move 5 places down'.

The inverse of $\begin{pmatrix} 2 \\ -1 \end{pmatrix}$ is $\begin{pmatrix} -2 \\ 1 \end{pmatrix}$

4 Write down the inverse of each of these.
- **a** 3 places right
- **b** 2 places down
- **c** 4 places left
- **d** 1 place up
- **e** 2 places right and 3 places down
- **f** 3 miles north
- **g** 6.1 miles south
- **h** 0.8 km east
- **i** 5 miles north east
- **j** 5 km west and 3 km north

5 These column vectors represent translations.
Write down the column vector of the inverse of each one.

a $\begin{pmatrix} 4 \\ 1 \end{pmatrix}$ **c** $\begin{pmatrix} 3 \\ -1 \end{pmatrix}$ **e** $\begin{pmatrix} -5 \\ 0 \end{pmatrix}$

b $\begin{pmatrix} -5 \\ 2 \end{pmatrix}$ **d** $\begin{pmatrix} -6 \\ -4 \end{pmatrix}$ **f** $\begin{pmatrix} 0 \\ 7 \end{pmatrix}$

6 In Logo, instructions are given to control the movement of the **turtle**.

Instruction	Meaning
fd 50	move forward 50 units
bk 30	move back 30 units
rt 90	turn to the right through 90°
lt 60	turn to the left through 60°

Write down the inverse of each of the following Logo instructions.
- **a** fd 60
- **b** rt 20
- **c** bk 350
- **d** lt 125

Object	The shape you start with is called the **object**.
Image	The transformed shape is called the **image**.
Reflection	The diagram shows the image of the object pattern after **reflection** in the line AB.

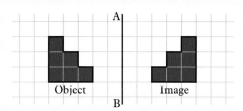

Exercise 1:4

1　**a**　Copy the diagram. Reflect shape A in the line PQ.
Label the image B.
　　b　Reflect shape A in the line RS. Label the image C.

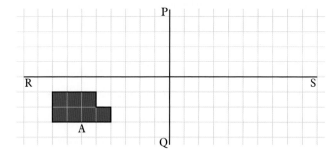

2　Copy the diagram. Reflect the labelled points in the line $y = 1$.
Label the image of point A as A′, the image of B as B′ and so on.

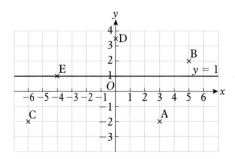

3 **a** Draw x and y axes labelled from -3 to 3.
 b Plot the points A(2, 3), B(-1, -1) and C(3, -2). Draw triangle ABC.
 c Reflect triangle ABC in the line $x = 1$. Label the image A′B′C′.

The image of (2, 1) after reflection in the line $x = 4$ is (6, 1).
You can write this as (2, 1) → (6, 1) or (2, 1) **maps to** (6, 1).

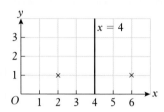

The same reflection maps (6, 1) to (2, 1).

**Inverse of a
reflection**

A second reflection, in the same line, always undoes the effect of
the first. The **inverse of a reflection** is the same reflection.

Mirror line

The line that you use to reflect an object is called the
mirror line.

---

4 Melissa is exploring the effect of repeating reflections in the same
mirror line.

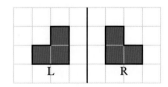

She finds that:
 The image of L after one reflection is R.
 The image of L after two reflections is L.

Write down the image of L when the number of reflections is:
 a 5 **b** 18 **c** 47 **d** even **e** odd
 f a prime number that is bigger than 2

Rotation

A **rotation** turns a shape about a fixed point. This point is called the **centre of rotation**.

When you describe a rotation you must give these three things:
(1) the angle
(2) the direction (clockwise or anticlockwise)
(3) the centre.

In the diagram, A is mapped on to B by a rotation of **90° clockwise** with centre (0, 0)

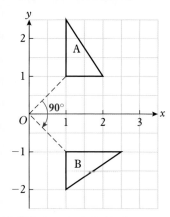

Exercise 1:5

1 You are going to draw the image of C after a rotation of 90° clockwise about (0, 0).

a Copy the diagram.

b Place a piece of tracing paper on the diagram. Trace the shape C and the red cross at the origin.

c Put the point of your pencil on the origin to hold the tracing paper firmly in place.

d Turn the tracing paper through 90° clockwise. Use the cross at the origin to help you.

e Copy the new position of C on to your axes.
This is the image of C after a rotation of 90° clockwise about (0, 0).
Label it D.

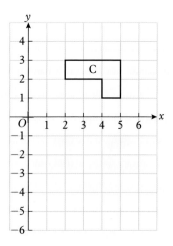

2 a Copy the diagram.
b Draw the image of F after a rotation of 90° anticlockwise about (2, 2).
Label the image G.
c Rotate G through 180° clockwise about (2, 2).
Label the image H.
d What is the single clockwise rotation that would map F on to H?

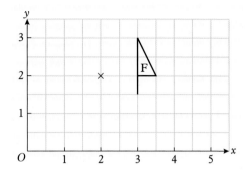

3 Describe these rotations. Remember to give the angle, the direction and the centre.
a P on to Q
b Q on to R
c P on to R
d Q on to S
e S on to Q
f R on to P

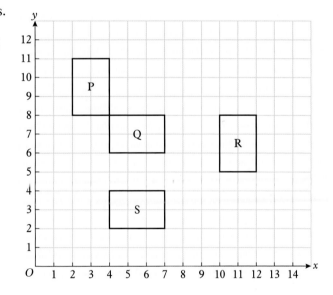

4 The diagram shows a regular hexagon ABCDEF with centre at O.
a Find the smallest angle of rotation about O so that A → B.
b What is the order of rotational symmetry of a regular hexagon?

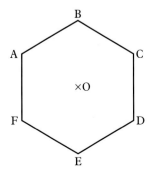

| Inverse of a rotation | The **inverse of a rotation** is also a rotation. The angle and the centre are the same but the turn is in the opposite direction. |

Example The inverse of a rotation of 60° **clockwise** about (5, 7) is a rotation of 60° **anticlockwise** about (5, 7).

5 Write down the inverse of each of these:
  a 90° clockwise about (8, 1)
  b 27° anticlockwise about (−3, 5)
  c 48° anticlockwise about (−7, −10)
  d 123° clockwise about (11, −6)

6 **a** Copy the diagram. Rotate P through 90° clockwise about (3, 3).
        Label the image Q.
     b Rotate Q through 90° anticlockwise about (5, 3). Label the image R.
     c Describe the single transformation that would map P on to R.

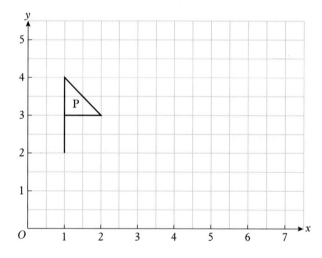

| Enlargement | An **enlargement** changes the size of an object.
When you describe an enlargement you must give these two things:
(1)   the centre
(2)   the scale factor |

Example	Enlarge triangle ABC with scale factor 2 and centre O.
	
	(1) Join OA and extend.
	
	(2) Measure OA.
	
	(3) OA' = OA × 2
	     = 3 cm
	
	(4) Measure 3 cm from O.
	    Label this point A'.
	
	(5) Do the same for point B.
	
	(6) Do the same for point C.
	
	(7) Draw the triangle A'B'C'.

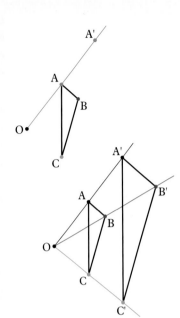

Triangle A'B'C' is an enlargement of triangle ABC.
A and A', B and B' and C and C 'are pairs of corresponding points.

Centre of enlargement	Lines drawn through corresponding points pass through the **centre of enlargement**.
Scale factor	The **scale factor** tells you how many times bigger the enlargement is. You multiply an object length by the scale factor to get the corresponding image length. So A'B' = AB × 2

Exercise 1:6

1 **a** Measure the lengths of PQ and P'Q'.
     b Use your answers to find the scale factor of the enlargement.

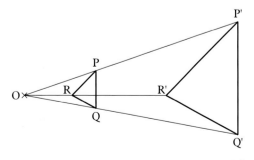

2 Jim has started to enlarge the rectangle with centre at O.
Find the scale factor of the enlargement.

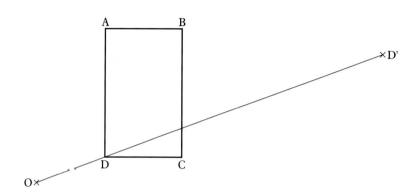

For enlargements with centre at the origin:
co-ordinates of object × scale factor = co-ordinates of image

Example   Find the image of P(3, 1) under an enlargement with scale
factor 3, centre at the origin.

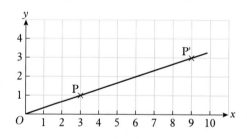

The image of P(3, 1) is P'(9, 3).
The co-ordinates of P have been multiplied by 3.

3 Find the image of these points under an enlargement with scale factor 4
and centre at the origin.
  a (3, 2)   **e** (0, −6)
  b (1, 7)   **f** (−3, −5)
  c (2, −3)   **g** (2.5, 3)
  d (−3, 0)   **h** (−3.5, 1.25)

3 Combined transformations

The three Great Pyramids do not lie in a straight line.
If you draw the position of the three stars in Orion's belt, then enlarge
and rotate the diagram, it will fit exactly over the positions of the Great
Pyramids.

Combination of transformations

You can often describe a movement by a **combination of transformations**.

Shape A is moved to B by a combination of two transformations.

The first transformation is a **translation** 5 units across and 4 units up.
The second transformation is a **rotation** 90° clockwise, about the point O.

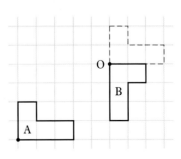

Exercise 1:7

1 These shapes have been moved by a translation followed by a rotation.

For shape S:
  a Write down the translation that moves the point A to A′.
  b Write down the rotation that has been used.

For shape T:
  c Write down the translation that moves the point B to B′.
  d Write down the rotation that has been used.

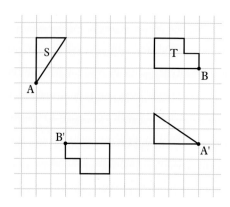

2 The shape T is moved by a translation followed by a rotation to shape B.
Point P is translated to P′.
Write down:
  a the translation
  b the rotation

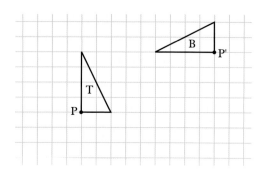

3 Part of a picture has been enlarged to give this pattern of pixels.
A block of 4 pixels appears in the corner at the origin.
You can transform this block to make the patterns at A, B and C.
  a Give the translation for A.
  b Give the rotation for B.
  c Give the translation, to combine with a rotation of 180°, centre (1, 1) for B.
  d Give the reflection for C.
  e Give the translation to combine with reflection in $y = 2$ for C.
  f Give the rotation to map A to C.
  g B is given a translation $\begin{pmatrix} 0 \\ -4 \end{pmatrix}$

  Give the rotation so that the image maps to A.

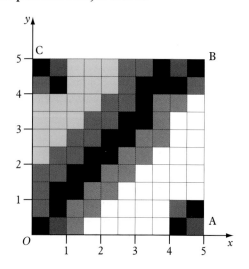

Sometimes a combination of transformations can be replaced by a single transformation.

Shape A is reflected in the *y* axis to give the image B.

Shape B is rotated 180° anticlockwise about the origin to give the image C.

There is a single transformation that maps shape A onto shape C. The transformation is a reflection in the *x* axis.

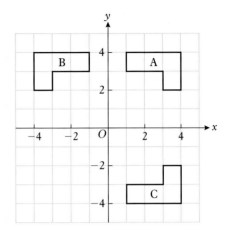

Exercise 1:8

1 a Copy the axes and the shape A onto squared paper.
   b Reflect A in the *x* axis. Label the image B.
   c Reflect B in the *y* axis. Label the image C.
   d Write down the single transformation that maps A to C.

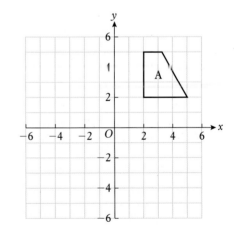

2 a Draw another set of axes like those in question **1**.
   b Draw the triangle with the vertices $(-4, 2)$, $(-2, 2)$ and $(-4, 6)$. Label the triangle P.
   c Rotate triangle P 180° clockwise about the origin. Label the image Q.
   d Reflect triangle Q in the *y* axis. Label the image R.
   e Write down the single transformation that maps triangle P to triangle R.

3　**a**　Copy the axes and triangle P on to squared paper.

　　b　Reflect triangle P in the y axis. Label the image Q.

　　c　Reflect triangle Q in the line $y = x$. Label the image R.

　　d　Write down the single transformation that maps triangle P to triangle R.

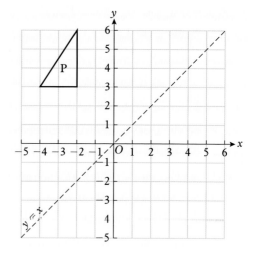

4　**a**　Draw a set of axes with x and y from -6 to 6. Draw the triangle with vertices $(2, 1)$, $(3, 1)$ and $(2, 4)$. Label this triangle A.

　　b　Use triangle A to check if the following statement is true:

A reflection in the x axis followed by a rotation of 90° anticlockwise about the origin	is the same as	a rotation of 90° anticlockwise about the origin followed by a reflection in the x axis.

5　**a**　Draw a set of axes and triangle A as in question **4**.

　　b　Use triangle A to check if the following statement is true:

A reflection in the x axis followed by a reflection in the y axis	is the same as	a reflection in the y axis followed by a reflection in the x axis.

6　Here are some Logo instructions. Write down the instructions that would return you to the starting point in each part.

　　a　fd 80

　　b　rt 45

　　c　fd 30　rt 60

　　d　fd 50　lt 30　fd 80

　　e　fd 50　rt 90　fd 50　rt 90　fd 50　rt 90

1 Write down the co-ordinates of each point.

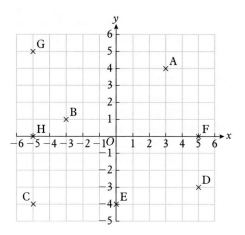

2 Write down the equation of each line.

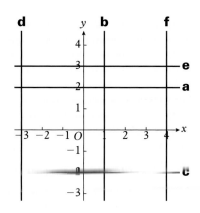

3 These arrows represent translations. Write down the column vectors for each one.

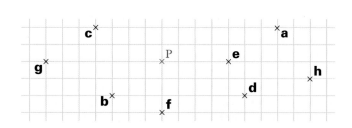

4 Give the translations from **P** to each of the other points.

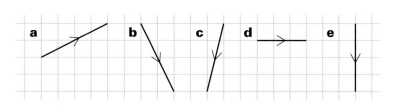

5 Reflect these shapes in the mirror lines.

a 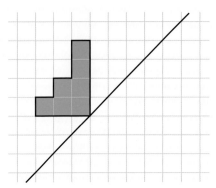   **b**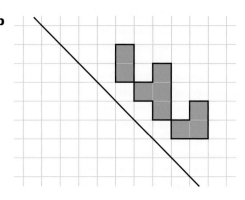

6 Which of these shapes cannot be mapped on to P by a rotation?

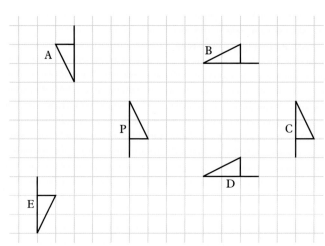

7 Each shape can be mapped on to L by a single transformation. Describe each transformation fully.

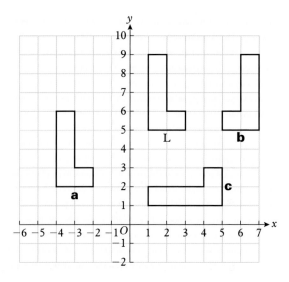

8 **a** The rectangle PQRS is reflected in the line $y = x$ to give rectangle P′Q′R′S′. What are the co-ordinates of S′?

  b The rectangle PQRS is enlarged with scale factor 2, centre the origin to give rectangle P″Q″R″S″. What are the co-ordinates of Q″?

  c The rectangle PQRS is rotated 90° clockwise about (0, 0) to give rectangle P‴Q‴R‴S‴. What are the co-ordinates of R‴?

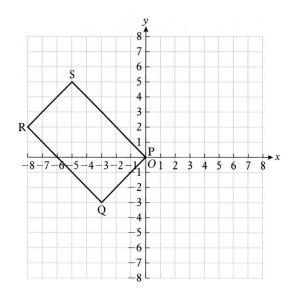

9 **a** Copy the axes and shape A.
  b Reflect shape A in the line $y = 4$. Label the shape B.
  c Rotate the shape A 180° clockwise about the origin. Label the shape C.
  d Reflect shape A in the x axis. Label the shape D.

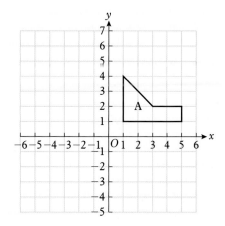

10 **a** Draw a set of axes on to squared paper. Use values of x and y from -8 to 8.
  b Plot the points $(1, -1)$, $(3, -1)$ and $(3, -4)$. Join them up with straight lines. Label the triangle P.
  c Reflect the triangle in the line $y = x$. Label this triangle Q.
  d Reflect triangle Q in the x axis. Label this triangle R.
  e Which single transformation maps triangle P onto triangle R?

1 **a** Copy the diagram.
   b Translate shape A 5 units
      to the left and 2 units up.
      Label the image B.
   c Reflect shape A in the
      line $y = -x$.
      Label the image C.
   d Rotate shape A through
      $450°$ clockwise about $(-1, -1)$.
      Label the image D.

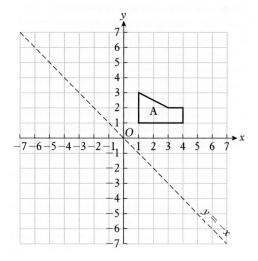

2 Describe the translation that maps $(3, 5)$ to the point:
   a $(6, 9)$ **b** $(3, 5)$ **c** $(0, -2)$ **d** $(-3, 6)$

3 **a** Draw a set of axes on to squared paper.
      Use values of x and y from -6 to 6.
   b Plot the points $(1, 0)$, $(0, 3)$ and $(3, 4)$.
      Join them up. Label the triangle A.
   c Reflect triangle A in the x axis. Label the image B.
   d Reflect triangle B in the line $y = x$. Label the image C.
   e Write down the single transformation that maps triangle A to
      triangle C.

4 **a** Draw a set of axes on to squared paper.
      Label the x and y axes from -8 to 8.
   b Draw the line $y = x$.
   c Reflect these points in $y = x$.
      A $(4, 5)$ C $(-3, 2)$ E $(-1, 0)$
      B $(2, 6)$ D $(0, -4)$ F $(-2, -1)$
      Label the image points A', B', etc.
   d Use your answers to part **c** to describe what happens to the
      co-ordinates of a point when it is reflected in the line $y = x$.
   e Investigate what happens to co-ordinates of points when they are
      reflected in:
      (1) $y = -x$ (3) $y = 1$ (5) $x = 2$
      (2) $y = 3$ (4) $x = 1$ (6) $x = 4$

1 a Write down the co-ordinates
of the points A, B, C and D.

  b Write down the equations
of the lines P, Q, R and S.

  c Write down the equation of
(1) the x axis
(2) the y axis.

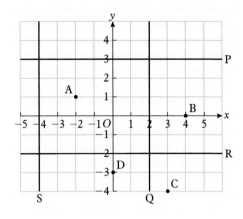

2 a Use words to describe this translation.

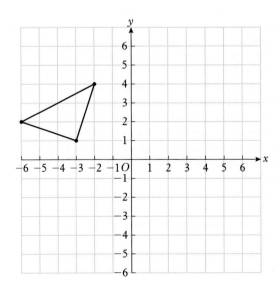

  b Draw a line to show the translation:

(1) $\begin{pmatrix} -3 \\ 4 \end{pmatrix}$ 　　　　　　(2) $\begin{pmatrix} 0 \\ -2 \end{pmatrix}$

3 a Copy the diagram.

  b Reflect the shape in the y axis. Label the new shape b.

  c Rotate the shape 90° anticlockwise about (0, 0). Label the new shape c.

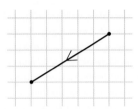

4 Write down the inverse of each of these:
   a a translation 3 squares up and 2 squares to the left

   b a translation of $\begin{pmatrix} 3 \\ -4 \end{pmatrix}$

   c a rotation of 270° clockwise about the point $(2, -3)$

5 **a** Copy the diagram.
   b Enlarge the triangle with
      scale factor 3, centre $(1, 2)$.

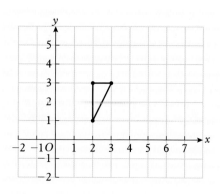

6 **a** Copy the diagram.
   b Reflect shape T in the y axis.
      Label the image B.
   c Rotate shape T 90° clockwise with centre the origin.
      Label the image C.
   d Write down the single transformation that maps B onto C.

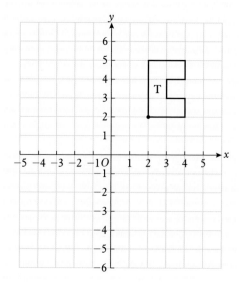

2 Numbers: approximating and rounding

1 Place value
Using place value up to thousands
Reading and writing whole numbers
Using place value up to millions
Putting numbers in order of size
Writing inequalities

2 Rounding
Rounding to the nearest 10
Rounding to the nearest 100
Rounding to the nearest 1000
Rounding to 1 significant figure
Rounding to any number of significant figures

CORE

3 Estimating and checking
Rounding to 1 sf to give an estimate
Solving problems and checking by estimating
Checking answers by working back
Estimating square roots
Estimating using cancelling

4 Fractions and decimals
Changing a fraction into a decimal
Changing a decimal into a fraction
Putting fractions and decimals in order of size
Multiplying and dividing by decimals

QUESTIONS

EXTENSION

TEST YOURSELF

1   Place value

It would be impossible to build a house without numbers!
You need to know how many bricks to use.
You need to know how many tiles to use.
You need to know how many metres of copper piping to use.
Then you need to work out the cost of everything.

Numbers help you to understand size.

Place value

Look at the number 234

It is made from the digits 2, 3 and 4.
You can make these numbers from the same digits:

234   243   324   342   423   432

They all have different values!

The order of the digits in a number is important.

Numbers can be written in columns.
The columns have names for their values.

Millions	Hundred Thousands	Ten Thousands	Thousands	Hundreds	Tens	Units
M	HTh	TTh	Th	H	T	U
				2	3	4

This number is 2 hundreds 3 tens and 4 units.
In these positions: the 2 is worth   200
                      the 3 is worth   30
                      the 4 is worth   4
                      this adds up to   234

Exercise 2:1

1   Write down the value of the coloured digit in each of these numbers.

	Thousands	Hundreds	Tens	Units
a		2	8	9
b		4	3	6
c		7	4	7
d	7	9	9	5
e	8	8	7	9
f	9	9	9	9

2   Write down the **total** value of the coloured digits in each of these numbers.

	Thousands	Hundreds	Tens	Units
a		9	2	3
b		4	2	4
c		7	9	5
d	6	9	2	7
e	8	9	7	6
f	9	3	8	9

3 Write down the value of the coloured digit in each of these numbers.

a 245	**c** 2345	**e** 8742	**g** 5891	● **i** 7098
b 327	**d** 2629	**f** 5192	**h** 8810	● **j** 6006

4 Write down the **total** value of the coloured digits in each of these numbers.

a 172	**c** 2417	**e** 3165	**g** 7689	● **i** 9999
b 595	**d** 1752	**f** 4928	**h** 8761	● **j** 8098

5 Barbara uses each of the digits 3 4 5 to make a three digit number.
  a What is the largest three figure even number that she can make?
  b What is the smallest three figure odd number that she can make?

6 Ade wins £8950 in prizes from his premium bonds in a year. The £8950 is a collection of £50, £100 and £1000 prizes. If he has won fifteen £50 prizes and eight £1000 prizes, how many £100 prizes has he won?

7 Jerome collects £270 in £10 travellers cheques.
  How many cheques is this?

● **8** In the village of Toneland all the telephone numbers are made from the digits 5 4 3 2. How many telephone numbers begin with a 3?

Digit Dodgems

Look at the digits **1 2 3**
How many ways can you use these digits to make a 3 digit number?

Here are two of the ways: 123, 132
Write down all of the ways in order. Start with the smallest.

Look at the digits **1 2 3 4**
How many ways can you use these digits to make a 4 digit number?
Here are two of the ways: 1234, 1243
Write down all of the ways in order. Start with the smallest.

How many ways can you write a 5 digit number? Use the digits 1 2 3 4 5.
How many ways can you write a 6 digit number? Use the digits 1 2 3 4 5 6.
Look at the pattern of your answers.
Can you predict how many ways you could write a 9 digit number?

Reading and writing whole numbers

Claire has just won the lottery!

She has won £2 658 496.
You need to be able to
write numbers in words.

Look at the number.
You write down the number
of millions that there are.
When you get to the gap
write '**million**'.
Then you write down
the number of thousands
that there are.

M		HTh	TTh	Th		H	T	U

£ 2 , 6 5 8 , 4 9 6

two **million**   six hundred   **thousand**   four hundred
and fifty-eight   and ninety-six

When you get to the gap write '**thousand**'.
Then you write the rest of the number.

The digits are always grouped in threes from the right.
All big numbers have digits grouped like this.

Example   Write these numbers in words

  a 4056   **b** 22 507   **c** 9 601 457

  a four thousand and fifty-six
  b twenty-two thousand five hundred and seven
  c nine million, six hundred and one thousand, four hundred
       and fifty-seven

Exercise 2:2

1 These are attendance figures for the first day of the 1997/8 football
   season. Write the numbers in words.
   a Gillingham   6562   **e** Wimbledon   26 106
   b Grimsby   6220   **f** Middlesbrough   29 414
   c Southampton   15 206   **g** Leicester   20 304
   d Norwich   17 230   **h** Birmingham   20 608

2 These are possible populations of cities in the year 2000.
   Write the numbers in words.
   a Leicester   291 756   **c** Birmingham   1 017 094
   b Bristol   402 175   **d** Mexico   22 721 495

Here is the number of spectators at
an American baseball match:

one hundred and forty-two thousand, seven hundred and twenty-nine

You need to be able to write numbers in figures.
First write down the number of thousands.
Then leave a small space.
Then write down the rest of the number.

| one hundred and forty-two | thousand | seven hundred and twenty-nine |

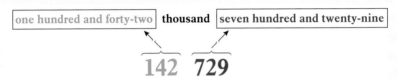

142 729

Example

Write these numbers in figures.
a Twenty-two thousand and seventy-eight
b Nine hundred and eight thousand, three hundred and six
c Seventy-nine million, six hundred and one thousand, four hundred and two

a 22 078 **b** 908 306 **c** 79 601 402

Exercise 2:3

1 Write these numbers in figures.
a Two thousand, three hundred and fifteen
b Fifty-seven thousand, three hundred and eighty-two
c Nine thousand, six hundred and ninety-seven
d Twelve thousand, four hundred and sixty-eight
e Six hundred and fifty-seven thousand, eight hundred and eleven
f Eight million, nine hundred and sixty-four thousand, one hundred and twenty-two
g Forty-two million, six hundred and seventy-eight thousand, nine hundred and forty-five

2 Write the amount of money on this cheque in figures.

The Royal Bank of Whatland	
	Date _____ 19 ____
Pay *Mr A. Smith*	
Three million and forty-one pounds only	£

Exercise 2:4

1 Write down the value of the coloured digit in these numbers.

	M	HTh	TTh	Th	H	T	U
a	2	9	4	5	7	3	6
b	8	2	7	9	1	2	1
c	9	9	9	9	9	9	9

2 Write down the value of the coloured digit for each of these numbers.

a 789 245   c 8 742 417   e 7 898 965   g 4 626 313
b 4 862 345   d 5 581 223   f 9 729 164   h 7 610 003

3 Write down the **total** value of the coloured digits for each of these numbers.

a 375 172   d 5 117 736   g 3 065 469   • j 4 101 202
b 600 432   e 2 211 165   h 7 090 403   • k 3 412 610
c 9 442 417   f 1 202 020   • i 9 999 999   • l 9 098 908

Putting whole numbers in order

Write any numbers that you are trying to put in order in columns.

		M	HTh	TTh	Th	H	T	U
Numbers that are different lengths				4	2	1	1	1
The number with the most digits is the biggest.					5	6	9	9

Numbers that are the same length

		M	HTh	TTh	Th	H	T	U
Look at the digits with the highest place value.								
Here 80 000 is bigger than 70 000.				8	3	1	2	3
So 83 123 is bigger than 75 468.				7	5	4	6	8

For these two numbers, the digits with the highest place value are the same.

		M	HTh	TTh	Th	H	T	U
Look at the thousands column.								
Here 5 000 is bigger than 3 000.				7	3	4	6	8
So 75 123 is bigger than 73 468.				7	5	1	2	3

If the first two columns are the same go to the column with the next highest value.

		M	HTh	TTh	Th	H	T	U
Here this is hundreds.								
400 is bigger than 100.				7	5	4	6	8
So 75 468 is bigger than 75 123.				7	5	1	2	3

Carry on like this, working towards the right.
Look at one column at a time until the value is different.

Exercise 2:5

1 Write these numbers in order of size. Start with the smallest.

a	Th	H	T	U
	1	4	1	9
	1	7	9	8
	1	4	7	6

c	Th	H	T	U
	2	3	6	6
	2	3	7	7
	2	3	7	6
	2	3	6	7

b	Th	H	T	U
	3	4	7	8
	3	1	8	7
	3	4	7	7

d	Th	H	T	U
	3	7	4	8
	3	4	4	8
	3	4	7	8
	3	4	8	7

2 These are insurance claims. Arrange them in order of size.
Start with the smallest.

a	£4768	£4689	£496	£47 689	£47 766
b	£89 464	£93 291	£92 319	£93 192	£89 646
c	$927 893	$932 879	$927 998	$9 276 789	$932 998
d	£1 221 122	£2 121 122	£1 212 121	£1 212 212	£2 122 122

Game: Digits for hire!

You need to play this with two other people.
You will need a set of digit cards from your teacher.

You also need rough paper.

`0` `0` `1` `1` `2` `2` `3` `3`

Choose a dealer.
The dealer shuffles the cards.

`4` `4` `5` `6` `7` `8` `9` `9`

The dealer deals out 6 cards and lays them on the table facing the other
2 players.
The other 2 players leave the cards where they are.
They write down the biggest number possible using the digits on the cards.
The winner of the turn is the fastest player to do this.
The winner of the game is the first player to win 6 turns.
Play the game again but change the dealer.
Then change the dealer and repeat the game.

Inequalities

Some numbers are greater than others.
You need to know how to write this.

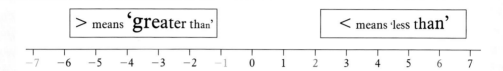

| > means 'greater than' | | < means 'less than' |

Look at the number line.
The number 2 is less than the number 6.
This is because it is further to the left.
You write this as $2 < 6$

The number -1 is greater than the number -7.
This is because it is further to the right.
You write this as $-1 > -7$

Exercise 2:6

1   Copy these pairs of numbers.
    Put the correct symbol in between them. Choose from $<$ or $>$.
    a 2 4   **c** 13 3   **e** 157 175   **g** -2 4   **i** -2 -4
    b 9 10   **d** 12 4   **f** 10 0   **h** -2 0   **j** -23 -22

2   These are the lengths Sheena jumped in her triple jump competition:

    842 cm   896 cm   658 cm   919 cm

    Copy this. Fill it in. Use a whole number of centimetres.
    Sheena jumped distances > 657 cm and $<$ ....

3   These are some fishing quotas for trawlers:

Trawler	Baywatch	Bunter	Hunter	Shellshock
Quota in tonnes	2786	9247	6785	9427

    Copy this. Fill it in. Use a whole number of tonnes.
    The quotas are $>$ .... tonnes and < 9428 tonnes.

4   Marie needs a cooker that must fit a space in her kitchen. She says 'the cooker must be > 75 cm but < 68 cm'. What mistake has she made?

5   Alan is watching a marathon. The runners with numbers 71 to 80 are from his club. He wants to know how many runners from his club finish in the first twenty.

   a   Copy this. Fill it in.

      Alan has to look for the runners with
      numbers > ....
      and for runners with
      numbers < ....

   The times of Alan's clubmates are
   between 3 hours 1 minute and
   7 hours 59 minutes.

   b   Copy this. Fill it in.

      The times of Alan's clubmates are > ...... hours and < ...... hours.

Putting decimals in order of size

Look at the numbers before the decimal point first.
e.g. 2.43 is bigger than 0.81 because 2 is bigger than 0.
You can write   2.43 > 0.81

$$2 . 4 \ 3$$
$$0 . 8 \ 1$$

If the numbers before the decimal point are the same
then look at the first figures after the decimal point.
e.g. 38.72 is bigger than 38.59 because 7 is bigger than 5.
You can write   38.72 > 38.59

$$3 \ 8 . 7 \ 2$$
$$3 \ 8 . 5 \ 9$$

Carry on like this. Look at one decimal place at a time.

6   Copy these pairs of numbers.
   Put the correct symbol in between them. Choose from < or > .
   a   2.3   4.9   **e**   7.34   7.14
   b   8.9   7.2   **f**   0.098   0.096
   c   11.56   12.87   **g**   0.0089   0.00891
   d   97.45   97.29   • **h**   −2.0986   −2.0896

• 7   These are the heights Jack jumped in his high jump competition:
   1.42 m   1.56 m   1.58 m   1.49 m
   Copy the sentence below and fill it in. Use numbers to 2 decimal places.
   Jack jumped heights > .... and < ....

2 Rounding

This is the crowd at Leicester City.

The usual attendance at Leicester City is 20 000.

This does not mean that exactly 20 000 people come to every game.

The number has been rounded to the nearest 1000.

You often need to round numbers to a sensible degree of accuracy.

Rounding to the nearest 10

Examples

1 Round the number 63 to the nearest 10.

60   63   70

63 is nearer to 60 than to 70,
It is rounded to 60 to the nearest 10.

2 Round the number 85 to the nearest 10.

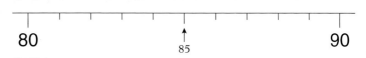

80   85   90

85 is half way between 80 and 90.
It is rounded to 90 to the nearest 10.

Exercise 2:7

1 Round these numbers to the nearest 10.

a	17	**d**	48	**g**	52	● **j**	237
b	84	**e**	55	**h**	99	● **k**	299
c	18	**f**	79	● **i**	142	● **l**	1857

2 2478 people went to the first match of the 1997/98 season at Chester City.
Write this number to the nearest 10.

Rounding to the nearest 100

Examples   **1**   Round the number 683 to the nearest 100.

683 is nearer to 700 than to 600.
It is rounded to 700 to the nearest 100.

2   Round the number 650 to the nearest 100.

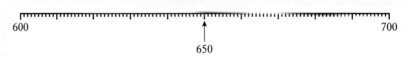

650 is halfway between 600 and 700.
It is rounded to 700 to the nearest 100.

3   Round these numbers to the nearest 100.
a	347	**d**	428	**g**	523	● **j**	4264
b	259	**e**	650	**h**	999	● **k**	1999
c	186	**f**	389	● **i**	1425	● **l**	2307

4   20 304 people went to the first match of the 1997/98 season at Leicester
City.
Write this number to the nearest 100.

Rounding to the nearest 1000

Examples   **1**   Round the number 6125 to the nearest 1000.

6125 is nearer to 6000 than to 7000.
It is rounded to 6000 to the nearest 1000.

2 Round the number 4500 to the nearest 1000.

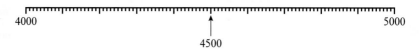

4000   5000

4500

4500 is halfway between 4000 and 5000.
It is rounded to 5000 to the nearest 1000.

---

5 Round these numbers to the nearest 1000.

a	1473	**d**	3276	**g**	3501	**j**	42 454
b	5694	**e**	5500	**h**	9999	**k**	129 999
c	1256	**f**	7555	**i**	14 251	**l**	412 867

6 These are the attendances at the first matches of the Premier League for
the 1997/98 football season.
Write each attendance to the nearest 1000.

Barnsley	18 667	Leicester	20 304
Blackburn	23 557	Newcastle	36 711
Coventry	22 686	Southampton	15 206
Everton	35 716	Wimbledon	26 106
Leeds	37 993		

7 Write each attendance in question **6** to the nearest 10 000.

Significant figure	In any number the first **significant figure** is the first digit which isn't a 0. For most numbers this is the first digit. The first significant figure is the digit in red. 21.4 312 45.78 0.81
Rounding to 1 significant figure (1 sf)	To **round to 1 significant figure (1 sf):** (1) Look at the digit after the first significant one. (2) If it is 5, 6, 7, 8 or 9 add one on to the first digit. If it is 0, 1, 2, 3 or 4 ignore it. (3) Be careful to keep the number about the right size and fill in the spaces with zeros. 21.4 is 20 to 1 sf. It is *not* 2! 46.78 is 50 to 1 sf. 312 is 300 to 1 sf. It is *not* 3. 0.81 is 0.8 to 1 sf.

Exercise 2:8

1 Round these numbers to 1 significant figure.

a	12	**d**	317	**g**	3529	**j**	0.455
b	59	**e**	550	**h**	9999	**k**	0.356
c	15	**f**	7218	**i**	0.584	**l**	0.777

Rounding to any number of significant figures

To **round to any number of significant figures:**
(1) Look at the first unwanted digit.
(2) Use the normal rules of rounding.
(3) Be careful to keep the number about the right size.

341.4 to 2 sf is 340. It is *not* 34!

The 1 is the first unwanted digit. This does not change the 4 when you round.

7945.78 to 1 sf is 8000

The 9 is the first unwanted digit. This changes the 7 to an 8 when you round.

0.002 034 5 to 3 sf is 0.002 03

Here the 0 after the 2 is significant because it comes after the first significant figure. A 0 is only significant when it appears on the right of the first significant figure.

---

2 Round these calculator displays to 2 sf.

a 136783   **c** 3.9586287   **e** 0.4652357

b 24.897912   **d** 14456   **f** 0.03521

3 Round these calculator displays to 3 sf.

a 2.4367866   **c** 325347   **e** 0.795379

b 24.887912   **d** 188656   **f** 0.0050831

4 Round these numbers.

a	3.7824 to 3 sf	**c**	273 to 1 sf	● **e**	0.039 892 to 2 sf
b	58.344 to 3 sf	**d**	255 643 to 2 sf	● **f**	0.000 359 6 to 3 sf

● **5** Write down the number of significant figures in each of these numbers.

     a 3.8457   **b** 0.243   **c** 0.0003   **d** 34.017

3 Estimating and checking

This is a picture of the Channel Tunnel.

The original estimate of the cost was £3 billion.
The tunnel actually cost £10 billion.

Some estimates are very difficult to do!

You often work things out on a calculator.
One way to check your answers is by estimating.
To get an estimate, round each number to 1 significant figure.

Example　　Work out 3.9 × 5.2

Calculation:　**3** **.** **9** **×** **5** **.** **2** **=**　Answer 20.28

Estimate:　　3.9 is 4 to 1 sf.
　　　　　　5.2 is 5 to 1 sf.
　　　　　　3.9 × 5.2 is about 4 × 5 = 20
　　　　　　20 is near to 20.28
　　　　　　so the answer is probably right.

Exercise 2:9

1 Work these out. Write down the answer and an estimate for each one.
　a 2.7 × 6.1　　**c** 3.4 × 7.7　　**e** 5.5 × 45　　**g** 1.9 × 7.32
　b 6.3 × 2.7　　**d** 3 × 8.5　　　**f** 5 × 7.1　　　**h** 0.7 × 4.42

Example　　Work out 67 × 32

Calculation:　**6** **7** **×** **3** **2** **=**　Answer 2144

Estimate:　　67 is 70 to 1 sf.
　　　　　　32 is 30 to 1 sf.
　　　　　　67 × 32 is about 70 × 30 = 2100.
　　　　　　2100 is near to 2144
　　　　　　so the answer is probably right.

---

2 Work these out. Write down the answer and an estimate for each one.

   a   46 × 24   **c**   28 × 71   **e**   55 × 22   **g**   30 × 71

   b   37 × 13   **d**   57 × 32   **f**   60 × 57   **h**   80 × 65

Example   Work out 232 × 286

         Calculation: `2` `3` `2` `×` `2` `8` `6` `=`   Answer 66 352

         Estimate: 232 is 200 to 1 sf.

                    286 is 300 to 1 sf.

                    232 × 286 is about 200 × 300 = 60 000

                    60 000 is near to 66 352

                    so the answer is probably right

---

3 Work these out. Write down the answer and an estimate for each one.

   a   324 × 176   **c**   568 × 212   **e**   398 × 623   **g**   200 × 652

   b   273 × 513   **d**   434 × 897   **f**   300 × 525   **h**   800 × 233

4 Work these out. Write down the answer and an estimate for each one.

   a   7.3 × 26   **c**   3.9 × 58   **e**   21 × 34.9   **g**   1.9 × 435

   b   325 × 58   **d**   153 × 76.8   **f**   26.1 × 24   **h**   20.89 × 338

5 Work these out. Write down the answer and an estimate for each one.

   a   6.2 + 2.6   **d**   2.4 + 7.5   **g**   5.7 − 2.1   **j**   8.923 − 2.731

   b   31.5 ÷ 4.2   **e**   18 ÷ 4.8   **h**   234 + 567   **k**   315 − 189

   c   437 − 95   **f**   4.8 ÷ 1.2   **i**   248 ÷ 49.6   **l**   499.2 ÷ 9.6

● 6 Seema is doing this calculation.
    She writes the answer 4599.
    How can you tell that this is wrong
    without doing the calculation?

Exercise 2:10

When you answer questions you should
always do an estimate to check your answer.
In this exercise:

   a   Work out the answers using a calculator.
        You may have to round your answer.

   b   Write down an estimate to check that each answer is about right.

1 The height of a television stand is 53 cm.
The television is 65 cm high.
How high is the television and the stand
together?

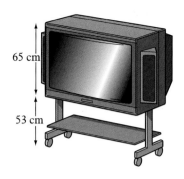

65 cm

53 cm

2 The height of a fridge-freezer is 210 cm.
The freezer is 57 cm high.
How high is the fridge?

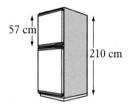

57 cm

210 cm

3 Phil buys 13 packets of crisps.
Each packet costs 23 p.
How much does he pay?

4 A bag of fun size Mars bars costs £2.19
There are 18 bars in the bag.
How much is 1 fun size bar?

5 A bag of chicken pieces costs £4.89
The bag contains 8 pieces of chicken.
What is the cost of 1 piece?

6 A chart CD costs £13.99
Find the cost of 11 chart CDs.

● **7** Stamps cost 26 p.
Sharon has £8.
How many stamps can Sharon buy?

● **8** 164 pupils went on a school trip by coach.
Each coach could carry 46 pupils.
How many coaches were used?

This is going to be a new Sports Hall.
John is the quantity surveyor who has to
decide how much it will cost to build the
Sports Hall.

He has to estimate the cost.

In this exercise you are going to estimate
the cost of building this Sports Hall.

Exercise 2:11

1 This is a plan of the Sports Hall floor.
  a Work out the area of the floor.
  b Round this area to 1 significant figure.
  c Is this estimate too big or too small?

```
                          36 m
 24 m
```

2 John is estimating the cost of the foundations.
The foundations cost £49.40 per square metre.
   a Round this cost to 1 significant figure.
   b Estimate the cost of the foundations.

3 The site needs preparing before work begins.
All of these costs are estimated by using the floor area.

Item	Cost per square metre (£)
site work	27.15
drainage	40.26
services	16.14
external work	103.94

   a Round each cost to 1 significant figure.
   b Estimate the cost of each of these items.

4 All of these costs are estimated by using the floor area.

Item	Cost per square metre (£)
roof	91.38
floor finish	9.44
ceiling finish	8.40
fittings	18.14
heating system	68.36

   a Round each cost to 1 significant figure.
   b Estimate the cost of each of these items.

5 The sports hall will be 8 metres high.
   a Work out the area of each wall.
   b Work out the total area of the walls.
   c Round this area to 1 significant figure.
   d Is this estimate too big or too small?

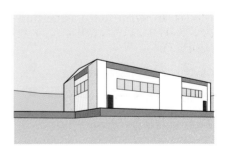

6 The walls cost £76.49 per square metre.
   a Round this cost to 1 significant figure.
   b Estimate the cost of the walls.

7 All of these costs are estimated by using the wall area.

Item	Cost per square metre (£)
wall finishes	22.13
internal walls	9.60
internal finishes	39.97

   a Round each cost to 1 significant figure.
   b Estimate the cost of each of these items.

8 The Sports Hall needs 2 external doors and 10 internal doors.
An external door costs £86 and an internal door costs £31.
Estimate the cost of the doors.

9 What is your total estimate for the cost of the Sports Hall?
Do you think that your estimate is too high, too low or about right?
Explain your answer.

You know that you can estimate an answer to check
that it is about the right size.

You can also check your answers by reversing the problem.
This is a different way of checking.

Example   Work out 234×45

$$\boxed{2}\ \boxed{3}\ \boxed{4}\ \boxed{\times}\ \boxed{4}\ \boxed{5}\ \boxed{=}\quad \text{Answer } 10\,530$$

The reverse of multiplying is dividing,
so you can check your answer by
doing a division question.
You can work out $10\,530 \div 45$
You should get 234

$$234 \longrightarrow \boxed{\times\ 45} \longrightarrow 10530$$

$$234 \longleftarrow \boxed{\div\ 45} \longleftarrow 10530$$

Exercise 2:12

For each question:
a Work out the answer on your calculator.
b Write down a question that you can use to check your answer.

1 24×367 **4** 683×289 **7** $573 + 2998$

2 45×167 **5** 23×28.98 **8** $387 \div 3$

3 365×289 **6** 39.39×1987 **9** $19\,875 - 2876$

Estimating square roots

Square numbers You need to round the numbers to the nearest square number.

$$1, \quad 4, \quad 9, \quad 16, \quad 25, \quad \ldots \text{ are the \textbf{square numbers}}$$
$$1 \times 1 \quad 2 \times 2 \quad 3 \times 3 \quad 4 \times 4 \quad 5 \times 5$$

Example   Estimate $\sqrt{23}$
$\sqrt{23} \approx \sqrt{25} = 5$
If you round $\sqrt{23}$ to 1 significant figure you get $\sqrt{20}$.
This is just as difficult to work out as the original question!

Exercise 2:13

For each question:

a Estimate the answer.
b Work out the answer using your calculator.
Give your calculator answer to 3 significant figures.

1 $\sqrt{34}$ **3** $\sqrt{5}$ **5** $\sqrt{46}$ **7** $\sqrt{103}$

2 $\sqrt{14}$ **4** $\sqrt{10}$ **6** $\sqrt{67}$ **8** $\sqrt{120}$

Sometimes you have to estimate in stages.

Example

Estimate the answer to

$$\sqrt{\frac{23 \times 489}{35}}$$

To do this start by rounding
the numbers to 1 significant figure

$$\approx \sqrt{\frac{20 \times 500}{40}}$$

Work this out

$$= \sqrt{\frac{10\,000}{40}}$$

Now look for the
nearest square number

$$= \sqrt{250}$$
$$\approx \sqrt{256}$$

Square root to get the answer

$$= 16$$

Exercise 2:14

For each question:

a Estimate the answer.
b Work out the answer using your calculator.
Give your calculator answer to 3 significant figures.

1 $\sqrt{\dfrac{212 \times 64}{310}}$ **4** $\sqrt{\dfrac{234 \times 46}{52}}$ **● 7** $\sqrt{\dfrac{189 \times 97}{22 \times 564}}$

2 $\sqrt{\dfrac{86 \times 47}{153}}$ **5** $\sqrt{\dfrac{178 \times 68}{47}}$ **● 8** $\sqrt{\dfrac{16^2 \times 13}{167}}$

3 $\sqrt{\dfrac{197 \times 24}{38}}$ **● 6** $\sqrt{\dfrac{184 \times 43}{82 \times 31}}$ **● 9** $\sqrt{\dfrac{48 \times 36}{24 \times 52}} + \sqrt{\dfrac{8^2 \times 3^2}{24}}$

When you are estimating the answer to a question that involves a fraction there is a way of getting a much better estimate than by rounding to 1 sf.

Examples   **1**   Estimate the answer to $\dfrac{65.9 \times 56.1}{42}$

If you do this question by rounding each number to 1 sf you get

$$\frac{65.9 \times 56.1}{42} \approx \frac{70 \times 60}{40} = \frac{4200}{40} = 105$$

The actual answer is 88.0 to 3 sf.
105 isn't too far from 88 but you can get much closer!
Start by rounding all of the numbers to the nearest whole number.

$$\frac{65.9 \times 56.1}{42} \approx \frac{66 \times 56}{42}$$

Now you need to be clever and see that you can split the 42 in the denominator into 6×7 and cancel the fraction like this:

$$\frac{66 \times 56}{42} = \frac{66 \times 56}{6 \times 7} = \frac{66}{6} \times \frac{56}{7} = 11 \times 8 = 88$$

This gives an excellent approximation!
To do this you must try to cancel parts of the fraction.

2   Estimate the answer to $\dfrac{78 \times 41}{6.9 \times 8.4}$

The numbers in the denominator round to 7×8 so change the numbers in the numerator to multiples of 7 and 8.

$$\frac{78 \times 41}{6.9 \times 8.4} \approx \frac{77 \times 40}{7 \times 8} = 11 \times 5 = 55$$

Exercise 2:15

For each question:
a   Estimate the answer by rounding so that numbers will cancel.
b   Work out the exact answer using your calculator.
Give your calculator answer to 3 significant figures if you need to round.

1 $\dfrac{24.2 \times 41.8}{35}$ **4** $\dfrac{12.7 \times 102.5}{30}$ **7** $\dfrac{36.2 \times 38.9}{4.7 \times 8.1}$

2 $\dfrac{16.3 \times 35}{24}$ **5** $\dfrac{32.1 \times 17}{45}$ **8** $\dfrac{18.1 \times 33.4}{2.46 \times 6.89}$

3 $\dfrac{15.8 \times 40}{35}$ **6** $\dfrac{39.1 \times 43.4}{5.3 \times 6.8}$ **9** $\dfrac{46.7 \times 50.1}{7.89 \times 3.15}$

4   Fractions and decimals

One is not amused.

To turn the fraction $\dfrac{a}{b}$ into a decimal you divide **a** by **b**.

You can do this without a calculator using short division.

Example   Change $\frac{1}{4}$ into a decimal.

You need to divide 1 by 4.

$$0.$$
$$4\overline{)1.^10}$$

First do $1 \div 4$. This is 0 with 1 left over.
Put the 0 above the 1 and carry the 1.
Put in the decimal point and add a 0 in the tenths column.

$$0.\ 2$$
$$4\overline{)1\ ^10^20}$$

Now do $^10 \div 4$.
This is 2 with 2 left over.
Put the 2 above the ^{10} and carry the 2 into the next column.
Add a 0 in the hundredths column.

$$0.\ 2\ 5$$
$$4\overline{)1.^10^20}$$

Now do $20 \div 4$.
This is 5. Put the 5 above the ^{20}.

So $\frac{1}{4} = 0.25$

When you do this you will always get
   either   a decimal that stops
   or   a recurring decimal.

Terminating decimal

A **terminating decimal** is one which stops.

0.5, 0.867, 0.373 645 651 2 are all terminating decimals.

Recurring decimal

A **recurring decimal** is one which does not stop but which repeats.

$\frac{1}{9} = 1 \div 9 = 0.111\ 111\ 111 \ldots$

The 1s carry on forever. You write this with a dot over the 1 like this:

$$0.111\ 111\ 111\ldots = 0.\dot{1}$$

$$\tfrac{1}{7} = 1 \div 7 = 0.142\ 857\ 142\ 857\ 142\ 857\ldots$$

The 142 857 part carries on for ever. You show this by putting dots over the first and last digits that repeat like this:

$$0.142\ 857\ 142\ 857\ 142\ 857\ldots = 0.\dot{1}42\ 85\dot{7}$$

Exercise 2:16

1 Work out the values of each of the fractions $\tfrac{1}{2}, \tfrac{1}{3}, \tfrac{1}{4}$, etc. up to $\tfrac{1}{20}$.
Write each answer as a decimal.
Use the proper notation for the recurring decimals.

2   **a** Write down the value of $\tfrac{1}{9}$ as a decimal.
    b Work out the decimal for each of the fractions.
      (1) $\tfrac{2}{9}$ (2) $\tfrac{3}{9}$ (3) $\tfrac{4}{9}$
    c Use your answers to **a** and **b** to write down the decimals for
      (1) $\tfrac{5}{9}$ (2) $\tfrac{6}{9}$ (3) $\tfrac{7}{9}$
    d Explain how to write down the decimal for a fraction with a denominator of 9.
    e Use your answer to **d** to write down a recurring decimal for $\tfrac{9}{9}$.

You already know that every terminating decimal can be written as a fraction.
0.5 is 5 tenths because the 5 is in the tenths column.

So $0.5 = \tfrac{5}{10} = \tfrac{1}{2}$

0.32 is 32 hundredths because the 2 is in the hundredths column.

So $0.32 = \tfrac{32}{100} = \tfrac{8}{25}$

0.129 is 129 thousandths because the 9 is in the thousandths column.

So $0.129 = \tfrac{129}{1000}.$

Exercise 2:17

1 Write these decimals as fractions. Write each fraction in its simplest form.

    a 0.3   **d** 0.37   **g** 0.75   ● **j** 0.5125

    b 0.6   **e** 0.23   **h** 0.125   ● **k** 1.75

    c 0.8   **f** 0.25   **i** 0.375   ● **l** 2.125

2 Work out the decimal for each of these fractions.
Write down what you notice about the patterns of digits in your answers.

    a $\frac{1}{7}$ $\frac{2}{7}$ $\frac{3}{7}$ $\frac{4}{7}$ $\frac{5}{7}$ $\frac{6}{7}$

    b $\frac{1}{13}$ $\frac{2}{13}$ $\frac{3}{13}$ $\frac{4}{13}$ $\frac{5}{13}$ $\frac{6}{13}$ $\frac{7}{13}$ $\frac{8}{13}$ $\frac{9}{13}$ $\frac{10}{13}$ $\frac{11}{13}$ $\frac{12}{13}$

To **put fractions and decimals in order of size**:

(1) Change all of the fractions into decimals.
(2) Put the decimals in order of size.

Example   Put these in order. Start with the smallest.

$$\frac{1}{4}, \frac{2}{5}, 0.35, 0.42, \frac{2}{7}$$

Change the fractions to decimals.

$$\frac{1}{4} = 0.25 \qquad \frac{2}{5} = 0.4 \qquad \frac{2}{7} = 0.\dot{2}85\,71\dot{4}$$

Now put decimals in order like you did in section 1.

$$0.25, 0.\dot{2}85\,71\dot{4}, 0.35, 0.4, 0.42$$

Now you can answer the question. The order needed is:

$$\frac{1}{4}, \frac{2}{7}, 0.35, \frac{2}{5}, 0.42$$

Always give your answer with the fractions and decimals that were in the question.

---

3 Put these in order. Start with the smallest.

    a $\frac{1}{4}, 0.23, \frac{1}{5}$ **c** $\frac{5}{8}, 0.73, \frac{3}{5}$ **e** $\frac{3}{4}, 0.23, \frac{2}{5}, \frac{3}{8}, 0.576$

    b $\frac{2}{5}, 0.39, \frac{3}{4}, 0.79$ **d** $\frac{1}{6}, 0.15, 0.17$ ● **f** $\frac{1}{6}, \frac{3}{7}, \frac{4}{9}, 0.7776, \frac{7}{9}$

Exercise 2:18

1 Work these out using a calculator.

a	125×43	**i**	264×36	**q**	724×24
b	7.66×3	**j**	3.4×4	**r**	3.05×9
c	4.74×35	**k**	6.78×13	**s**	14.31×23
d	3.95×15	**l**	5.05×37	**t**	42.56×71
e	$375 \div 5$	**m**	$738 \div 9$	**u**	$784 \div 7$
f	$430 \div 5$	**n**	$336 \div 8$	**v**	$5725 \div 5$
g	$576 \div 12$	**o**	$768 \div 24$	**w**	$1400 \div 25$
h	$6.35 \div 5$	**p**	$4.36 \div 4$	**x**	$17.25 \div 5$

2 a Work these out using a calculator.

    (1) 20×0.3 (3) 20×0.13 (5) 20×0.7

    (2) 20×0.4 (4) 20×0.25 (6) 20×0.834

  b In part **a** you are multiplying 20 by decimal numbers.
The answers are all bigger or smaller than 20.
Write down what you notice about all of the answers to part **a**.

3 a Work these out using a calculator.

    (1) $20 \div 0.2$ (3) $20 \div 0.5$ (5) $20 \div 0.75$

    (2) $20 \div 0.4$ (4) $20 \div 0.25$ (6) $20 \div 0.8$

  b In part **a** you are dividing 20 by decimal numbers.
The answers are all bigger or smaller than 20.
Write down what you notice about all of the answers to part **a**.

4 Jason is working out 40×0.5 on his calculator.
He gets 80 as his answer.

  a Explain how you know that Jason must be wrong.

● **b** What has Jason done on his calculator?

5 Liza is working out $50 \div 0.4$ on her calculator.
She gets 12.5 as her answer.

  a Explain how you know that Liza must be wrong.

● **b** What has Liza done on his calculator?

1 Write down the value of the underlined digit in each of these numbers.
   a 1<u>2</u>3 **b** 187<u>6</u> **c** 4<u>4</u>44 **d** <u>2</u>468 **e** 99<u>9</u>9

2 Write down the total value of the underlined digits in each of these
   numbers.
   a 1<u>2</u>3 **b** <u>1</u>8<u>7</u>6 **c** <u>4</u>44<u>4</u> **d** 2<u>4</u>6<u>8</u> **e** <u>99</u>99

3 **a** The attendance at a rowing competition was 3056. Write this number
   in words.
   b The same day a premier league football game had a crowd exactly ten
   times as big. Write the size of this crowd in words.

4 **a** The sun is one million, three hundred and ninety-two thousand, one
   hundred and forty kilometres across. Write this distance in figures.
   b An astronomical unit is 92 955 807 miles. Write this distance in
   words.

5 Elspeth uses each of the digits 4 5 6 7 to make a four figure number.
   a What is the largest four figure even number that she could make?
   b What is the smallest four figure odd number that she could make?

6 These are the total runs scored by seven batsmen in their careers.
   39 832   61 237   43 423   50 138   43 551   39 802   50 551
   a Write these figures in words.
   b Put the totals in order. Start with the smallest.
   c Copy this pair of numbers: 39 832 ... 39 802
   Put the correct symbol in between.

7 These are second division football attendances on a Saturday in 1997.
   | Gillingham | 5083 | Watford | 10 125 |
   | Grimsby | 4404 | Wigan | 3761 |
   a Give each attendance to the nearest 1000.
   b Give each attendance to the nearest 100.
   c Give each attendance to the nearest 10.

8 These are the prices in £ of some cars.
Kia Pride	6679	Ford Mondeo	20 445
Fiat Punto	8099	Merc Benz S	69 725
Peugeot 106	8990	Aston Martin	189 950
   Give each price to:
   a 1 significant figure
   b 3 significant figures

53

9 These are the diameters of some industrial fibres in centimetres.

Xylon B6	0.006 742	Blotch 5Kdn	0.081 91
Mercuroid 22	0.009 226	Spagbolo Endgame	0.002 070 9
Narconic FJ7	0.000 545 4	Gyro IMB 98	0.002 960 998
Nils I4	0.497 73	Rosewell Arc 5	0.000 007 999 8

Give each diameter to:
a 1 significant figure
b 3 significant figures

10 Work these out. Write down the answer and an estimate for each one.
a $2.3 + 5.1 + 7.8$ **c** $12.2 - 4.9$ **e** 2.8×41 **g** $36 \div 9.1$
b $457 + 326$ **d** $792 - 309$ **f** 672×10.4 **h** $829 \div 20.3$

11 Two pupils are estimating answers to exam questions.
a Jessica says that 31×21 is about 600.
Show how she did this.
b Sylvester says that $2380 \div 39$ is about 60.
Show how he did this.

12 Joe is working at his local supermarket.
The supermarket sells about 8200 cans of beans each week.
The tins are packed in boxes. Each box contains 42 cans of beans.
Joe's supervisor asks him how many boxes of beans are needed each
week. Show how Joe can give him a quick estimate.

13 A bag of crisps costs 32 p. 178 pupils are out on a trip.
Mr Custer buys each pupil a bag. Estimate the cost of this.

14 For each part:
(1) Work out the answer on your calculator.
(2) Write down a calculation that you can use to check your answer.

a 23×562 **b** $8298 + 564$ **c** $684 \div 4$ **d** $28\,973 - 7629$

15 For each part:
(1) Estimate the answer.
(2) Work out the answer using a calculator.
Give your calculator answer to 3 significant figures.

a $\dfrac{279 \times 84}{24}$ **b** $\sqrt{79}$ **c** $\sqrt{\dfrac{8 \times 823}{322}}$

16 For each question:
(1) Estimate the answer by rounding so that numbers will cancel.
(2) Work out the exact answer using your calculator.
    Give your calculator answer to 3 significant figures.

a $\dfrac{4.1 \times 48.1}{24}$

c $\dfrac{14.8 \times 44.2}{25}$

e $\dfrac{36.2 \times 61.8}{8.7 \times 9.1}$

b $\dfrac{15.3 \times 24.7}{45}$

d $\dfrac{31.6 \times 14.3}{4.7 \times 7.3}$

f $\dfrac{17.1 \times 27.64}{7.46 \times 3.89}$

17 **a** Work out the decimal for each of these fractions.

(1) $\frac{1}{99}$ (3) $\frac{7}{99}$ (5) $\frac{29}{99}$

(2) $\frac{2}{99}$ (4) $\frac{18}{99}$ (6) $\frac{70}{99}$

b Use your answers to **a** to write down the decimals for:

(1) $\frac{2}{99}$ (2) $\frac{35}{99}$ (3) $\frac{98}{99}$

c Explain how to write down the decimal for a fraction with a denominator of 99.

18 **a** Work out the decimal for each of these fractions.

(1) $\frac{1}{999}$ (3) $\frac{15}{999}$ (5) $\frac{123}{999}$

(2) $\frac{8}{999}$ (4) $\frac{11}{999}$ (6) $\frac{330}{999}$

b Use your answers to **a** to write down the decimals for:

(1) $\frac{5}{999}$ (2) $\frac{58}{999}$ (3) $\frac{389}{999}$

c Explain how to write down the decimal for a fraction with a denominator of 999.

19 Write these decimals as fractions. Write each fraction in its simplest form.

a 0.4   c 0.325   e 0.525   g 0.4728
b 0.56   d 0.275   f 0.145   h 0.1825

20 Write these fractions and decimals in order of size.
Start with the smallest.
Write all the fractions as decimals first to help you.

a $\frac{1}{4}, 0.13, \frac{1}{5}, \frac{1}{8}, 0.1576$

b $\frac{2}{5}, \frac{3}{7}, \frac{5}{11}, 0.4776, \frac{4}{9}$

1 **a** Write these numbers in words.

(1) 22 346 901 (2) 22 364 109 (3) 22 436 910

b Write these numbers in order of size. Start with the smallest.

2 A dinosaur lived seventy two million, four hundred and five thousand, nine hundred and two years ago. Write this number in figures.

3 Every year the people of Masutoland eat 4.8 million coconuts. Write this as an ordinary number.

4 **a** A group of pensioners have ages > 67 years but < 82 years. You can write this as 67 < age < 82 Write down the ages in years that they could be.

b A group of children have ages 9, 10, 11, 12, 13, 14. Write this using < signs.

5 Indira is trying to work out the answer to a substitution.

She is using this formula $s = \dfrac{d \times n}{k}$

She has these values for d, n and k

$d = 293.25,$ $n = 9.8711$ $k = 588.6942$

Indira puts the numbers in the formula to give

$$s = \frac{293.25 \times 9.8711}{588.6942}$$

a Work out the actual value of s using your calculator. Give your calculator answer to 3 significant figures.

b Write down the numbers Indira could use in the formula to estimate the value of s.

c Work out an estimate for the value of s.

6 **a** Use your calculator to work out the value of

$$\sqrt{\frac{(6.982)^2 \times 38.719}{8197 + 7774 - 5186}}$$

Give your calculator answer to 3 significant figures.

b Estimate the value of this expression. Show all your working. You will need to use BODMAS.

1 Write down the value of the **red** digit in each of these numbers.

   a 2734

   b 173 500

2 One hundred and forty thousand, seven hundred and nine people visited a National Trust Manor House.

   a (1) Write this number in figures.

      (2) Write this number to the nearest thousand.

95 082 of the visitors were members of the National Trust.

   b (1) Write this number in words.

      (2) Write this number to the nearest hundred.

3 The table gives the prices of new cars in July 2000.

Car	Price in £	Price to nearest £100
Ford Ka	9595	
Nissan Micra	9550	
Peugeot 106	9070	
Rover Mini Cooper	9630	
Vauxhall Corsa	9295	
Fiat Punto	9995	

   a Copy the table. Fill in the last column.

   b Write down the cars in order of price. Start with the cheapest.

4 Ken is trying to improve his long jumping. These are the lengths, in metres, of his last 8 long jumps.

   2.65   2.98   3.07   2.07   2.54   2.91   2.3   3.1

Write the lengths in order of size.

Start with the smallest.

5 Put the correct symbol between each of these pairs of numbers.
Choose from < and >.
a 2978 ... 2798   **c** 2.17 ... 2.71
b −7 ... −9   **d** 0 ... −10

6 Arvind uses the digits 4, 5, 6 and 7 to make a four-digit number.
Write down
a the smallest number he can make.
b the largest odd number he can make.

7 Round these numbers.
a 75 to the nearest 10   **d** 384 to 1 significant figure
b 4039 to the nearest 100   **e** 0.836 45 to 2 significant figures
c 67 299 to the nearest 1000   **f** 56.0782 to 3 significant figures

8 Dave fills his car with petrol. It costs 80.9 p per litre.
The total cost is £39.07
How many litres is this? Give your answer to the nearest litre.

9 Estimate an answer for each of these.
Show clearly how you get your estimate.

a $\dfrac{102 - 57}{19.35}$ **b** $\sqrt{78}$ **c** $\sqrt{\dfrac{5.83 \times 6.7}{2.95}}$

10 Write these decimals as fractions. Write each fraction in its simplest
form.
a 0.4   **b** 0.22   **c** 0.375

11 Put these in order. Start with the smallest.
$\frac{7}{8}, 0.83, \frac{4}{5}, \frac{91}{100}$

3 Dealing with data

1 Presenting data
Drawing bar-charts
Drawing pie-charts
Drawing pictograms
Drawing scatter graphs
Drawing histograms
Drawing frequency polygons
Time series graphs

CORE

2 Questionnaires
Taking samples
Asking biased questions
Asking leading questions
Obtaining a notion of fairness

3 Stem and leaf diagrams
Drawing stem and leaf diagrams

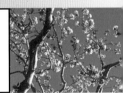

QUESTIONS

EXTENSION

TEST YOURSELF

CORE

1 Presenting data

Ian Hatem is the Headteacher of Adeney School. He is preparing a report for parents on the Key Stage 3 results in Maths, English and Science.

He has to report separately on boys' and girls' results. He has to decide which diagrams are best to make the results clear to the parents.

Here are some of the diagrams he has produced so far.

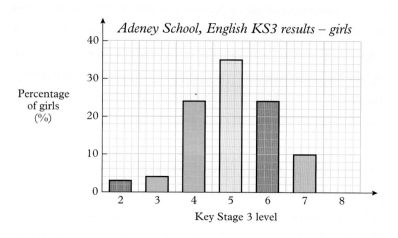

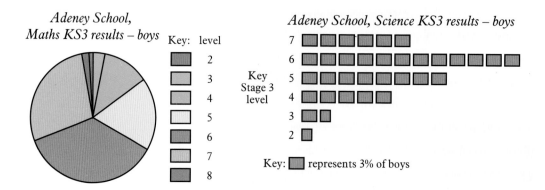

Exercise 3:1

1 Look at the bar-chart.
- **a** What percentage of girls gained level 7 in English?
- **b** What percentage of girls gained more than level 4?
- **c** Which is the modal level?
- **d** There are 5 girls who gained level 7.
  How many girls gained level 6?

2 Look at the pie-chart.
- **a** What level are most boys at in Maths?
- **b** Estimate the percentage of boys who gained level 7.
- **c** Estimate the fraction of boys who gained level 6.

3 Look at the pictogram.
- **a** What percentage of the boys does ▨ stand for?
- **b** What percentage of boys gained level 6 in their test?
- **c** What percentage of boys gained level 3?
- **d** 100 boys sat the Science test. How many boys passed at level 5?

4 Look at the 3 diagrams.
- **a** Explain the advantages of each diagram for displaying the data.
  (Think about whether you can read the percentages off the diagrams accurately.)
- **b** Explain the disadvantages of each diagram for displaying the data.

▼W 5 Draw a bar-chart of the English results for boys at Bishop's School, using the data on Worksheet 3:1. Don't forget a title and labels.

▼W 6 Draw a pictogram to show the Science results at Bishop's School for the girls. Make sure that your diagram has a key.

One of the diagrams that Mr Hatem is considering is a pie-chart.
All the data he is using is in percentages.

Pie-chart

A **pie-chart** shows how something is divided up.
The angle of the sector represents the number of items.
It is not useful for reading off accurate figures.

Example

This table shows the percentage of boys gaining each level in the Key Stage 3 Maths tests.

Level	2	3	4	5	6	7	8
Percentage of boys	1	6	15	24	24	18	12

Show these results in a pie-chart.

1 Divide up the 360°.
There is 100% in total. 1% = 360° ÷ 100 = 3.6°

2 Work out the angle for each level.
This is easy to do in a table.
You will need to round the angles to the nearest degree.

Level	Percentage	Working	Angle	Angle (rounded)
2	1	1 × 3.6°	3.6°	4°
3	6	6 × 3.6°	21.6°	22°
4	15	15 × 3.6°	54°	54°
5	24	24 × 3.6°	86.4°	86°
6	24	24 × 3.6°	86.4°	86°
7	18	18 × 3.6°	64.8°	65°
8	12	12 × 3.6°	43.2°	43°

3 Check that the angles add up to 360°:
4 + 22 + 54 + 86 + 86 + 65 + 43 = 360

When the angles have been rounded, they might not add up to 360°.
If this is the case, add or take 1° from the biggest angle.
It will never be noticed!

4 **a** Draw a circle. Mark the centre.
Draw a line to the top of the
circle.

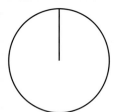

c Measure the next angle (22°)
from the line that you have
just drawn.

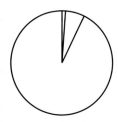

b Draw the first angle (4°).

d Carry on until you have
drawn all the angles.

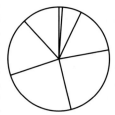

e Colour your pie-chart. Add a key.

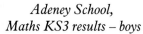

*Adeney School,
Maths KS3 results – boys*

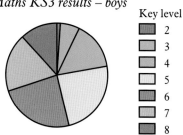

Key level

▓	2
☐	3
☐	4
☐	5
▓	6
☐	7
▓	8

Each section of the pie-chart is a
sector of the circle.

Exercise 3:2

1 **a** Look at the data for Adeney School boys' Maths results on
Worksheet 3:1.
Copy this table.

Level	Percentage	Working	Angle	Angle (rounded)
2	1	1 × 3.6°	3.6°	4°
3	3	3 × 3.6°	10.8°	11°
4	12	12 × 3.6°	43.2°	43°
5	18	18 × 3.6°	64.8°	65°
6				
7				
8				

b Fill in the rest of the table and calculate the angles.
c Check that the angles add up to 360°.
d Draw a pie-chart of this data.
e Add a key and a title to your pie-chart.

2 **a** Look at the girls' Maths results at Adeney School.
Draw a table similar to the one in question **1**.
b Fill in your table. Round off the angles.
c Draw a pie-chart for this data.
d Add a key and a title to your pie-chart.

3 Copy and complete these sentences.
Choose one word each time where there is a choice.

'These two pie-charts are quite similar/different.'
'Slightly/Lots more boys/girls than boys/girls gained a level 5, but more
boys/girls than boys/girls gained a level 7.'

4 a Draw pie-charts for the boys' Maths results at Bishop's School.
You will need to draw a table first.
  b Draw a pie-chart for the girls' Maths results at Bishop's School.
  c Write a couple of sentences about any differences between the two pie-charts
that you have drawn.

The Head also wants to compare the Maths, Science and English results.
He wants to see if the students are doing equally well in all 3 subjects.
He decides to plot the students' results in Maths and Science on a scatter graph.
He uses the actual test scores rather than the levels.

Scatter graph

A **scatter graph** is a diagram that is used to see if there is a
connection between two sets of data.
One value goes on the x axis and the other on the y axis.
It doesn't matter which way round they go.

This is a scatter graph showing test results in Maths and Science.
If a student scores **35** in Maths and **40** in Science, a point is
plotted at (**35**, **40**).

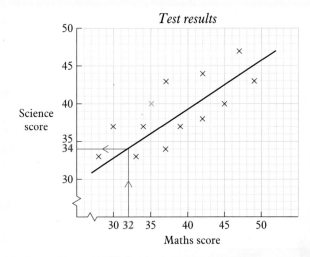

Line of best fit

The points on this graph lie roughly in a straight line.
This line is called a **line of best fit**. It goes through the middle
of the points.

The line of best fit is used to estimate other data values.
To do this, draw from one axis to the line and then to the other axis.

Example

Ben scored 32 in Maths but missed the Science test.
Work out an estimate for his Science score.

(1) Find **32** on the Maths axis.

(2) Draw a line up to the line of best fit.

(3) Draw across to the Science axis.

(4) Read off the Science score.

The estimate is shown by the **red** line on the graph.
The estimate for science is **34**.

Exercise 3:3

1 Here are the Maths and Science results for some pupils in 9P.

Maths	27	34	26	28	34	27	40	21	35	27	29
Science	29	38	22	29	27	32	43	20	32	25	31

  a Plot a scatter graph for this data.
     Scale both your axes from 20 to 45.
  b Draw a line of best fit on your graph.
  c Dave scored 33 in Maths. Use your line to estimate his score in
     Science.

2 These are the English results for the same pupils in 9P.

    English: 35 40 20 22 28 21 35 29 30 26 40

  a Draw a scatter graph of Maths against English.
  b Draw a line of best fit on your graph.
  c Liam scored 37 in English.
     Use your line to estimate his score in Maths.

3 **a** Draw a scatter graph of the Science and English scores.
  b Draw a line of best fit on your graph.
  c Louise scored 37 in English.
     Use your line to estimate her score in Science.

3

Correlation	**Correlation** is a measurement of how strongly connected two sets of data are.
	There are different types of correlation.

Positive correlation	This scatter graph shows the weights and heights of people. As the weight increases so does the height. This is **positive correlation**.	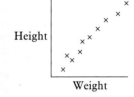

Negative correlation	This graph shows the values of cars and their ages. As age increases, value decreases. This is **negative correlation**.	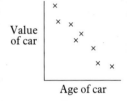

Zero correlation	This graph shows the height of some students against their maths scores. There is no connection between these two things. There is **zero correlation**.	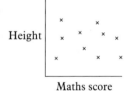

Correlation can be strong or weak.

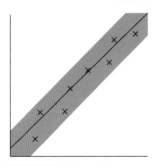   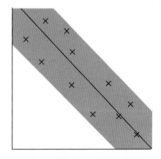

Strong correlation
The points all lie close to the line of best fit.

Weak correlation
The points are well spread out from the line of best fit but still follow the trend.

Exercise 3:4

1 The ages of 10 Ford Escorts and their sale values are shown in this table.

Age	3	6	5	4	2	6	5	3	6	5
Value (£)	6000	2500	2900	3500	6500	2300	3100	5800	2100	3300

   a Plot a scatter graph to show this data.
   b Draw a line of best fit.
   c Describe the type of correlation that this data shows.
   d Estimate the age of a Ford Escort that is worth £5500.
   e Estimate the value of $3\frac{1}{2}$ year old Ford Escort.

2 Two judges awarded marks in an art competition.
Judge A scored out of 20. Judge B scored out of 15.
Here are the results of the judging for 10 paintings.

Judge A	15	12	8	19	7	6	17	8	15	16
Judge B	12	9	7	13	8	3	12	5	12	14

   a Plot a scatter graph to show this data.
   b Draw a line of best fit.
   c Describe the type of correlation that this data shows.
   d Judge A gives a piece of work 14 marks.
      Estimate the score Judge B would give.

3 LoPrice supermarkets are doing a survey of their customers.
They asked how many visits people made to the supermarket during a 3 month
period. They also asked how far away from the store the people lived.
Here are the results for 15 customers.

Number of visits	9	7	12	11	14	12	6
Length of journey (miles)	7	5	5	8	3	4	8

Number of visits	8	15	13	5	12	2	9
Length of journey (miles)	5	3	6	10	1	7	6

   a Plot a scatter graph to show this data.
   b Draw a line of best fit.
   c Describe the type of correlation that this data shows.
   d Estimate the number of visits made by a shopper living 9 miles away.
   e Say how reliable you think this estimate is.
      What other factors could affect your answer?

The Head of the Maths department is looking at the Maths results in more detail.
She is looking at the marks the pupils scored, not just the levels.
She decides to draw a histogram to show the results.

Histogram

A **histogram** looks like a bar-chart but there are several important differences.

- It can only be used to show **continuous** numerical data. This means that you can't draw a histogram of favourite colours. Data is continuous when it can take any value in a certain range. When data can only take certain individual values (like the levels in the previous exercise) it is called **discrete** data.

- Data for a histogram is always grouped. You must make the widths of all the groups the same.
  The height of the bar then tells you the number in each group.

- The scale along the bottom of a histogram must be like a graph scale like this:

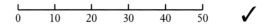

✓

You never label it in categories like this:

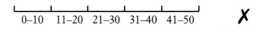

✗

Exercise 3:5

1 Look at this histogram.
It shows the Maths results at Adeney School.
  a How many pupils scored between 0 and 10?
  b How many pupils scored between 30 and 40?
  c How many pupils scored more than 70?

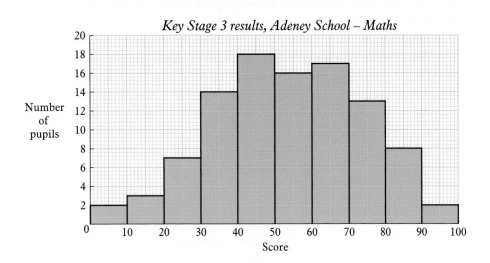

2 Here are the same results for Bishop's School.

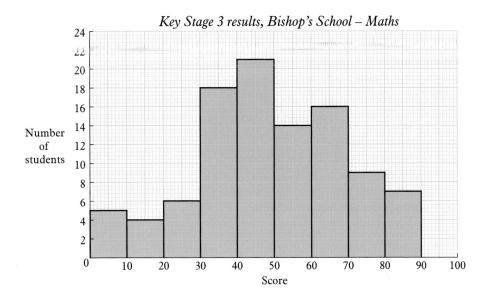

a How many pupils scored between 20 and 30?
b How many pupils scored between 40 and 60?
c How many pupils are there altogether?

3 Here are the scores for the Science exams at Adeney School.

Score	0 up to 10	10 up to 20	20 up to 30	30 up to 40	40 up to 50
Number of pupils	3	10	8	14	18

Score	50 up to 60	60 up to 70	70 up to 80	80 up to 90	90 up to 100
Number of pupils	16	17	9	3	2

Draw a histogram of these results. Don't forget labels and a title.

4 Here are the scores for the Science exams at Bishop's School.

Score	0 up to 10	10 up to 20	20 up to 30	30 up to 40	40 up to 50
Number of pupils	2	7	6	14	19

Score	50 up to 60	60 up to 70	70 up to 80	80 up to 90	90 up to 100
Number of pupils	20	13	8	7	4

Draw a histogram of these results.
Don't forget labels and a title.

5 The Headteacher at Adeney School is also looking at attendance figures.
Each pupil can attend a maximum of 380 half days per year.
Here are the attendance figures for Year 9 last year:

Number of sessions attended	Number of pupils
100 up to 140	1
140 up to 180	2
180 up to 220	4
220 up to 260	9
260 up to 300	15
300 up to 340	37
340 up to 380	32

a Draw these axes on graph paper.
Continue the vertical scale up to 40
and the horizontal scale across to 380.
b Draw a histogram to show the attendance data.

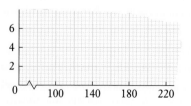

6 Here are the attendance figures for Bishop's School.

Number of sessions attended	Number of pupils
100 up to 140	0
140 up to 180	1
180 up to 220	6
220 up to 260	12
260 up to 300	16
300 up to 340	25
340 up to 380	40

a Draw these axes on graph paper. Continue the vertical scale up to 40 and the horizontal scale across to 380.

b Draw a histogram to show this data.

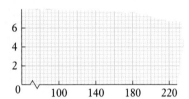

Frequency polygon

Frequency polygons are often used to compare two sets of data. You use straight lines to join up the mid points of the top of the bars. This makes a frequency polygon

This diagram shows a histogram with the **frequency polygon** drawn in **red**. You must make sure that you use straight lines to join the **mid-points** of the tops of the bars.

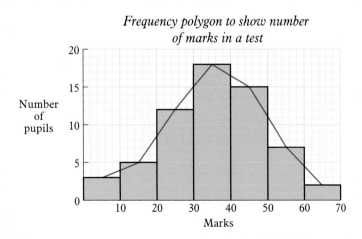

Frequency polygon to show number of marks in a test

Exercise 3:6

1 Look at this histogram. It shows the Maths Key Stage 3 results for Adeney School.

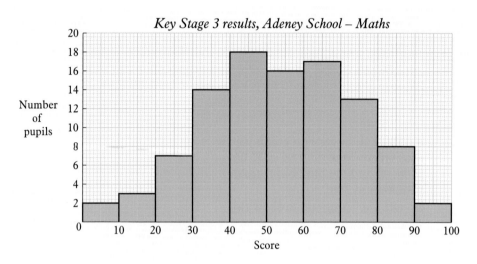

Key Stage 3 results, Adeney School – Maths

a Copy the histogram on to graph paper.
b Put a small cross in the middle of the top of each bar.
c Join up your crosses with straight lines.
   You have now drawn a frequency polygon.

It is possible to draw a frequency polygon without drawing the histogram first. This table shows the scores of Year 7 pupils in a French test.

Score	0 up to 10	10 up to 20	20 up to 30	30 up to 40	40 up to 50
Number of pupils	4	8	16	20	12

To draw a frequency polygon

(1) First work out the mid-point of each group in the table.
   This is easy to do by adding a row to the table.

Score	0 up to 10	10 up to 20	20 up to 30	30 up to 40	40 up to 50
Number of pupils	4	8	16	20	12
Mid-point	5	15	25	35	45

(2) Label the horizontal axis like this:

(3) The vertical axis shows the number of pupils.

(4) Plot the mid-points and join them with straight lines.

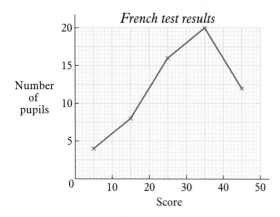

(5) You can label the vertical axis 'Frequency' if you want to

2   This table shows the scores of Year 7 pupils in a Science test.

Score	0 up to 10	10 up to 20	20 up to 30	30 up to 40	40 up to 50
Number of pupils	0	6	14	26	14

a   Copy the table and add another row.
    Write 'mid-point' at the beginning of this row.
b   Work out the mid-point of each group and complete the table.
c   Draw a pair of axes using the same scale as question 1.
d   Draw the frequency polygon by plotting the mid points and joining
    them up with straight lines.
e   Don't forget labels and a title.

3 Here are the scores for the English tests at Adeney School.

Score	0 up to 10	10 up to 20	20 up to 30	30 up to 40	40 up to 50
Number of pupils	2	8	12	18	20
Mid-point	5	15	25		

Score	50 up to 60	60 up to 70	70 up to 80	80 up to 90	90 up to 100
Number of pupils	22	15	1	0	2
Mid-point					

a Copy the table.
b Fill in the mid-points.
   The first few have been done for you.
c Draw these axes on graph paper.
   Continue the vertical scale up to 25
   and the horizontal scale across to 100.
d Draw a frequency polygon of the results.

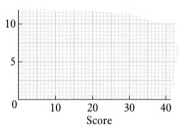

4 Here are the scores for the English tests at Bishop's School.

Score	0 up to 10	10 up to 20	20 up to 30	30 up to 40	40 up to 50
Number of pupils	0	2	7	10	13
Mid-point					

Score	50 up to 60	60 up to 70	70 up to 80	80 up to 90	90 up to 100
Number of pupils	17	15	18	10	8
Mid-point					

a Copy the table and fill it in.
b Draw a frequency polygon of the results.
   Use the same axes as question **3**.
c Look at the frequency polygon for Adeney School in question **3**.
   Write down the main differences between the English test results at
   these schools.

Trend   The mid-points are joined together in a frequency polygon to
show the **trend**. The **trend** shows how the data is changing.

---

5 Here are the results of the Science tests at Adeney School and Bishop's School.

Score	0 up to 10	10 up to 20	20 up to 30	30 up to 40	40 up to 50
Pupils at Adeney	3	10	9	16	18
Pupils at Bishop's	2	7	6	10	19

Score	50 up to 60	60 up to 70	70 up to 80	80 up to 90	90 up to 100
Pupils at Adeney	16	14	9	3	2
Pupils at Bishop's	22	15	7	8	4

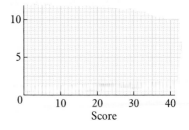

  a Copy the tables.
  b Add a new row and work out the mid-
     points.
  c Draw these axes on graph paper.
     Continue the vertical scale up to 25
     and the horizontal scale across to 100.
  d Draw a frequency polygon for both
     schools on the same graph.
     Don't forget labels and a title.

6 Look carefully at the two frequency polygons in question 5.
  Write a brief report describing the trend in each graph and the
  differences between the graphs.
  Here are some hints to help you write your report.
  ● Which school has the most students scoring
     in the 0–45 range?
  ● How do the graphs show you this?
  ● Which school is doing better in this range?
  ● Which school has the least students scoring
     in the 45–95 range?
  ● How do the graphs show you this?
  ● Which school is doing better in this range?
  ● What do you notice about the general trend
     of both graphs?
  ● Which school do you think produced the
     'better/worse' set of results?

7 Miss Carver is a new Mathematics teacher at Bishop's School.
She is helping her Year 10 class with their coursework.
They have collected information on weekly pocket money from the
pupils in the school.
This table shows their results.

Pocket money (£)	0 up to 2	2 up to 4	4 up to 6	6 up to 8	8 up to 10	10 up to 12
Girls	38	68	88	32	22	18
Boys	34	58	106	56	30	12

a Copy the table.
b Add a new row and work out the mid-points.
c Draw a frequency polygon for boys and girls on the same graph.
d Don't forget the labels and titles.
e Write a brief report for Miss Carver comparing boys' and girls'
pocket money.

8 Bishop's Belters and Adeney Acers are two cycle clubs.
This table shows the number of cyclists from each club that achieved
various speeds in a time trial.

Speed (mph)	5 up to 10	10 up to 15	15 up to 20	20 up to 25	25 up to 30	30 up to 35
Bishop's Belters	13	23	36	20	6	2
Adeney Acers	20	25	32	19	9	0

a Draw a frequency polygon for both clubs.
Use the same set of axes.
b The trainers for both clubs write separate reports for the local
newspaper comparing the results.
(1) Write the Bishop's Belters report.
(2) Write the Adeney Acers report.

9 Doctor Jones and Doctor Hay recorded
the time spent with each of their
patients at their surgery.
The table shows the results.

Time spent (minutes)	Dr Jones (no. of patients)	Dr Hay (no. of patients)
0 up to 5	14	10
5 up to 10	14	11
10 up to 15	10	15
15 up to 20	8	9
20 up to 25	4	5

a Draw a frequency polygon for each
doctor.
Put both diagrams on the same pair
of axes.
b What conclusions can you come to
from the two sets of results?

Time series graphs

Time series graphs are used to show trends in statistics.
This graph shows the trends in work over the last 50 years.

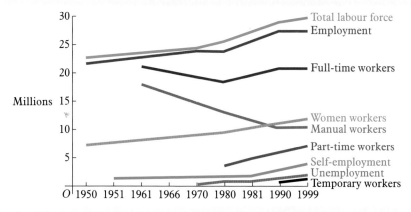

Exercise 3:7

Answer questions **1** and **2** by reading the information from the graph above.

1 **a** How many people were working full time in 1961?
    b How many people were working full time in 1999?
    c How many manual workers were there in 1961?
    d How many manual workers were there in 1999?

2 Copy these and fill in the gaps.
    a Between 1961 and 1999 the number of full time workers has …
    b Between 1961 and 1999 the number of manual workers has …
    c The trend is for … people to work part time.
    d The trend is for … people to be self-employed.
    e The trend is for … people to have manual jobs.

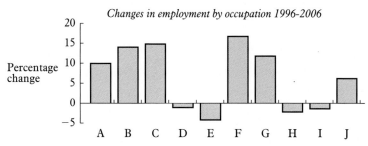

A – managers and administrators
B – professional occupations
C – associate professional and technical
D – clerical and secretarial
E – craft and skilled manual
F – personal and protective services
G – sales occupations
H – plant and machine operatives
I – other occupations
J – whole economy (excludes armed forces)

3 Look at the graph on the previous page which shows changes in the types of job that people may have. The graph is a prediction.

   a Which type of job is predicted to increase the most?

   b Which type of job is predicted to decrease the most?

   c Which type of job is predicted to increase by 10%?

● **d** Which type of job is predicted to increase the least?

4 Look at this graph. It shows car ownership since 1950.

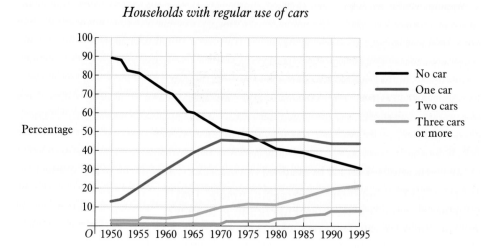

Households with regular use of cars

   a What percentage of families did not have a car in 1950?

   b What percentage of families did not have a car in 1995?

   c Describe the trend in families without a car.

● **d** Why has the number of families with one car levelled out whilst the total number of cars has gone up?

5 This table shows the number of people who attend different types of churches. The numbers are in thousands.

	1980	1985	1990	1995	2000	2005
Anglican	968	921	918	839	794	748
Baptist	201	196	198	213	224	230
Methodist	438	421	395	347	313	279

a Copy these axes onto graph paper.

b Plot a graph to show the number of people who attend an Anglican church in each year.

c Plot the graphs for the Baptist and the Methodist churches **on the same axes**.

d Write a sentence to describe the trend for each type of church.

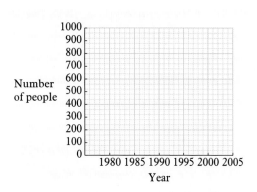

6 This table shows how spending on certain items has changed since 1971. The numbers in the table come from setting the amounts in 1971 at 100 and then comparing the amounts in each of the other years to this. These are called index numbers.

	1971	1981	1986	1991	1996
Food	100	104	109	115	125
Alcohol	100	127	134	132	131
Tobacco	100	89	74	71	59
Recreation	100	112	156	102	206

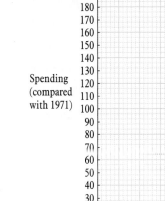

a Copy these axes onto graph paper.

b Plot the graph for Food.

c Plot the graphs for Alcohol, Tobacco and Recreation on the same axes. Use different colours if you can.

d Which type of spending has increased the most?

e Which type of spending has decreased the most? Say why you think this is.

7 This graph shows how the UK population is expected to change up to the year 2051. Write about the trends in this graph.

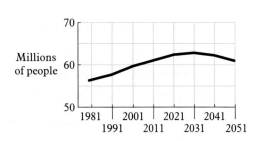

2 Questionnaires

To get information, you often need to ask questions.

The questions have to be carefully thought out.

You also have to decide who you are going to ask.

If you want to know what the people living in Derbyshire think of their bus services, you can't ask them all! You can only ask a small number of people. These people have to represent everyone in Derbyshire.

Sample   A small group of people who represent a much larger group of people is called a **sample**.

You need to make sure you get a good spread of people so that your sample represents a wide range of views.

Exercise 3:8

1 Imagine you are doing a survey about what people think of the bus services in your area.
Read this list of ideas for choosing the sample.
   a All the people taking part should be regular bus users.
   b Choose a Saturday for the survey when the buses are busiest.
   c Make sure that half the sample are men and half are women.
   d Don't ask people with bus passes, because they don't have to pay.
   e Do the survey in the middle of the day when most of the shoppers are using the buses.
   f Make sure there is a good spread of ages.
   g Just ask people 'What do you think of the bus service?'
Asking lots of small questions will take too much time.

2 Say which ideas in question **1** you think are sensible and which are not. Just write down the letter of each idea.

3 For each idea you think is not sensible, write down your reason. For each bad idea, write down what you think would be more sensible.

Once you have decided on a sensible sample, you must then plan your questions. It is very important that your questions are not biased.

Biased	A question is **biased** if it makes you think that one particular answer is right. A question that does this is called a **leading question**.
Example	This is a leading question: 'Most people think the bus service is poor. Do you agree?' The question should not say 'Most people think ...' It is leading people to agree.

Exercise 3·9

Here is a list of questions.
a 'Do you think the bus service is better than it used to be?'
b 'Most people think that the buses should run more often? Do you agree?'
c 'Which bus company in your area gives the best service?'
d 'Richer people tend to have their own car or use taxis. Do you use buses or cars and taxis?'
e 'Do you think smoking should be banned on buses?'
f 'School children often behave badly on buses. Do you think all children should travel on special school buses?'

1   Which of the questions do you think is biased?
    Write down their letters.

2   Write down what makes these questions biased.

3   Write better questions to replace the ones that you thought were biased.

It is important to choose the right size for your sample. It would not be sensible to ask just 10 people in Derbyshire what they thought of the buses and hope that this would represent the whole of the county. 1000 would be the minimum.

Reliable

Surveys that have a sensible sample size are called **reliable**. This means that it is likely that the sample represents the views of all of the people.

You often hear about **margins of error** when surveys are reported on TV. More reliable surveys have smaller margins of error.

Exercise 3:10

Suggest sensible sample sizes for each of the surveys in questions 1–5.

1   Music survey amongst 100 Year 10 pupils.

2   School uniform survey in a school of size 650.

3   Computer games survey from 20 000 magazine readers.

4   Survey on the standards of bus services in a city of 200 000 people.

5   Survey of TV programmes watched on a Saturday night in the whole of the UK.

Exercise 3:11

Read these descriptions of how surveys were organised.
For each one, say what is wrong with the organisation.
Also say how the survey could be improved.

Think about:

(1) The sample of people.
(2) The time of the survey.
(3) The size of the sample.
(4) The questions that were asked.

1 A bus company wanted to know how many people in a town used their buses. One Monday morning, they telephoned 200 people and asked them if they used their buses.

2 Rajiv wanted to know how many people in his school had school lunch. He asked the 30 pupils in his Year 10 group, 'Are you having a school lunch today?'

3 Nathan is doing a survey for his Sports Studies exam. He wants to know how much exercise Year 10 pupils do. He asks all 55 people who take Sports Studies how many hours exercise they do each week. He plans to change his answers to percentages and use them to write a report about the whole school.

4 Dangerfield's supermarket want to know if people in a local town would like a new large supermarket. Their researcher stands outside a local corner shop all day on a Monday and asks everyone questions which include:

a Do you think supermarkets are cheaper than small shops?

b Do you get a wider choice in larger shops?

c Isn't it easier to pay for your shopping using a credit card?

d Do you find that the fruit is fresher in a large supermarket?

e Do you like being offered extra services such as dry cleaning and film processing?

f Would you like to see a new out-of-town supermarket in this area?

3   Stem and leaf diagrams

There is another way of showing data. You split the data values into two parts.
The first part is called the stem and the second part is called the leaf. This is like a branch of this tree which has its leaves growing out from the stem.

Stem and leaf diagram

A **stem and leaf diagram** shows the shape of a set of data. It is like a bar chart with the numbers forming the bars.

Example

These are the times, in minutes, taken by 10 pupils to solve a page of puzzles.

   18   25   23   31   20   19   28   35   22   33

Draw a stem and leaf diagram to show these times.

Each number has a tens digit and a unit digit   e.g.   **18**, **35**

The tens digits form the stems, the units digits form the leaves.

Stem	Leaf
1	8 9
2	5 3 0 8 2
3	1 5 3

Now put the leaves (units) in size order.

Give your diagram a title and a key.

Times taken by pupils to solve puzzles

Stem	Leaf
1	8 9
2	0 2 3 5 8
3	1 3 5

Key: 2|3 means 23 minutes

Exercise 3:12

1 The stem and leaf diagram
shows the ages, in years,
of a group of people.
  a What is the age of
   (1) the youngest
   (2) the eldest?
  b How many people are in
   the group?

Ages of people

Stem	Leaf
1	4 7 8 8 9
2	0 1 3 5 5 8
3	4 5 8 9
4	0 2 3 5
5	2 7

Key: 4|2 means 42 years

2 These are the highest daytime temperatures, in °C, in Adeney during a
two-week period in August.

    18   20   19   21   25   17   23
    22   16   17   29   18   24   30

Draw a stem and leaf diagram to show this data.

These are the weekly attendances at a sports club for eight weeks.

    351   169   265   291   304   178   250   265

With larger numbers you need to decide how to split them into a stem and leaves.

Use the hundreds unit for the stem.

Stem	Leaf
1	69 78
2	65 91 50 65
3	51 4

Putting the leaves in order gives
the final diagram.

Weekly attendance

Stem	Leaf
1	69 78
2	50 65 65 91
3	4 51

Key: 2|65 means 265

---

3 Dawn has done a survey on the miles travelled by people on an intercity
train. These are her results.

    234   189   306   271   165   284   316   166   217   178   305

Draw a stem and leaf diagram to show this data.

4 Rory measures the lengths in centimetres of 20 earthworms. These are his results.

> 7.5 4.8 3.9 5.1 3.5 4.7 8.2 4.3 6.0 5.7
> 8.5 4.6 7.7 3.8 4.2 5.4 4.8 6.1 4.2 5.8

Draw a stem and leaf diagram for this data.
Use the units for the stem and the first decimal place for the leaves.
Don't forget a key.

Some stem and leaf diagrams have a
small number of stems and a lot of leaves.
This diagram shows the ages of people
in a block of retirement flats.

Stem	Leaf
6	1 2 3 3 5 6 7 8 8 9
7	0 2 2 3 3 4 5 6 7 7 8
8	1 1 4 6 8 9 9

For this type of diagram you split
each stem number into two rows.
The first row contains the
leaves 0, 1, 2, 3 and 4.
The second row contains
the leaves 5, 6, 7, 8 and 9.

Stem	Leaf
6	1 2 3 3
6	5 6 7 8 8 9
7	0 2 2 3 3 4
7	5 6 7 7 8
8	1 1 4
8	6 8 9 9

Key: 7|2 means 72

---

5 Mr Williams has to write 24 reports for his form.
He recorded the time it took to write each report.
These are his times in minutes.

> 7.8 6.3 7.2 8.1 6.5 7.0 7.7 6.0 8.4 7.1 6.7 8.9
> 6.8 7.5 7.2 8.2 8.9 7.1 6.6 7.4 6.5 7.5 7.0 6.8

Draw a stem and leaf diagram to show his results.
Use two rows for each different stem value.

6 Tom is testing a machine to check that it delivers the correct weight
of sweets.
He takes a sample of 20 packets and weighs them.
These are his results.
The weights are in grams.

> 248 244 237 240 237 245 240 247 236 249
> 235 234 246 250 232 238 245 241 239 251

Using two rows for each stem, draw a stem and leaf diagram to show
Tom's data.
Use the values 23, 24, ... as the stems.

1 Alison asked her friends for their star signs.
Here are her results.

Star sign	♈	♉	♊	♋	♌	♍	♎	♏	♐	♑	♒	♓
Number of friends	4	5	2	7	1	3	2	3	2	4	1	2

  a How many friends did Alison ask?
  b Draw a pie-chart to show the star signs.
     You will need to draw a table first.
  c Colour your pie-chart. Don't forget to add a key and a title.

2 Simon read an article about the daily activities for an average teenager.
He was surprised to read the following information.

Activity	Time (h)
sleeping	7
eating	1.5
at school	6.5
travelling to and from school	1
watching television	2.5
playing tapes/CDs	2
doing homework	1.5
on the telephone	0.5
other	1.5

  a Draw a pie-chart to show these activities.
  b What activities could be in the 'other' category?

3 Sinita did a survey on the favourite sports at her school.
These are her results for 300 pupils.

Sport	hockey	football	basketball	tennis	swimming
Number of pupils	42	88	64	30	76

Draw a pictogram to show these sports.
Don't forget to add a key and a title.

4 Helen is designing hats. She needs to know how to make them.
She measures the head circumference of 100 friends in centimetres to the nearest centimetre.
She represents her results in a histogram.

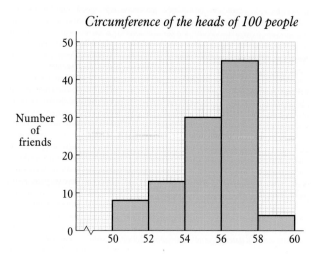

Circumference of the heads of 100 people

a Copy the table.
b Fill it in. Leave the third row empty for now.

Head circumference (cm)	50 up to 52	52 up to 54	54 up to 56	56 up to 58	58 up to 60
Number of friends	8				

c Write 'mid-point' in the third row of the table and fill it in.
d Draw a frequency polygon of Helen's results.
e What advice would you give Helen for making the hats?

5 Richard and Pauline were looking at some old questionnaires.
These are some of the questions they found.
(1) 'Do you think chocolate is bad for you?'
(2) 'Don't you think that soaps are the best programmes on television?'
(3) 'Do you agree that only rich people go on winter ski holidays?'
(4) 'Most people prefer to live in the city and not the country. Don't you agree?'
(5) 'Do you regularly use the town library?'
    a Which of these questions do you think are biased?
    b Write down what makes these questions biased.
    c Write better questions in place of the ones that are biased.

6 The stem and leaf diagram shows the ages of some of Naomi's relatives.
Write down the age of:
  a the oldest
  b the youngest

Stem	Leaf
1	2 3 3 5 6
2	0 2 7
3	6 8
4	5 6 9
5	1

Key: 4|6 means 46 years

7 Rory measures the time for a ball to roll down a track in his Physics lesson. He does this 12 times. This is his data.
The times are to the nearest second.

24 18 25 31 25 32
20 19 20 17 36 22

Draw a stem and leaf diagram to show this data.
Don't forget to include a key.

8 Cara cycles to school each day. She writes down how long each journey takes. She does this for two weeks.
These are her times to the nearest tenth of a minute.

6.8 8.4 7.3 8.0 7.9 6.2 7.1 7.5 6.8 7.6

Draw a stem and leaf diagram to show this data.
Don't forget to include a key.

9 Mrs Rice entered 18 students for a piano exam.
These are the marks that they scored.

105 127 139 108 114 128 140 137 112
138 126 120 128 130 119 127 132 121

Draw a stem and leaf diagram to show this data.

1 Lucinda did a survey on how many bars of chocolate were bought by 30 school friends in one week. Here are her results.

$$12 \quad 3 \quad 6 \quad 16 \quad 22 \quad 6 \quad 9 \quad 10 \quad 15 \quad 12 \quad 25 \quad 7 \quad 5 \quad 18 \quad 11$$
$$19 \quad 5 \quad 9 \quad 6 \quad 14 \quad 17 \quad 21 \quad 5 \quad 13 \quad 15 \quad 9 \quad 7 \quad 12 \quad 5 \quad 8$$

a Copy the table.
b Fill it in. The table has been started for you.

Number of bars of chocolate	0 up to 5	5 up to 10	10 up to 15	15 up to 20	20 up to 25	25 up to 30
Frequency	1					

c Draw a histogram to show these results.
d Which interval has the largest frequency?
e Why do you think this is?

2 The table shows the number of accidents in four districts.

District	North	East	South	West
Number of accidents	432	696	184	328

The results are to be displayed in a pictogram.

Which key would you choose from the following?

a = 8 vehicles   **c** = 100 vehicles

b = 200 vehicles   **d** = 50 vehicles

Give a reason for your choice.

3 The table shows some Key Stage 3 results in three subjects.

Key Stage 3 level	2	3	4	5	6	7	8
English	2%	10%	23%	31%	18%	7%	1%
Mathematics	2%	11%	28%	21%	12%	20%	4%
Science	2%	9%	26%	35%	17%	4%	0%

a Draw a frequency polygon to show these results on one graph. Use a different colour for each subject.
b Write a report to explain the differences between the subjects.

1 Pam has done a survey on the drinks sold from the drinks machine in the youth club. This is her data for one evening.

Drink	cola	orange	water
Number sold	27	11	22

Draw a pie-chart to show this data.

Use a table to work out the angles.

2 Arum is looking at widths and lengths of pebbles for a science project. The table shows his data for 10 pebbles.

Length (mm)	23	50	15	33	58	10	43	23	55	35
Width (mm)	19	34	13	22	40	13	30	16	35	27

  a Plot a scatter graph to show this data.

  b What type of correlation does your graph show?

  c Draw a line of best fit on your graph.

  d Use your line to estimate the length of a pebble with width 21 mm.

3 Paula recorded how long she took to read each chapter of her book. This is her data.

Time (minutes)	Number of chapters
0 up to 5	3
5 up to 10	5
10 up to 15	8
15 up to 20	4
20 up to 25	1

  a Draw a histogram to show this data.

  b Use your histogram to draw a frequency polygon for the data.

4 The graph shows how the numbers of people using different forms of transport has changed in the last 50 years.
Write about the trends shown in the graph.

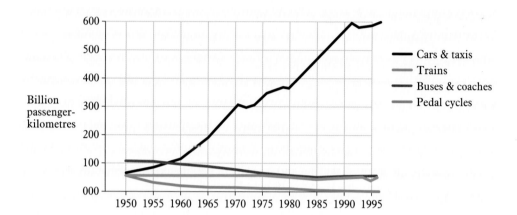

5 Keith records how long it takes him to swim a length of the swimming pool. These are his results.
They are written to the nearest second.

35 28 41 39 32 27 30
44 29 31 38 40 42 36

Draw a stem and leaf diagram to show this data.

6 Janine has grown 15 sunflowers.
The diagram shows the heights of these sunflowers.

Stem	Leaf
14	3 7 9
15	1 3 6 7
16	0 5 5 8 9
17	1 3 4

Key: 15|3 means 153 cm

a What is the height of the tallest sunflower?
b Two sunflowers are the same height.
What is this height?

4 Patterns: lining up

1 Patterns in numbers
Odd numbers
Even numbers
Multiples
Lowest common multiples
Factors
Prime factors
Highest common factor (HCF)
Square numbers
Triangle numbers
Number sequencing
Number sequencing from patterns and shapes

CORE

2 Finding a formula
Formulas for sequences using times tables
Two part formulas for sequences
Finding formulas for patterns with shapes

QUESTIONS

EXTENSION

TEST YOURSELF

1   Patterns in numbers

You can use patterns in number to help you do calculations in your head quickly.

There is a quick way of adding the numbers 1 to 5:

$1 + 2 + 3 + 4 + 5$ Write the numbers this way.

$\dfrac{5 + 4 + 3 + 2 + 1}{6 + 6 + 6 + 6 + 6}$ Write the numbers round the other way.
Add each pair of numbers.

$6 + 6 + 6 + 6 + 6 = 30$ Each pair gives the answer 6.
                                    (1 more than 5)
              $5 \times 6 = 30$ There are 5 pairs.

so $5 \times (5 + 1) = 30$

But you wrote the numbers out twice.
You need to halve the answer.

So $1 + 2 + 3 + 4 + 5 = 30 \div 2$
                              $= 15$

Example   Add the numbers 1 to 10.

Each pair will give the answer 11   (1 more than 10)
There will be 10 pairs.
$10 \times 11 = 110$
The answer is $110 \div 2 = 55$

Exercise 4:1

Use the method given above to add these numbers.

1   1 to 4   **3**   1 to 8   **5**   1 to 100

2   1 to 6   **4**   1 to 20   **6**   1 to 1000

These are some special types of numbers:

Odd numbers	The **odd numbers** are	1, 3, 5, 7, 9, 11, 13, ...
Even numbers	The **even numbers** are	2, 4, 6, 8, 10, 12, 14, ...
Multiples	The **multiples** of 2 are	2, 4, 6, 8, 10, 12, 14, ...
	The **multiples** of 5 are	5, 10, 15, 20, 25, 30, ...
	The **multiples** of 12 are	12, 24, 36, 48, 60, 72, ...

7 From the numbers 8, 9, 10, 11, 12, 13, 14, 15, 16
write down the numbers which are
   a even   **b** odd   **c** multiples of 4

8 Write down the first five multiples of 10.

9 Find each of these numbers using the clues.
   a It is a multiple of 10   **b** It is a multiple of 5
      It is a multiple of 4   It is less than 60
      It is less than 35   It is a multiple of 9

You can use multiples to solve problems

Example	Paul and David are playing arcade games.
	Paul's game takes 3 minutes to play.
	David's game takes 5 minutes to play.
	They start playing at the same time.
	How long is it before they finish a game at the same time?

The multiples of 3 are   3, 6, 9, 12, **15**, 18, 21, 24, 27, **30**, 33 ...
The multiples of 5 are   5, 10, **15**, 20, 25, **30**, 35, 40 ...
They both finish after **15** minutes.

Common multiples	The multiples 15 and 30 appear in both lists.
	They are called **common multiples**.
	You can find more common multiples if you write down more multiples of 3 and 5.

Lowest common multiple	15 is the lowest of all the common multiples.
	It is the **lowest common multiple**.

10 Find the lowest common multiple of
   a 5 and 7   **b** 6 and 9

11 Mia and Anne run circuits of the park to get fit.
They both start at the gate at the same time.
Mia takes 4 minutes to do the circuit. Anne takes 5 minutes.
How long will it be until they both arrive at the gate at the same time?

12 Two warning sirens ring at regular intervals.
One rings every 4 seconds and the other every 7 seconds.
They ring together at exactly 8 a.m.
   a What time is it when they both ring at the same time again for the
      first time?
   b What time is it when they ring together for the second time?
   c What time is it when they ring together for the tenth time?

Factor	A number that divides exactly into another number is called a **factor**. Factors are whole numbers. They come in pairs. When a pair of factors are multiplied the answer is the original number.

Example   Find the factors of   **a** 8   **b** 12

              a $8 = 1 \times 8$
                 $8 = 2 \times 4$ 1, 2, 4 and 8 are factors of 8
              b $12 = 1 \times 12$
                 $12 = 2 \times 6$
                 $12 = 3 \times 4$ 1, 2, 3, 4, 6 and 12 are factors of 12

Exercise 4:2

1 Write down the factors of each of these.
   a 6   **b** 16   **c** 20   **d** 30

Prime numbers	**Prime numbers** have only two factors, themselves and 1.

              $17 = 1 \times 17$ No other two numbers multiply to give 17
                                      17 is a prime number.

            The first 6 prime numbers are 2, 3, 5, 7, 11, 13
            1 is **not** a prime number.
            The first prime number is 2. It is the only even prime number.

2   **a**   Write down the factors of each of these numbers 15, 17, 19, 21, 23.
      b   Write down the prime numbers from the list.

3   Look at the numbers 20, 21, 22, 23, 24, 25, 26, 27, 28, 29, 30.
      Write down the numbers that are
      a   prime   **b**   factors of 100   **c**   multiples of 6

4   Find these numbers using the clues.
      a   It is a factor of 28   **b**   It is a factor of 11
         It is an odd prime number   It is not a prime number

---

Prime factors   The factors of 12 are 1, 2, 3, 4, 6, 12
                     The factors 2 and 3 are also prime numbers.
                     2 and 3 are called **prime factors** of 12.

Example   Find the prime factors of 30.

                                                          $30 = 1 \times 30$
                                                          $30 = 2 \times 15$
                     The factors of 30 are 1, 2, 3, 5, 6, 10, 15, 30 $30 = 3 \times 10$
                     The prime factors are 2, 3 and 5 $30 = 6 \times 5$

---

5   Find the prime factors of:
      a   20   **b**   44   **c**   48   **d**   100

                A number can be written as the product of its   24
                prime factors.
                You can use a factor tree to do this.   3   8

Example   Write 24 as a product of its prime factors.
                                                                4   2
                To start the tree use any two factors
                that multiply to give 24.   2   2

                Look at each of these factors.
                If it is prime, circle it and stop.
                If it is not prime, split it into two more factors.

                Multiply all the numbers in circles together. $24 = 3 \times 2 \times 2 \times 2$
                Then put them in order. $24 = 2 \times 2 \times 2 \times 3$

6 Write these numbers as products of their prime factors.

   a 30   **b** 28   **c** 36   **d** 50

7 Write these numbers as products of their prime factors.

   a 40   **b** 30   **c** 100   **d** 210

Common factor	If a number is a factor of two numbers then it is a **common factor.**
Example	Find the common factors of 15 and 40.

The factors of 15 are 1 3 5 15
The factors of 40 are 1 2 4 5 8 10 20 40
The common factors of 15 and 40 are 1 and 5.

Highest common factor	The **highest common factor** of two numbers is the biggest number that is a common factor of both numbers.

In the example above, the highest common factor of 15 and 40 is 5.

HCF	Highest Common Factor can be written as **HCF.**

---

8 Find the HCF of each of these pairs of numbers.
Write out all the factors of each number to help you.

   a 10 and 25   **b** 16 and 24   **c** 48 and 60

9 Find the HCF of the numbers 100, 48 and 56.

It is possible to calculate the HCF of two numbers using prime factors.

Example	Find the HCF of 24 and 30.

First, write each number as the product of prime factors:
$24 = 2 \times 2 \times 2 \times 3$
$30 = 2 \times 3 \times 5$

Then mark the common prime factors: $24 = 2 \times 2 \times 2 \times 3$
$30 = 2 \times 3 \times 5$

The factors have a 2 and a 3 in common.
This means that the HCF of 24 and 30 is $2 \times 3 = 6$.

---

10 Use the method of prime factors to find the HCF of these numbers.

    a 27 and 32   **b** 35 and 48   **c** 30 and 52

You can also use prime factors to spot recurring and terminating decimals.
To use this method, the fraction must be cancelled down to its lowest terms.
Some fractions always produce recurring decimals.
These are fractions which include $\frac{1}{3}$s, $\frac{1}{6}$s, $\frac{1}{7}$s and $\frac{1}{11}$s.

Fractions like $\frac{1}{2}$ and $\frac{1}{5}$ always produce terminating decimals.
These are decimals that do not go on forever.
For example $\frac{1}{2} = 0.5$ and $\frac{1}{5} = 0.2$

To tell if a fraction produces a recurring or a terminating decimal, write its
denominator as a product of prime factors.
If these prime factors are only 2s and 5s then the fraction will produce a terminating
decimal. If you find any other prime numbers then the fraction will produce a
recurring decimal.

Example   Decide if the following fractions are recurring or terminating.

         a $\frac{2}{15}$ **b** $\frac{1}{50}$ **c** $\frac{7}{16}$

        a Write 15 as the product of prime factors.

            $15 = 3 \times 5$

            Because of the 3, $\frac{2}{15}$ will produce a recurring decimal.

        b Write 50 as the product of prime factors.

            $50 = 2 \times 5 \times 5$

            Because there are only 2s and 5s, $\frac{1}{50}$ will produce a terminating
            decimal.

        c $16 = 2 \times 2 \times 2 \times 2$

            Because there are only 2s, $\frac{7}{16}$ produces a terminating decimal.
            The 7 on the top does not affect this.

---

11 Decide whether the fraction $\frac{5}{18}$ produces a recurring or a terminating
decimal.

12 Decide whether the fraction $\frac{7}{20}$ produces a recurring or a terminating
decimal.

13 Decide whether the fraction $\frac{11}{45}$ produces a recurring or a terminating
decimal.

14 Decide whether the fraction $\frac{13}{28}$ produces a recurring or a terminating decimal.

Some numbers are named after dot patterns.

Here are some square patterns.

$1 \times 1 = 1 \qquad 2 \times 2 = 4 \qquad 3 \times 3 = 9 \qquad 4 \times 4 = 16$

The number of dots in each pattern give you the square numbers.

Square numbers The **square numbers** are 1, 4, 9, 16, ...

Here are some patterns of triangles.

$1 \qquad 1 + 2 = 3 \qquad 1 + 2 + 3 = 6 \qquad 1 + 2 + 3 + 4 = 10$

The number of dots in each pattern give you the triangle numbers.

Triangle numbers The **triangle numbers** are 1, 3, 6, 10, ...

Exercise 4:3

1 Write down the first 10 square numbers.

2 Write down the first 6 triangle numbers.

3 Using the numbers 5, 6, 7, 9, 14, 15, 21, 25 write down
   a the prime numbers
   b the numbers that are multiples of 7
   c the triangle numbers
   d the square numbers
   e the numbers that are factors of 50
   f the two numbers that when added together give a square number
   g the two numbers that when subtracted give a triangle number

4 **a** Copy this multiplication square.
Fill it in.

×	1	2	3	4	5	6
1						
2						
3						
4						
5						
6						

  b Look for the line of symmetry
in your table.
What can you say about the
numbers on the line of symmetry?

5 Find the lowest number that fits each set of clues.
  a I am an even number. I am a factor of both 8 and 30.
  b I am an even number. I am a square number. I have 9 factors.
  c I am a multiple of both 2 and 3. If you add 1 to me you get a square
number.
  d I am an odd number. 15 is one of my factors. I am a multiple of 9.

When you do an investigation in Maths you often end up with a
sequence of numbers.
You can find the rule and predict the next numbers in the sequence.

Number sequence   A **number sequence** is a list of numbers that follow a rule.

Term   Each number in a sequence is called a **term**.

Example   **a** Write down the rule for this sequence:
5, 7, 9, 11, 13, 15
  b Write down the next two terms.

a 5   7   9   11   13   15
$+2$ $+2$ $+2$ $+2$ $+2$

Each new term is 2 more than the previous term.
The rule is 'add 2'.

b The next two terms are 17 and 19.

Exercise 4:4

For each of the sequences in questions **1–4** write down
a the rule   **b** the next two terms

1   4, 8, 12, 16, 20, ...   **3**   80, 72, 64, 56, 48, ...

2   30, 41, 52, 63, 74, ...   **4**   2, 4, 8, 16, 32, ...

For each of questions **5–8** write down
a the rule for the sequence   **b** the missing terms

5   12, 16, ..., 24, ..., 32   **7**   35, 33, ..., 29, 27, ...

6   70, 65, 60, ..., ..., 45   **8**   ..., 800, 400, 200, 100, ...

9   Look at this sequence of numbers: 2, 6, 14, 30
The rule that has been used to get the sequence is
     'add 1 and then multiply by 2'
Write down the next two numbers in the sequence.

A sequence can be made from a series of patterns.

Example

a   Write down the number of dots in each of these patterns.
b   Write down the rule for the sequence.
c   Write down the next two terms in the sequence.

a   The number of dots in the first three patterns are 5, 9, 13.
b   The rule is add 4.
c   The next two terms are 17 and 21.

Exercise 4:5

1 The numbers of matchsticks in these patterns form a sequence.

    a Draw the next pattern.
    b Write down the sequence of numbers.
    c Write down the rule for the sequence.
    d Write down the next three terms in the sequence.

2 These arrangements of cubes form a sequence.

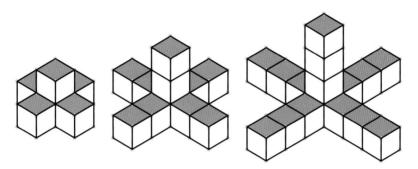

    a Write down the numbers of cubes in the sequence.
    b Write down the rule for the sequence.
    c Write down the next two numbers in the sequence.

3 **a** Copy the table for these patterns.
       Fill it in.

Number of squares	4	6	8	...	...
Number of dots	10	13	16	...	...
Number of lines	13	18	23	...	...

    b Write down the rule for the squares.
    c Write down the rule for the dots.
    d Write down the rule for the lines.

2 Finding a formula

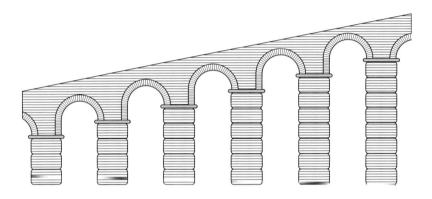

The blocks in the pillars give the sequence 3, 4, 5, 6, 7, 8, ...
Sequences are often found in investigational work.
You can find a formula for sequences.

Look at the sequence	5	10	15	20		...
Term number	1	2	3	4		n

The rule is 'add 5'.

$$5 \xrightarrow{+5} 10 \xrightarrow{+5} 15 \xrightarrow{+5} 20 \xrightarrow{+5} \qquad 5n$$

This is the 5 times table.

The first term is	$5 \times 1 = 5$	because the term number is 1
The second term is	$5 \times 2 = 10$	because the term number is 2
The third term is	$5 \times 3 = 15$	because the term number is 3

_n_th term   The term in the sequence with term number n is called the **_n_th term**.

So the nth term is $5 \times n = 5n$ because the term number is n

If you know the nth term you can work
out **any** term with a function machine.
You put the 5 from $5n$ in the function
machine.

Term number   1st term

$$1 \longrightarrow \boxed{\times 5} \longrightarrow 5$$

You can do more than one term at a time.

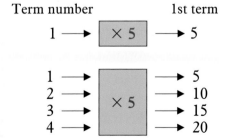

Exercise 4:6

1 The *n*th term of this sequence is **6*n***. The **6** is used in the function machine. Copy the function machine. Fill in the missing numbers.

Term number

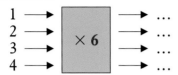

2 These are the *n*th terms of some sequences.
Use function machines to work out the first 4 terms.

a 8*n* $\boxed{\times 8}$ **d** 20*n* $\boxed{\times \ldots}$

b 9*n* $\boxed{\times 9}$ **e** 100*n* $\boxed{\times \ldots}$

c 10*n* $\boxed{\times \ldots}$ • **f** 2.5*n* $\boxed{\times \ldots}$

3 These are the *n*th terms of some sequences.
Work out the 5th, 6th, 7th and 8th terms for each one.

a 2*n* $\boxed{\times 2}$ **d** 6*n* $\boxed{\times \ldots}$

b 3*n* $\boxed{\times 3}$ **e** 22*n* $\boxed{\times \ldots}$

c 4*n* $\boxed{\times \ldots}$ **f** 100*n* $\boxed{\times \ldots}$

You can use a formula to find any term in a sequence.

Example   Find the 25th term in the sequence whose formula is **4*n***

Term number   25th term

25 $\longrightarrow$ $\boxed{\times 4}$ $\longrightarrow$ 100

---

4 Work out the 20th term for each of these sequences.
Use the function machines given.

a 2*n* $\boxed{\times 2}$ **d** 6*n* $\boxed{\times \ldots}$

b 3*n* $\boxed{\times 3}$ **e** 22*n* $\boxed{\times \ldots}$

c 4*n* $\boxed{\times \ldots}$ **f** 100*n* $\boxed{\times \ldots}$

You can write a formula which gives you any term in the sequence.
It is the same as the formula for the nth term.

Look at the sequence 　　3　　　6　　　9　　　12　　　...

Term number 　　　　1　　　2　　　3　　　4　　　...　　　　　n

The rule is 'add 3'

$$\overset{+3}{3 \quad 6} \quad \overset{+3}{\quad 9} \quad \overset{+3}{\quad 12} \quad ... \quad 3n$$

This comes from 　　3×1 　3×2 　3×3 　3×4 　　　　$3 \times n$

So:

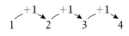
The formula for the 1 times table is $1n$
(but $1n$ is always written as n)

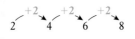
The formula for the 2 times table is $2n$

The formula for the 3 times table is $3n$

Example 　　　Write down the formula for this sequence 　7, 14, 21, 28, ...

Term number 　　　　1　　　2　　　3　　　4　　　...　　　　n

The rule is 'add 7'

$$\overset{+7}{7 \quad 14} \quad \overset{+7}{\quad 21} \quad \overset{+7}{\quad 28} \quad ... \quad 7n$$

This comes from 　7×1 　7×2 　7×3 　7×4 　　　$7 \times n$

These are the multiples of 7
So the formula for the sequence is $7n$.

You can check the formula by using it to find one of the terms in the question.
You could check the third term. This is when $n = 3$
So $7n = 7 \times 3 = 21$
This is the same as the third term in the question, so the formula is correct.

Exercise 4:7

For questions **1–10**:
a Copy down the sequence.
b Write down the rule.
c Write down a formula for each sequence.
d Check the formula by finding the third term.

1 4, 8, 12, 16, ...

6 8, 16, 24, 32, ...

2 5, 10, 15, 20, ...

7 100, 200, 300, 400, ...

3 6, 12, 18, 24, ...

8 9, 18, 27, 36, ...

4 10, 20, 30, 40, ...

9 22, 44, 66, 88, ...

5 20, 40, 60, 80, ...

10 90, 180, 270, 360, ...

11 a Copy these boxes.
b Connect each pair of boxes that match with an arrow.

Terms   Formula

2, 4, 6, 8, ...		$9n$
30, 60, 90, 120, ...		$11n$
11, 22, 33, 44, ...		$8n$
8, 16, 24, 32, ...		$100n$
12, 24, 36, 48, ...		$7n$
7, 14, 21, 28, ...		$12n$
100, 200, 300, 400, ...		$30n$
9, 18, 27, 36, ...		$2n$

Formulas with two parts

Look at this sequence. It is not the 5 times table!

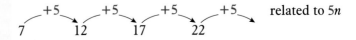

related to 5n

The rule for this sequence is **add 5,**
so it must have something to do with the 5 times table.
You can write related to 5n to help you.
The formula for the 5 times table is 5n.
Write the sequence 5n underneath. Compare the two sequences.

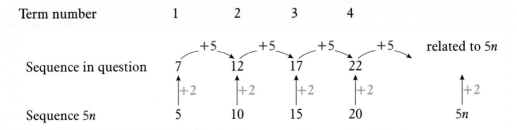

This is called a sequence diagram.

You need to **add 2** to every term in 5n to make the new sequence.
So the formula for the new sequence is 5n +2

Exercise 4:8

1 a Copy the sequence diagram below. Fill in the missing numbers.

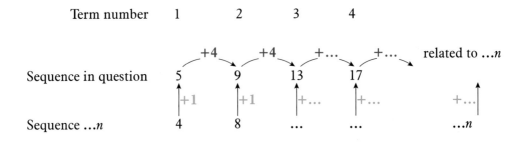

b Write down the formula for the new sequence.

2 **a** Copy the sequence diagram below.
   b Fill in the missing numbers.
   c Write down the formula for the sequence.

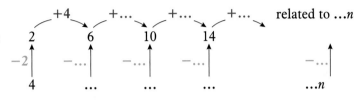

3 For each of these sequences:
   (1) draw diagrams   (2) find the formula
   a 7, 11, 15, 19, ...   **f** 3, 8, 13, 18, ...
   b 7, 10, 13, 16, ...   **g** 11, 17, 23, 29, ...
   c 7, 12, 17, 22, ...   **h** 9, 15, 21, 27, ...
   d 5, 7, 9, 11, ...   ● **i** 27, 29, 31, 33, ...
   e 3, 5, 7, 9, ...   ● **j** 5.5, 8, 10.5, 13, ...

4 **a** Copy these boxes.
   b Connect each sequence to the correct formula with an arrow

9, 15, 21, 27, ...		$7n + 3$
3, 8, 13, 18, ...		$5n - 2$
10, 17, 24, 31, ...		$6n + 3$

● **5** These 2 sequences are both based on $2n$.
   They have different formulas. Find the formula for each one.
   a 3, 5, 7, 9, ...   **b** 1, 3, 5, 7, ...

● **6** For each of these sequences:
   (1) draw diagrams
   (2) find the formula
   a 21, 19, 17, 15, ...   **b** 95, 90, 85, 80, ...

You can work out the terms for sequences like $2n + 3$ using function machines.

You need a function machine to work out $2n$ $\boxed{\times 2}$

You need another function machine to get from $2n$ to $2n + 3$

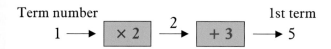

Term number   1st term

$1 \longrightarrow \boxed{\times 2} \overset{2}{\longrightarrow} \boxed{+ 3} \longrightarrow 5$

This is also useful for checking that formulas are correct.
Remember, you can do more than one term at a time!

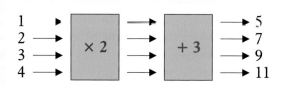

Exercise 4:9

1 Work out the first four terms for each sequence.
Show your working out.

a $2n + 4$ $\boxed{\times 2}$ $\boxed{+ 4}$ **e** $n + 5$ $\boxed{\times 1}$ $\boxed{+ \ldots}$

b $3n + 1$ $\boxed{\times 3}$ $\boxed{+ 1}$ **f** $2n - 3$ $\boxed{\times \ldots}$ $\boxed{- \ldots}$

c $3n - 2$ $\boxed{\times 3}$ $\boxed{- 2}$ **g** $6n - 5$ $\boxed{\times \ldots}$ $\boxed{- \ldots}$

d $4n + 5$ $\boxed{\times 4}$ $\boxed{+ 5}$ ● **h** $2.5n + 0.5$ $\boxed{\times \ldots}$ $\boxed{+ \ldots}$

2 Work out the 5th, 6th, 7th and 8th terms for each sequence.
Show your working out.

a $2n + 1$ $\boxed{\times 2}$ $\boxed{+ 1}$ **d** $6n + 2$ $\boxed{\times \ldots}$ $\boxed{+ \ldots}$

b $3n + 4$ $\boxed{\times 3}$ $\boxed{+ 4}$ **e** $22n - 10$ $\boxed{\times \ldots}$ $\boxed{- \ldots}$

c $4n - 4$ $\boxed{\times \ldots}$ $\boxed{- 4}$ ● **f** $100n - 200$ $\boxed{\times \ldots}$ $\boxed{- \ldots}$

You can use a formula to find any term in a sequence.

Example

Find the 22nd term in the sequence whose formula is $4n - 3$

Term number   22nd term

$$22 \longrightarrow \boxed{\times 4} \xrightarrow{\;88\;} \boxed{-3} \longrightarrow 85$$

3 Work out the 20th term for each of these sequences.

   a $2n + 3$ **d** $6n + 5$ **g** $10n + 5$

   b $3n + 7$ **e** $8n - 4$ **h** $2n - 36$

   c $7n - 2$ **f** $7n - 3$ ● **i** $8n - 200$

4 For each sequence:

   (1) Find the formula.

   (2) Check your formula by finding the fourth term.

   (3) Work out the 100th term.

   a 6, 10, 14, 18, ...   **b** 7, 16, 25, 34, ...   ● **c** 12, 23, 34, 45, ...

Gamoı It aauld be youľ

This is a game for 2 players.
Both of you need to write down this list of numbers:

   1 3 4 6 7 9 10 15 16 27

You need two dice. One is an ordinary dice numbered from 1 to 6.
You will need to put these formulas on the other dice:

n $n + 5$ $2n + 10$ $3n - 2$ $4n + 11$ $6n - 3$

Take it in turns to throw both dice.
The ordinary dice tells you the term number.
The other dice tells you the formulas that you need
to use.

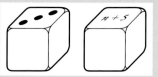

Katriona and Rhodri play the game.
Here is Katriona's throw.

Katriona works out the 3rd term for the formula $n + 5$.

She scores 8. As 8 is not on her list of numbers she cannot cross it out.

Rhodri then has his turn. He throws a '4' and '$4n + 11$'. He scores 27.
As 27 is on his list of numbers, he crosses 27 out.

The winner is the first player to match any six of the scores in their list.

Patterns with shapes

Look at these pillars.
Count the blocks for each
pillar.
There is a sequence.

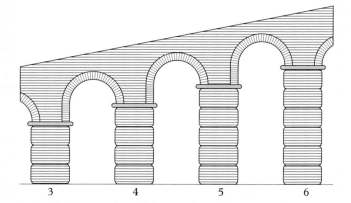

You can work out the formula for the sequence.

The sequence is	3	4	5	6	...
Term number	1	2	3	4	n

$$+1 \quad +1 \quad +1 \quad +1 \quad \text{related to } 1n$$

Sequence in question	3	4	5	6	
	+2	+2	+2	+2	+2
Sequence $1n$	1	2	3	4	$1n$

So the formula is $1n + 2$. Write this as $n + 2$.

Exercise 4:10

1 **a** Write the shape sequence as a number sequence.
   b Use a sequence diagram to work out the formula.

The sequence is   ...   .

2 **a** Write the shape sequence as a number sequence.
   b Use a sequence diagram to work out the formula.

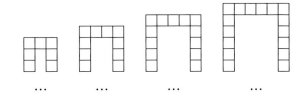

The sequence is   ...   .

3 Luciana has some patterns on
   her wall made from tiles.
   a Work out the formula for
       the sequence.
   b How many tiles would you need for the 8th pattern?

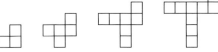

4 The aliens are coming!
   a Write down how many are in the next group in the pattern.
   b Work out the formula for their flying formation.

5 These penguins were seen on an ice floe watching RAF aircraft.
   a How many are in the next group in the pattern?

   b Work out the formula for their formation.

1 From the numbers 20, 21, 22, 23, 24, 25, 26, 27, 28, 29, 30
Write down the numbers which are
a even   **b** odd   **c** multiples of 4

2 **a** Write down the first ten multiples of 5.
   b Write down the first ten multiples of 7.
   c Use your answers to write down the lowest common multiple of 5 and 7.

3 Tim and Andy are bell ringing.
Tim rings his every 4 seconds. Andy rings his every 10 seconds.
They both start to ring the bells at the same time.
   a How long is it before they both ring the bells at the same time again?
   b How long is it from the start before they ring the bells together for the second time?

4 Two warning lights flash at different intervals.
One flashes every 2 seconds, the other every three seconds.
How often do they flash together?

5 Find the smallest number that fits each set of clues.
   a It is a multiple of 7   **b** It is a multiple of 5
       It is an even number   It is a square number
       It is 1 less than a prime number   It is more than 30

6 Write down the factors of these numbers.
   a 20   **b** 24   **c** 32   **d** 50

7 Look at the numbers 10, 11, 12, 13, 14, 15, 16, 17, 18, 19, 20.
Write down the numbers that are
   a prime   **b** factors of 90   **c** multiples of 5

8 Find these numbers using the clues.
   a It is a factor of 50   **b** It is a factor of 12
       It is a square number   It is a prime number
                              It is an odd number

9 Find the prime factors of:
   a 24   **b** 40   **c** 33   **d** 39

10 Write these numbers as products of their prime factors.
   a 20   **b** 34   **c** 45   **d** 60

11 Write down the first 6 square numbers.

12 Write down the first 5 triangle numbers.

13 Using the numbers 5, 6, 8, 14, 15, 16, 18, 25, 30, write down
    a the prime numbers   **c** the triangle numbers
    b the numbers that are multiples of 6   **d** the square numbers

    e the numbers that are factors of 60
    f the two numbers that when added together give a square number
    g the two numbers that when subtracted give a triangle number.

14 For each of these sequences write down the rule and the next two terms.
    a 5, 15, 25, 35, 45, …
    b 6, 9, 12, 15, 18, …
    c 20, 18, 16, 14, 12, …
    d 20, 15, 10, 5, 0, …

15 For each of these sequences write down the rule and the missing terms.
    a 10, 14, …, 22, …, 30,
    b 25, …, 19, 16, …, …,

16 Look at this sequence of numbers: 3, 4, 7, 16, …
The rule that has been used to get the sequence is

   'multiply by 3 and subtract 5'

Write down the next two numbers in the sequence.

17 The rule for a sequence is 'multiply by 10 and add 6'
The sequence starts with the number 3
Write down the first five terms of the sequence.

18 The rule for a sequence is 'multiply by 2 and add 5'
The sequence starts with the number 4
Write down the first five terms of the sequence.

19 A supermarket sells four different sizes of bath oil.

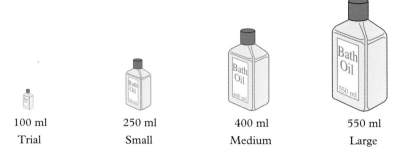

| 100 ml | 250 ml | 400 ml | 550 ml |
| Trial | Small | Medium | Large |

    a The contents follow a rule. Write down the rule.
    b The next size is a Large Economy size. It also follows the rule.
       What are the contents of this size?

20 Write down the formula for each of these.
    a 11, 22, 33, 44, 55, …
    b 7, 14, 21, 28, 35, …
    c 13, 26, 39, 52, 65, …
    d 15, 30, 45, 60, 75, …

21 Find the 20th term in the sequence whose formula is:
    a $3n$ **b** $5n$ **c** $12n$

22 Work out a formula for each of these.
    a 5, 7, 9, 11, 13, …
    b 3, 7, 11, 15, 19, …
    c 12, 22, 32, 42, 52, …
    d 10, 17, 24, 31, 38, …

23 Work out the 3rd, 4th, 5th and 6th terms for the sequence.
    a $3n + 2$ **b** $5n - 1$ **c** $7n + 4$

24 Find the 20th term in the sequence whose formula is:
    a $2n + 6$ **b** $n - 5$ **c** $8n - 25$

25 **a** Write this pattern of shapes as a number sequence.
    b Use a sequence diagram to work out the formula.

26 **a** Write this pattern of shapes as a number sequence.
    b Use a sequence diagram to work out the formula.

27 **a** Write this pattern of shapes as a number sequence.
b Use a sequence diagram to work out the formula.

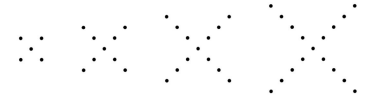

28 **a** Write this pattern of shapes as a number sequence.
b Use a sequence diagram to work out the formula.

1 **a** Look at this sequence of numbers: 2, 3, 5, 9, 17
   The rule that has been used to get the sequence is

   'multiply by 2 and subtract 1'

   Write down the next two numbers in the sequence.

b Use the same rule to write the first five terms of the sequence that starts with 7.

   7, ..., ..., ..., ...

c Using the same rule but another starting number the second term is 21.
   Find the starting number.

2 A formula for a sequence is $3n + 4$.
   Which term has the value:
   a 19   **b** 28   **c** 34   **d** 43?

3 A formula for a sequence is $5n + 2$.
   Which term has the value:
   a 12   **b** 32   **c** 47   **d** 52?

4 A formula for a sequence is $4n - 2$.
   Which term has the value:
   a 26   **b** 42   **c** 18   **d** 58?

5 A sequence has the formula $2n - 5$.
   Which of these numbers belong to the sequence:
   a 14   **b** 17   **c** 43   **d** 55?

6 **a** Find the formula for the sequence 2, 5, 8, 11, ...
   b Find the formula for the sequence 4, 7, 10, 13, ...
   c Add the two formulas together. Simplify your answer.
   d Add the two sequences together to get the new sequence
      2 + 4, 7 + 5, ...
      6, 12, ...
      Find the formula for the new sequence.
   e Compare your answers to parts **c** and **d**.

1 Look at these numbers: 1, 2, 3, 8, 10, 13, 16, 21
Write down the numbers which are
  a odd
  b square
  c triangle numbers
  d multiples of 4
  e prime numbers
  f factors of 24

2 Sam has two flashing disco lights.
The red light flashes every 3 seconds.
The blue light flashes every 5 seconds.
How often do they flash at the same time?

3 **a** Write 420 as a product of its prime factors.
  b Use the method of prime factors to find the highest common factor
    of 420 and 220.

4 Explain why the fraction $\frac{1}{24}$ gives a recurring decimal.

5 Write down the next two terms in each of these sequences
  a 23   19   15   11   ...   ...
  b 2   6   18   54   ...   ...
  c 0.06   0.09   0.12   0.15   ...   ...

6 The rule for a sequence is 'multiply by 10 and subtract 20'.
The first term is 4.
Write down the second and third terms.

7 The nth term of a sequence is $11n$.
Write down the first 5 terms of the sequence.

8 Write down the formula for each of these sequences.
  a 6, 12, 18, 24, 30, ...
  b 9, 18, 27, 36, 45, ...

9 These two sequences are based on $5n$.
They have different formulas.
Find the formula for each one.

   a 6, 11, 16, 21, 26, …

   b 2, 7, 12, 17, 22, …

10 Look at this sequence:

        11   17   23   29

   a Draw a sequence diagram.

   b Find the formula for the sequence.

11 Look at these patterns of triangles.

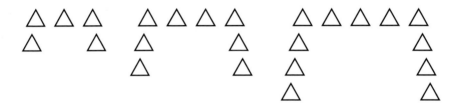

   a Draw the next pattern in this sequence.

   b Write this pattern of triangles as a number sequence.

   c Use a sequence diagram to work out the formula.

12 The formula for a sequence is $6n - 5$

   a Find the first 3 terms.

   b Find the 20th term.

   c Which term has the value 55?

5 Negative numbers

LEADERBOARD

Player	Score
David Arnold	-5
Robert Elswit	-3
Allan Cameron	-1
Anthony Waye	0
Bruce Firstein	0
Michael G. Wilson	1
Roger Spottiswoode	2
Albert R. Broccoli	4

CORE

QUESTIONS

EXTENSION

TEST YOURSELF

1 Adding and subtracting

LEADERBOARD

Player	Score
David Arnold	-5
Robert Elswit	-3
Allan Cameron	-1
Anthony Waye	0
Bruce Firstein	0
Michael G. Wilson	1
Roger Spottiswoode	2
Albert R. Broccoli	4

This is the scoreboard from a golf tournament.
The players in the lead are 'under par'.

This means that they have taken fewer shots than the standard set for the course.
The player who is in the lead is 5 shots under par.
His score is shown as −5.

Golf uses lots of positive and negative numbers in its scoring.
Each hole has a par.
This is the standard number of shots a good player should take to play the hole.
If you play the hole in less shots you are under par.
There are special names for these scores.
They are shown in this table:

Albatross	3 under par	−3
Eagle	2 under par	−2
Birdie	1 under par	−1
Par		0
Bogey	1 over par	+1
Double	2 over par	+2

Example

A golf player plays the first five holes on a golf course.
She gets: Birdie, Birdie, Par, Par, Eagle.
What is her score?

Birdie	Birdie	Par	Par	Eagle
−1	−1	0	0	−2

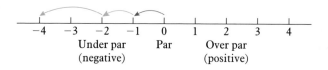

Under par
(negative)

Par

Over par
(positive)

Her score is −4.

Exercise 5:1

1 Work out the scores of each of these players.
Draw a scale like the one in the example if it helps.

Player	Hole 1	Hole 2	Hole 3	Hole 4	Hole 5
Duncan	Par	Par	Birdie	Par	Birdie
Fiona	Par	Birdie	Eagle	Par	Par
Lindsey	Eagle	Par	Par	Eagle	Birdie
Steve	Par	Par	Eagle	Birdie	Birdie

2 Work out the scores of each of these players.

Player	Hole 1	Hole 2	Hole 3	Hole 4	Hole 5
Anne	Bogey	Par	Eagle	Birdie	Par
Mohammed	Par	Bogey	Par	Birdie	Eagle
James	Bogey	Bogey	Birdie	Eagle	Eagle
Alison	Albatross	Eagle	Eagle	Birdie	Par

3 At the end of a round of golf, five friends have these scores:

Player	Score
Duncan	−4
Alison	−5
Dave	+2
Pardeep	−2
Tim	−3

a Who won the game?
b Who came last?
c Write the names and scores in order. Start with the winner.

4 In a tournament, competitors play 4 rounds of golf.
This table shows the scores for each round for the players.

Player	Round 1	Round 2	Round 3	Round 4	Total
Gary	−3	−4	−4	−1	
Tony	−4	−2	+1	+2	
Tiger	−4	−5	−1	+2	
Alan	−2	+2	+1	+3	
Brian	−3	−3	−3	+1	

a Copy the table. Fill in the 'total' column.
b Write the names and scores in order. Start with the winner.

Exercise 5:2 – Line out

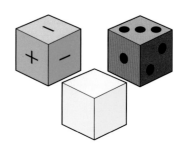

W You will need Worksheets 5:2 and
5:3, two special dice and a 1 cm
cube to play this game.

This is a game for two players.
One dice is marked with + and
− signs.
The other is an ordinary dice.
Place the cube on 0.

Positive player

Shake both dice. If you get a negative number, move to the left. If you
get a positive number, move to the right.

Negative player

Shake both dice. You move the same cube in the same way as the
positive player.

If the cube lands or goes past +27, the positive player wins.
If the cube lands or goes past −27, the negative player wins.

Record your moves on the sheet as you play.
Here is an example.
Notice that where the first player finishes, the second starts.

Positive player				Negative player		
Start	Move	Finish		Start	Move	Finish
0	−3	−3		−3	+2	−1
−1	+2	1		1	−6	−5
−5	+3	−2		−2	−4	−6

Now that you have used negative numbers, you need to be able to write down calculations.

Example

Work out: **a** $-3 + 4$ **b** $4 - 6$ **c** $-3 + -5$

You can use a scale to help you.
Start at the first number. For $+$, move to the right.
For $-$, move to the left.

a

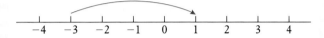

Start at -3 and move 4 to the right.

$$-3 + 4 = 1$$

b

Start at 4 and move 6 to the left.

$$4 - 6 = -2$$

c

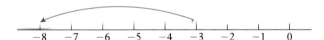

Adding a negative number is the same as taking away.
Start at -3 and move 5 to the left.

$$-3 + -5 = -8$$

Exercise 5:3

1   Work these out. Draw a scale to help you.

a $3 - 5$	**g** $-6 - 3$	**m** $-12 + -12$
b $12 - 15$	**h** $-5 - 7$	**n** $-15 + -9$
c $6 - 15$	**i** $-6 - 8$	**o** $-15 + 32$
d $-4 + 6$	**j** $8 + -6$	**p** $-17 - 25$
e $-5 + 16$	**k** $15 + -7$	**q** $62 - 100$
f $-3 + 9$	**l** $16 + -16$	**r** $-100 - 100$

2 Copy this table of temperatures. Fill it in.

Starting temperature	Change	Warmer or colder?	New temperature
−15	+6		
4	−10		
−12	+7		
−6	+6		
−4	−5		

3 Copy each of these patterns.
Write down the next three numbers in each pattern.
a 6 4 2 0 −2 ... ...
b 3 0 −3 ... ...
c 10 5 0 ... ...
d −5 −8 −11 ... ...
e $\frac{1}{2}$ 0 −$\frac{1}{2}$ ... ...
f −25 −20 −15 ... ...

4 Put a greater than sign (>) or a less than sign (<) between each of these pairs of numbers:
a   6 ... −4
b   −3 ... −5
c   −6 ... −4
d   −7 ... −7
e   10 ... −24
f −32 ... −35

5 ***A negative maze***
  a Copy this maze.

−7	3	−6	4	Out
2	−2	7	−2	
7	−1	2	0	
−3	−4	2	−4	
In				

Move only up, down or across.
You must not move diagonally.

You can only visit each square once.

Start at 'In' and finish at 'Out'.
Add the numbers as you go.

  b Read the rules next to the maze.
     Your aim is to get the smallest total you can.
     Try different routes through the maze.

These are the scores given by 4 judges at an ice skating contest.

If you add up the scores you get:
$$8 + 5 + 3 + -2 = 14$$

The judge who gave the negative score was taken out.
The total is now: $8 + 5 + 3 = 16$
It has gone up.

Taking away the negative score makes the total go up.
It is the same in maths calculations.
Taking away a negative number is the same as adding.

Example

Work out   **a** $3 - -6$ **b** $-5 - -2$ **c** $-4 - -10$

a Taking away -6 is the same as adding 6.
   $3 - -6 = 3 + 6 = 9$

b Taking away -2 is the same as adding 2.
   $-5 - -2 = -5 + 2 = -3$
   Another way of looking at it is

-1
-1
-1
-1
-1

-1
-1
-1
-1
-1

-1
-1
-1

-5 $-$ -2 $=$ -3

c Taking away -10 is the same as adding 10.
   $-4 - -10 = -4 + 10 = 6$

Exercise 5:4

1 Work these out:
   a $5 - -7$ **c** $2 - -2$ **e** $-3 - -6$
   b $3 - -5$ **d** $5 - -5$ **f** $-6 - -10$

2 Work these out:

a $-6 - -7$ **c** $6 - 9$ **e** $-7 - 7$

b $-5 - -5$ **d** $6 - -9$ **f** $-35 - -25$

3 Look through these calculations.

(1) $6 + -5 = 1$
(2) $6 - 5 = 1$
(3) $6 - -2 = -8$
(4) $-3 - -5 = -8$
(5) $-4 - 4 = -8$
(6) $-6 - -9 = -3$

a Write down the numbers of the calculations that you think are wrong.

b Re-write the ones that you thought were wrong.

4 These are magic squares.
The diagonals, rows and columns always add up to the same total.
Copy the magic squares. Fill them in.

a

-1		-3
	0	2
3		1

b

	5	-9
	-3	
3		

c

-6		
-11	-4	-9

5   *Line out 2 – Now it gets nasty!*

You will need Worksheets 5:2 and 5:3. You will also need two dice: the $+$ and $-$ dice you used last time in Exercise 5:2, and a new number dice. This dice has the numbers $1, -2, -3, 4, -5$ and 6 on it.
The rules of the game are exactly the same (see p. 124) but you need to watch for double negatives! If you get a $-$ on the sign dice and throw a -3, this becomes $- -3$ which is the same as $+3$.
Good luck!

Exercise 5:5

1 Work these out:

a $4 - 6$ **d** $3 - 9$ **g** $6 - -5$

b $18 - 19$ **e** $-3 - 9$ **h** $-14 - 14$

c $-6 + 12$ **f** $-3 - -9$ **i** $-6 + -8$

2 Copy these tables. Fill them in.

a

Second number

+	−4	−7	−2	−6
−5	−9	−12		
−3	−7			
−7				
−2				

b

Second number

−	−4	−7	−2	−6
−5	−1	+2		
−3	+1			
−7				
−2				

3 **a** Copy this diagram on to squared paper.

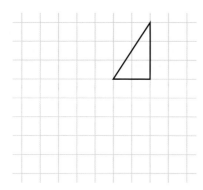

b Translate this shape by $\begin{pmatrix} -3 \\ -2 \end{pmatrix}$

c Translate your new shape by $\begin{pmatrix} -1 \\ -3 \end{pmatrix}$

d Write down the translation that will take the original shape to the last one.

● **e** A shape is translated by $\begin{pmatrix} -4 \\ -2 \end{pmatrix}$ then by $\begin{pmatrix} -3 \\ 1 \end{pmatrix}$

Write down the total translation.

2 Multiplying and dividing

It would be a golfer's dream to play three Eagles at the start of a tournament.

Eagle,	Eagle,	Eagle
(-2)	(-2)	(-2)

This would give a score of 6 under par.

You can show repeated scores as a multiplication.

Example

Write down the score for Eagle, Eagle, Eagle as a multiplication. Find the total score.

$$\text{Eagle, Eagle, Eagle} = 3 \text{ Eagles}$$
$$= 3 \times -2$$
$$\text{Total score} = -6$$

Exercise 5:6

1 Copy and complete each of these:

a Eagle, Eagle, Eagle, Eagle = ... Eagles
$$= ... \times -2$$
$$\text{Total score} = ...$$

b Birdie, Birdie, Birdie, Birdie, Birdie = ... Birdies
$$= ... \times -1$$
$$\text{Total score} = ...$$

c Albatross, Albatross, Albatross = ... Albatrosses
$$= ... \times -3$$
$$\text{Total score} = ...$$

2 Use multiplication to find the total of each of these scores:
 a Albatross, Albatross
 b Eagle, Eagle, Eagle, Eagle, Eagle
 c Albatross, Albatross, Albatross, Albatross

3 Write the information shown in each diagram as a multiplication:

 a

 b

 c

 d

4 Copy these. Fill in the spaces.
 a $-4 - 4 - 4 - 4 - 4 = \ldots \times -4 = \ldots$
 b $-12 - 12 - 12 - 12 = \ldots \times -12 = \ldots$
 c $-6 - 6 - 6 - 6 - 6 - 6 = \ldots \times -6 = \ldots$
 d $-8 - 8 - 8 - 8 - 8 - 8 - 8 - 8 - 8 = \ldots \times 8 \ldots$
 e $3.1 \quad 3.4 - 3.4 - 3.4 - 3.4 - 3.4 - 3.4 - 3.4 - 3.4 = \ldots \times -3.4 = \ldots$

5 Work out:
 a 5×-4 **c** 4×-9 **e** 4×-2.5
 b 6×-2 **d** 10×-7 **f** 100×-1.6

Order of multiplication

Numbers can always be multiplied in any order without changing the answer.
For example, $7 \times 4 = 28$ and $4 \times 7 = 28$

The same is true when negative numbers are involved.
For example, $5 \times -2 = -10$ and so $-2 \times 5 = -10$

Always look for the easiest way when multiplying three numbers together.
For example, $5 \times -7.9 \times 2$ is the same as
$5 \times 2 \times -7.9 = 10 \times -7.9 = -79$

Exercise 5:7

1 Work out:

a -3×5 **d** -4.3×10 **g** $-5 \times 1.63 \times 2$

b -4×6 **e** $3 \times -2 \times 4$ **h** 100×-0.143

c -10×1.7 **f** $8.7 \times -5 \times 2$ **i** $25 \times -0.217 \times 4$

2 Copy these. Fill them in.

a $4 \times \ldots = -12$ **d** $0.5 \times 47 \times -2 = \ldots$ **g** $50 \times -3.71 \times 2 = \ldots$

b $-3 \times \ldots = -15$ **e** $0.5 \times \ldots \times -2 = -76$ **h** $25 \times -0.48 \times \ldots = -48$

c $-5 \times 2 \times \ldots = -30$ **f** $0.5 \times \ldots \times 2 = -39$ **i** $4 \times \ldots \times 25 = -23$

Squares and cubes

When you multiply two negative numbers, the answer is **positive**.
For example, $-3 \times -2 = 6$

When you **square** a negative number, the answer is always **positive**.
For example, $(-5)^2 = -5 \times -5 = 25$

When you **cube** a negative number, the answer is always **negative**.
For example, $(-2)^3 = -2 \times -2 \times -2 = 4 \times -2 = -8$

Exercise 5:8

1 Work out:

a -4×-2 **d** $(-4)^2$ **g** $(-1)^3$

b -5×-6 **e** $(-10)^2$ **h** $(-4)^3$

c -7×-3 **f** $(-1)^2$ **i** $(-10)^3$

2 a Multiply each of these numbers by -1.

    (1) 5 (2) -4 (3) 27 (4) -5.3 (5) 14.9 (6) -0.76

   b How does a number change when it is multiplied by -1?

3 Copy these. Fill them in.

a $-3 \times \ldots = 6$ **d** $\ldots \times (-4)^2 = -32$ **g** $-2 \times \ldots \times 5 = 30$

b $-5 \times \ldots = 5$ **e** $\ldots \times (-1)^2 = -9$ **h** $4 \times -3 \times \ldots = 12$

c $\ldots \times (-3)^2 = 9$ **f** $\ldots \times (-1)^3 = -8$ **i** $2 \times (\ldots)^3 = -128$

Dividing

When you divide numbers of the **same** sign you get a **positive** answer.
For example, $-6 \div -2 = 3$

When you divide numbers of **different** signs you get a **negative** answer.
For example, $-10 \div 2 = -5$ and $14 \div -2 = -7$

Exercise 5:9

1 Work out:
  a $12 \div -3$
  b $16 \div -8$
  c $-15 \div 3$
  d $-27 \div -9$
  e $-18 \div -3$
  f $-16 \div 4$
  g $36 \div -9$
  h $100 \div -4$
  i $-6.4 \div 2$
  j $12.6 \div -3$
  k $-9 \div -2$
  l $-16.7 \div 10$

2 **a** Divide each of these numbers by -1.
     (1) -5 (2) 4 (3) -9 (4) -11 (5) 7.2 (6) -14.8
  b How does a number change when it is divided by -1?

3 Copy these.
  Fill in the spaces.
  a $\ldots \div -2 = 4$
  b $\ldots \div 3 = -5$
  c $\ldots \div -1 = -27$
  d $14 \div \ldots = -7$
  e $-15 \div \ldots = -3$
  f $-18.6 \div \ldots = 18.6$
  g $-18.6 \div \ldots = 9.3$
  h $174 \div \ldots = -17.4$
  i $(-4)^2 \div \ldots = 16$

4 Simplify:
  a $\dfrac{-6}{2}$
  b $\dfrac{12}{-4}$
  c $\dfrac{-3 \times 4}{6}$
  d $\dfrac{24}{-2 \times -4}$
  e $-3 \times \dfrac{20}{-10}$
  f $\dfrac{-15}{3} \times \dfrac{-16}{-8}$

5 Copy these.
  Fill in the spaces.
  a $\dfrac{-10}{\ldots} = 5$
  b $\dfrac{42}{\ldots} = -6$
  c $\dfrac{-100}{\ldots} = 4$
  d $\dfrac{\ldots}{2} = -11$
  e $\dfrac{\ldots}{-3} = -9$
  f $\dfrac{\ldots}{-10} = 5$

Using negative numbers in formulas

You can use negative numbers in formulas.

Example

Use the formula $v = u + at$ to find v when
$u = 10$, $a = -4$ and $t = 3$.

Write the formula:	$v = u + at$
Replace the letters with their values:	$v = 10 + -4 \times 3$
Do the multiplication first.	$= 10 + -12$
	$= 10 - 12$

So $v = $ 2

Exercise 5:10

1   Use the formula $v = u + at$ to find v when $u = 20$, $a = -3$ and $t = 4$.

2   Use the formula $t = 50 - 10d$ to find t when:
   a $d = 3$ **b** $d = 6$ **c** $d = 2.8$ **d** $d = 7.9$ **e** $d = -3$

3   The formula $f = \dfrac{uv}{u + v}$ is used in Physics. Find the value of f when:

   a $u = -10$ and $v = 5$ **b** $u = 3$ and $v = -12$

4   Use the formula $F = 10x - 30$ to find F when:
   a $x = 4$ **d** $x = 0$ **g** $x = -2$
   b $x = 3$ **e** $x = 0.5$ **h** $x = -5$
   c $x = 1$ **f** $x = 2.25$ **i** $x = -6.8$

5   The gradient of a line passing
   through the points $(3, 2)$ and (x, y).
   is given by:

   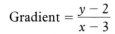

   $$\text{Gradient} = \frac{y - 2}{x - 3}$$

   Find the gradient when $x = 5$ and $y = -7$.

Scientific calculators are designed to make it easier to use formulas.

Example
Use the formula $F = 11.8 + 1.6x$ to find F when $x = -23.7$
Give your answer to three significant figures.

Write the formula: $F = 3.8 + 1.6x$
Replace x with -23.7 $F = 3.8 + 1.6 \times -23.7$
Key in:

$\boxed{3}\ \boxed{.}\ \boxed{8}\ \boxed{+}\ \boxed{1}\ \boxed{.}\ \boxed{6}\ \boxed{\times}\ \boxed{+/-}\ \boxed{2}\ \boxed{3}\ \boxed{.}\ \boxed{7}\ \boxed{=}$

$\boxed{3}\ \boxed{.}\ \boxed{8}\ \boxed{+}\ \boxed{1}\ \boxed{.}\ \boxed{6}\ \boxed{\times}\ \boxed{(-)}\ \boxed{2}\ \boxed{3}\ \boxed{.}\ \boxed{7}\ \boxed{=}$

This gives -34.12 and so $F = -34.1$ to three significant figures.

Exercise 5:11

1   Use the formula $P = 19.7 - 4.8x$ to find P when $x = 9.63$.
Give your answer to three significant figures.

2   In the formula $F = \dfrac{9C}{5} + 32$ the letters stand for temperatures.

Values of C are in degrees Celsius and values of F are in degrees Fahrenheit. Find F if the value of C is:
a   100
b -50
c -75
d -81
e -19
f -41.5

3   Use the formula $P = 17.3(5 - 3.125x)$ to find P for each of these values of x. Round your answers to three significant figures.
a   12.2
b   1.97
c -0.263
d -8.32
e -0.0619
f   1.6

● 4   The boiling point of oxygen is $-297\,°F$.

Use the formula $C = \dfrac{5(F - 32)}{9}$ to find this temperature in degrees Celsius.

1   Andy, John and Martin played four rounds of golf.
Their scores are shown in this table.

	Round 1	Round 2	Round 3	Round 4
Andy	-3	-2	$+2$	-3
John	-4	-3	-4	-1
Martin	-2	$+2$	$+1$	-3

Work out each person's score after the four rounds.

2   Temperatures are recorded in towns around Britain each day.
These are some of the temperatures for one day in January.

Town	Temp. (°C)
Aberdeen	-7
London	1
Bristol	-2
Orkney	-10
Sheffield	-5
Exeter	3

Write these temperatures in order.
Start with the smallest.

3   Write down the next three numbers in each of these patterns.
a -12 -10 -8 ... ...
b 6 4 2 ... ...
c -10 -7 ... ...

4   Complete this magic square.

-4		-6
	-3	-1
0		-2

5   Fill in the missing numbers in each of these sequences.
   a   −6   0   2   ...
   b   −8   ...   ...   −17   −20   ...
   c   ...   ...   −5   ...   −9   −11

6   Copy this multiplication square. Fill it in.

×		−2		−8
	12	8		
2	−6			
−1			5	
				24

7   Copy these. Fill in the spaces.

   a $7 \times (...) \times (...) = 21$ d $\dfrac{...}{3} = -4$ g $... \times \dfrac{-17}{3} = -20$

   b $5 \times ... \times -2 = -60$ e $\dfrac{...}{-2} = 5$ h $(-3)^2 \times ... = -90$

   c $... \times 17.9 \times 0.5 = -17.9$ f $\dfrac{-3 \times 4}{...} = 12$ i $\dfrac{8}{(...)^3} = -8$

8   An approximate formula for changing from one temperature scale to another is $F = 2C + 30$
   Use the formula to estimate F when $C = -50$.

9   $P = 10 - \dfrac{x}{0.83}$

   Use a calculator to find the value of P when $x = -2.79$.
   Give your answer to three significant figures.

1   A triangle is translated by $\begin{pmatrix} -3 \\ -1 \end{pmatrix}$ and then by $\begin{pmatrix} -2 \\ 3 \end{pmatrix}$.

What is the total translation?

2   Karen is trying to do $8 - -6$ on her calculator.

She presses: `8` `–` `–` `6` `=`

She gets the answer 2.
  a   What is the correct answer?
  b   What keys should Karen have pressed?

3   The temperature at the base of a mountain is $-3\,°C$.
Rod climbs 500 ft to the top of the mountain.
He notices that the temperature drops by $2\,°C$ per 100 ft.
What is the temperature at the top of the mountain?

4   Angela says 'Two minuses make a plus'.
Brian says that this means that $-2 - 6 = +8$.
Is Brian right?
Explain your answer.

5   Write down the value of $(-1)^n$ when:
  a n is odd   **b** n is even

6   Copy this division square. Fill it in.

÷	−3		3
12	−4	−6	
	2		
		1.5	

7   A stone is thrown upwards with velocity 20 m/s. The velocity of the
stone t seconds later is v m/s, where $v = 20 + at$.
The value of a is -10.
Find v when:
  a $t = 1$ **b** $t = 2$ **c** $t = 3$

1 Work these out:

a $-3 + 5$ **c** $-6 + -2$

b $2 - 7$ **d** $-11 - 4$

2 Rachel plays a game using two 6-sided dice.
The sides of the dice are marked with positive and negative numbers.
Rachel adds the two numbers on the top faces to get the score.
Write down the score for each of these:

a

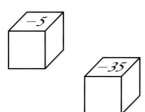

b

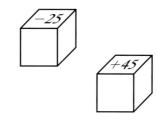

3 This is a net of a dice.
The numbers on opposite
faces of the dice add up to -1.
Fill in the missing numbers
marked by letters.

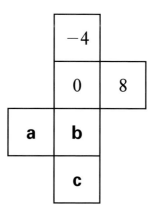

4 Write down the next two numbers in each sequence.

a   4 -1 -6 ...   ...

b -320 -160 -80 ...   ...

5 Put the correct symbol between each of these pairs of numbers.
Choose from < or > .

a 3 ... −2 **b** −6 ... −9 **c** −1 ... 0

6 Competitors play 4 rounds of golf in a tournament.
These are their scores.

Player	Round 1	Round 2	Round 3	Round 4
Brian	−3	−2	−1	−2
Norma	2	−1	−3	0
Julia	−2	−4	−3	−1

a Work out the total score for each player.
b Write the players and scores in order. Start with the winner.

7 Work these out:
a 4×-3 **c** -5×7
b 10×-5.8 **d** -2×-9

8 Work these out:
a $(-4)^2$ **b** $(-3)^3$ **c** $(-5)^3$

9 Work these out:
a $14 \div -2$ **b** $-12 \div -4$ **c** $-24 \div 8$

10 Copy these. Fill in the missing numbers.
a $5 \times \ldots = -40$ **e** $-100 \div \ldots = -4$
b $-6 + \ldots = 10$ **f** $-30 \times \ldots = 120$
c $7 - \ldots = 2$ **g** $2.05 \times \ldots = -2050$
d $\dfrac{-12}{\ldots} = 6$ **h** $\dfrac{\ldots}{-7} = 1$

11 a Use the formula $w = 4p - 12$ to find w when $p = -5$.
b Use the formula $v = u + at$ to find v when $u = -15$,
$a = -8$ and $t = 9$.

6 Simplifying and solving

1 Collecting terms
  Collecting algebraic terms
  Multiplying algebraic terms
  Multiplying out brackets

2 Solving equations
  Solving one step equations
  Solving two step equations

3 Trial and improvement
  Solving equations with whole number answers
  Looking for two solutions for a quadratic
  equation
  Solving to 1 dp and 2 dp
  Solving worded problems

CORE

QUESTIONS

EXTENSION

TEST YOURSELF

1 Collecting terms

Graham is adding his bottles to the bottle bank.

He must make sure that the different coloured bottles are all collected together.

There is a different collecting bin for each colour.

In algebra, you can collect terms together as long as they are the same type.

| **Term** | A **term** is the name given to one part of an equation or formula. In the formula $y = kv + 3v^2$, kv and $3v^2$ are terms. |

| **Collecting terms** | **Collecting terms** means adding or subtracting terms in an equation or formula to make it simpler. To collect terms together they must have exactly the same letters in them. |

Example

Simplify these by collecting terms.
a $t + t + t + t + t$ **b** $b + b + b + c + c$

a Adding five ts together gives 5 lots of t.
$$t + t + t + t + t = 5 \times t = 5t$$
b You can collect together the three bs and the two cs.
You can't add the bs to the cs.
$$b + b + b + c + c = 3b + 2c$$

Exercise 6:1

1 Simplify these by collecting terms.
   a $g + g + g + g + g$ **d** $r + r + r + r - r - r$
   b $k + k + k + k + k + k$ **e** $y + y$
   c $t + t + t$ **f** $a + a + a - a$

2 Simplify these by collecting terms.

a $g + g + h + h + h$

b $m + m + m + k + k + k$

c $t + t + s + s + s - s$

d $r + r + r + r + w + w$

e $y + y + h + h + h + h + h$

• **f** $a + a + a - b - b + c + c$

Often, the letters are already in groups.

Remember that $5t$ means $5 \times t$ or 5 lots of t.

Example

Simplify these by collecting terms.

a $5a + 3a + 2a$

b $3a + 6bc + 2a - 4bc$

a All the terms involve just a so they can all be added together.

$5a + 3a + 2a = 10a$

b The terms involving a can be collected together.

So can the terms with bc in them.

You can't collect the as and the bcs together.

$3a + 6bc + 2a - 4bc = 5a + 2bc$

---

3 Simplify these by collecting terms.

a $3g + 3g + 2g + 5g$

b $5m + 2m + 5m + 3k + 5k$

c $3t + 2t + 5s - 4s + 3s$

d $3r - 6r + 5w - 8w$

e $3y - 6y + 7h - 4h + y$

• **f** $5a - 9a + 7b - 11b + 10c + 4c$

4 Simplify these by collecting terms.

a $3ab + 5ab$

b $5mn - 2mn + 4mn$

• **c** $3ts + 2st$

d $3pr - 6pr + 5kw - 10kw$

e $5xy - 12xy + 9z - 4z + y$

• **f** $6ad - 9da + 8bc - 6cb + 15c - 24c$

Power

$k^4 = k \times k \times k \times k$

The **power** 4 tells you how many ks are multiplied together.

You can only collect terms with powers when

- they are of the same letter or groups of letters
- they are exactly the same power

Example

Simplify these by collecting terms where possible.

a $x^2 + 3x^2 + 5x^2$ **c** $3x^2 + 5x$

b $3ab^2 + 5ab^2 - 2ab^2$ **d** $3a^2b + 5ab^2$

a All the letters and all the powers are the same so these can be collected.
$$x^2 + 3x^2 + 5x^2 = 9x^2$$

b The terms all involve ab^2 so these can be collected.
$$3ab^2 + 5ab^2 - 2ab^2 = 6ab^2$$

c Both terms involve just x, but they are **different powers**. These terms **cannot** be collected.

d Both terms involve a and b and squared, but the power 2 is on a different letter in each term. These terms **cannot** be collected.

Exercise 6:2

1 Simplify these by collecting terms where possible. When it is not possible to collect terms, give a reason.

a $6x^2 + 5x^2$ **d** $3r^2s + 6r^2s$

b $9x^2 - 3x^2$ **e** $3y^3 + 6y^3 - y^3$

c $3t^2 + 2t^3$ **f** $5a^2 - 3a^2 + 7a^2$

2 Simplify these by collecting terms where possible. When it is not possible to collect terms, give a reason.

a $3x^2 + 2x^2 + 6y^2 - 3y^2$ **d** $6a^2b + 5a^2b - 3a^2b$

b $9x^2 - 3x^2 - 7z^2 - 2y^2$ **e** $4xy^2 + 7xy - 8x^2y$

c $3t^2 - 5h^2 + 6t^3 + 6h^3$ • **f** $7ab^2 - 4ab^2 + 5b^2a$

3 Simplify these as far as possible by collecting terms.

a $5x + 4x^2 + 6x - 3y$ **d** $7a + 9a^2b - 4ab^2$

b $7x^2 - 3x - 4x^2 - 2x$ **e** $4y^2 + 4x^2y - 9x^2y$

c $5t^2y - 8h + 6t^2y + 6h$ • **f** $4x^2yz + 3yx^2z - zyx^2$

Equations or formulas often have **brackets** in them.
You need to multiply out the brackets before you can simplify them.
Before you multiply out brackets, here is a reminder of how to multiply terms together.

Example

Simplify these by multiplying.

a $f \times g$ **c** $4g \times 7h$

b $3z \times y$ **d** $3y \times 2y$

a When two letters are multiplied together you should miss out the $\times$ sign.
This is because the $\times$ sign can get confused with the letter x.
$$f \times g = fg$$

b Numbers always come before letters.
Letters should be in alphabetical order.
$$3z \times y = 3yz$$

c When you have two numbers, multiply them together as well.
$$4g \times 7h = 28gh$$

d When the letters are the same, they should be written as powers.
$$3y \times 2y = 6 \times y \times y = 6y^2$$

Exercise 6:3

1 Simplify these by multiplying.

a $t \times s$ **d** $6w \times 3y$

b $3 \times 5c$ **e** $3a \times 5b$

c $7r \times 5$ **f** $5y \times 2y$

2 Simplify these by multiplying.

a $3p \times 5p$ **d** $(3h)^2$

b $6t \times 8t$ **e** $4c \times 2c \times 3c$

• **c** $4z \times (-2z)$ **f** $2a \times 3b \times 6c$

3 Simplify these by multiplying.

a $3t \times 5s$ **d** $3t \times 8t \times 4s$

b $8p \times 6p \times 2q$ **e** $p \times t \times r \times p \times t \times r$

• **c** $3c \times 4d \times (-6e)$ • **f** $(2p)^3$

Multiplying out brackets

It is easiest to start with numbers before looking at letters.
To work out 2(3 + 6) you need to use the **BODMAS** rule.

First you do   **B**rackets
then   powers **O**f
Next you do   **D**ivision
and   **M**ultiplication
Then you do   **A**ddition
and   **S**ubtraction

So, to work out 2(3 + 6) you need to work out the bracket: $3 + 6 = 9$
Then multiply by the 2: $2 \times 9 = 18$

Another way to work this out is to **multiply out** the bracket.

To do this you multiply everything inside the bracket by the number outside.
$$2(3 + 6) = 2 \times 3 + 2 \times 6$$
$$= \quad 6 \quad + \quad 12$$
$$= \quad 18$$

Exactly the same method works with letters.

Example   Multiply out these brackets.
   a $2(3 + x)$ **b** $-6(x^2 - 4)$ **c** $3(x^2 + 3x - 4)$

a   To work out $2(3 + x)$ multiply the 3 and the x by the 2.
$$2(3 + x) = 2 \times 3 + 2 \times x$$
$$= \quad 6 \quad + \quad 2x$$

b   Notice that there is a minus sign outside the bracket.
$$-6(x^2 - 4) = -6 \times x^2 + (-6) \times (-4)$$
$$= \quad -6x^2 \quad + \quad 24$$

c   It doesn't matter how many terms there are in the bracket.
They must *all* be multiplied by the number on the outside.
$$3(x^2 + 3x - 4) = 3 \times x^2 + 3 \times 3x + 3 \times (-4)$$
$$= \quad 3x^2 \quad + \quad 9x \quad - \quad 12$$

Exercise 6:4

Multiply out these brackets.

1 $4(x + 1)$ **4** $9(2x + 3)$ **7** $6(y^2 - 3y)$

2 $2(b + 3)$ **5** $5(3x - 5)$ **8** $8(f^2 - 3f - 4)$

3 $4(c - 8)$ **6** $4(x^2 + x)$ **9** $9(4x - x^3)$

Multiply out these brackets.
Watch the minus signs!

10 $-3(x + 4)$ **12** $-6(x^2 + 5)$ **14** $-4(x - y)$

11 $-5(x + 6)$ **13** $-5(2y - 6)$ **15** $-5(2x - x^2)$

You can also have letters outside the bracket.

Example

Multiply out these brackets.
a $c(d + 4)$ **b** $f(2f - 5)$ **c** $y^2(2y - x)$

a To work out $c(d + 4)$, multiply the d and the 4 by c.
$$c(d + 4) = c \times d + c \times 4$$
$$= cd + 4c$$
b In this part, notice that $f \times f$ gives you f^2
$$f(2f - 5) = f \times 2f - f \times 5$$
$$= 2f^2 - 5f$$
c Always make sure that letters are written in alphabetical order.
$$y^2(2y - x) = y^2 \times 2y - y^2 \times x$$
$$= 2y^3 - xy^2$$

Exercise 6:5

Multiply out these brackets.

1 $x(y + 1)$ **4** $x(x - 6)$ **7** $y(y^2 - 5y)$

2 $a(c + 5)$ **5** $x(3x + 4)$ **8** $g(g^2 + 5g - 2)$

3 $c(c - 8)$ **6** $y(x^2 + 5)$ ● **9** $y(xy - y^3)$

Exercise 6:6

Sharon has been learning about collecting terms.
Sadly, she has not been using Key Maths!
This is a copy of her last piece of work.
Look carefully through the work and spot all the errors.
Some of her answers are correct!
Re-write all the questions that Sharon has got wrong.

1 $t + t + t + t + t = t^5$

2 $3p + 2p + 4y + 5y = 5p + 9y = 14py$

3 $3ab + 5ab + 6ab = 14ab$

4 $6ad + 7da$ Can't be collected because the terms are different.

5 $x^2 + 3x^2 - 5x^2 = 9x^2$

6 $3x^2 + 5x^3 = 8x^5$

7 $3t^2 - 5h^2 + 6t^3 + 6h^3$ Can't be collected because the terms are different.

8 $t \times s = st$

9 $3p \times 5q = 15qp$

10 $4t \times 3s \times 5s = 60tss$

11 $2(x + 3) = 2x + 3$

12 $4(x^2 - 5) = 4x^2 + 20$

13 $g(g^2 + g) = g^3 + g^2$

14 $x(y^2 + 3x - 5) = xy^2 + 3x - 5x$

2 Solving equations

Dale, Vincent and Charlene are brothers and sister.

Dale is the youngest. Vincent is three years older than Dale. Charlene is three years older than Vincent.

Their ages add up to 39. How old are Dale, Vincent and Charlene?

Problems like this can be solved using linear equations.

Linear equations

Equations with simple letters and numbers are called **linear equations.**
Linear equations must not have any terms like x^2, x^3 or $\dfrac{1}{x}$ in them.

When you solve an equation, you are trying to work out the value of a letter.
You solve it by getting the unknown letter on to one side of the equation.

Example

Solve these equations:

a $x + 5 = 12$ **b** $2x = 7$ **c** $\dfrac{x}{6} + 3 = 5$

a To solve $x + 5 = 12$, notice that x has 5 added to it.
   To leave x by itself, take 5 from each side of the equation.
$$x + 5 - 5 = 12 - 5$$
$$x = 7$$

b In the equation $2x = 7$, the x has been multiplied by 2.
   To solve this equation, divide both sides by 2.

$$\frac{2x}{2} = \frac{7}{2}$$

$$x = 3.5$$

c You need to do two things to solve $\dfrac{x}{6} + 3 = 5$

The x has been divided by 6 and then 3 has been added.
To solve this, subtract the 3 then multiply by the 6.
This means doing the opposite operation in the opposite order.

$$\frac{x}{6} + 3 - 3 = 5 - 3$$

$$\frac{x}{6} \times 6 = 2 \times 6$$

$$x = 12$$

Exercise 6:7

1 Solve these equations.

a $x + 4 = 16$

b $3x = 18$

c $x + 6 = 19$

d $x - 12 = 14$

e $x - 4 = 14$

• f $2x = -3$

g $\dfrac{x}{5} = 6$

h $\dfrac{x}{7} = 4$

i $\dfrac{x}{3} = 9$

j $3x + 1 = 16$

k $4x - 3 = 13$

l $5x + 6 = 11$

m $7x - 6 = -13$

n $5x - 6 = 12$

• o $0.5x + 2 = 6$

p $\dfrac{x}{3} + 2 = 10$

q $\dfrac{x}{4} - 1 = 12$

r $\dfrac{3x}{2} + 5 = 26$

Some equations have letters on both sides.
To solve them, you need to change them so that they only have the letter on one side.

Example

Solve $5x = 3x + 14$

Look to see which side has least x.
In this example, the right-hand side (RHS) has only $3x$.

Subtract $3x$ from each side $5x - 3x = 3x - 3x + 14$
You now have x on just the LHS $2x = 14$
Divide both sides by 2 $x = 7$

Exercise 6:8

1 Solve these equations.

   a $5x = 3x + 8$

   b $7x = 3x + 24$

   c $12x = 7x + 35$

   d $3x = x + 19$

  ● **e** $9x - 8 = 7x$

   f $11x = 6 + 8x$

   g $3.5x = 2.5x + 8$

 ● **h** $5x = 2x - 12$

   i $4.5x = 2x + 10$

   j $15x = 8x + 147$

Sometimes, the side with the least x will be the left-hand side (LHS).
You can still solve the equations in the same way.

Example

Solve $4x + 9 = 7x$

Take $4x$ from both sides	$4x + 9 - 4x = 7x - 4x$
You now have x on just the RHS	$9 = 3x$
Divide by 3	$3 = x$
Usually you write this the other way around:	$x = 3$

---

2 Solve these equations.

   a $6x + 4 = 7x$

   b $4x + 7 = 11x$

   c $2x + 13 = 4x$

   d $3x + 9 = 6x$

  ● **e** $4x - 6 = 6x$

   f $4x - 21 = 11x$

   g $3x = 7x - 4$

 ● **h** $1.5x + 9 = 3.5x$

   i $3x - 6 = 5x$

   j $2x + 4.5 = 4x$

   k $5x - 3 = 7x$

   l $23x = 29x + 6$

3 Solve these equations.

   a $4x - 12 = 2x$

   b $7x + 4 = 5x$

   c $3x - 9 = 5x$

   d $6x = 4x - 10$

  ● **e** $4.5x = 6x - 9$

   f $4x - 9.5 = 5x$

Some equations have letters and numbers on both sides.
To solve these, change the equation so that it has x on only one side.
Then solve it as before.

Example

Solve $11x - 20 = 6x + 15$

The RHS has least x.

Take $6x$ from each side $\quad 11x - 6x - 20 = 6x - 6x + 15$
$$5x - 20 = 15$$

Now remove the numbers from the side with the x.
Add 20 to each side $\qquad 5x - 20 + 20 = 15 + 20$
$$5x = 35$$
Divide both sides by 5 $\qquad\qquad\quad x = 7$

Exercise 6:9

1 Solve these equations.

a $4x + 4 = 2x + 10$

b $2x - 7 = x + 3$

c $6x - 13 = 4x + 5$

d $8x + 9 = 4x + 13$

e $4x + 6 = 6x + 2$

f $7x - 21 = 3x - 5$

g $3x - 15 = x - 4$

● **h** $6x + 2 = 17 + x$

i $9x - 1 = 5x + 7$

j $12x + 7 = 12 + 2x$

● **k** $3.5x - 15 = x + 5$

l $5x + 25 = 3x + 25$

The method does not change if you have a minus sign in front of one of the letters.
A minus number is always less than a positive number.

$\quad$ Less than 0 $\qquad\qquad$ More than 0
$\quad$ (negative) $\qquad\qquad$ (positive)

This means that the side with the minus sign has the least x.
To remove the x from this side, add the same number of xs on to each side.

Example

Solve $4x + 5 = 20 - x$

First, remove the $-x$ from the RHS.
To do this, add x to each side $4x + 5 + x = 20 - x + x$
$$5x + 5 = 20$$
Subtract 5 from each side $5x + 5 - 5 = 20 - 5$
$$5x = 15$$
Divide both sides by 5 $x = 3$

2 Solve these equations.

a $6x + 6 = 20 - x$

b $5x + 7 = 21 - 2x$

c $x + 2 = 10 - x$

d $10x - 7 = 17 - 2x$

e $8x - 3 = 27 - 2x$

● **f** $-6x - 9 = 3 - 8x$

g $2.8x - 20 = 22 - 1.4x$

● **h** $7 - 3x = 4 + 2x$

Some equations have brackets in them.
To solve them, first multiply out the brackets.

Example

Solve $3(2x + 1) = 27$

Multiply out the bracket $3 \times 2x + 3 \times 1 = 27$
$$6x + 3 = 27$$
Now solve the equation as usual $6x = 24$
$$x = 4$$

Exercise 6:10

1 Solve these equations.

a $3(2x + 1) = 21$

b $4(7x - 4) = 40$

c $6(2x - 7) = 42$

d $5(8x - 1) = 35$

e $10(2x - 10) = 40$

f $9(3x - 5) = -18$

g $3(x - 1) = 2x - 2$

h $2(2x - 1) = x + 7$

i $2(x + 1) + 5 = 3(2x + 1)$

● **j** $3(x - 2) - 2(x + 1) = 5$

k $6(7x - 2) = 6(5x + 3)$

l $10(3x - 4) = 5(6 - x)$

You have already seen equations with a divide sign in them such as $\frac{x}{6} = 5$

Sometimes, the x is on the bottom of the fraction.
To solve the equation, you need to get the x back on the top.
To do this, multiply both sides of the equation by x.

Example

Solve the equation $\frac{3}{x} = 6$

First multiply both sides of the equation by x:

$$\frac{3}{x} \times x = 6 \times x$$

This gives

$$3 = 6x$$

Now divide both sides by 6:

$$0.5 = x$$

So, the solution to the equation is $x = 0.5$

Exercise 6:11

1 Solve these equations.

a $\dfrac{10}{x} = 2$ **c** $\dfrac{15}{x} = 3$ **e** $\dfrac{12}{3x} = -2$ ● **g** $\dfrac{-12}{x} + 1 = 4$

b $\dfrac{12}{x} = 4$ **d** $\dfrac{11}{2x} = 2$ **f** $\dfrac{4}{x} = -1$ ● **h** $\dfrac{1}{x} - 1 = 4$

3 Trial and improvement

Fred is trying to fence off a rectangular area to keep his sheep in.
He has 30 m of fencing.
He wants to make sure that each sheep has 1 m^2 of grass to graze in.
He has 50 sheep.
He wants to use the hedge as one side of the rectangle.
How would you build the fence?

Fred knows that he needs to solve a problem.
He can solve problems by guessing different answers.
He keeps trying different answers until he thinks he has found the best one.

This method is called **trial and improvement**.
You can use this method to solve any equation in Maths.
The method works for the linear equations that you solved in Section 2.
You would only do it this way if you were told to!

Example   Solve $12x - 35 = 163$

Value of x	Value of $12x - 35$		
10	$12 \times 10 - 35 = 85$	too small	
20	$12 \times 20 - 35 = 205$	too big	x is between 10 and 20
16	157	too small	x is between 16 and 20
17	169	too big	x is between 16 and 17
16.5	163	correct	

$x = 16.5$

Exercise 6:12

Solve these equations by trial and improvement.
For each question:
(1) Copy the table.
(2) Fill it in.
(3) Add more rows until you find the answer.

1 $4x - 13 = 33$

Value of x	Value of $4x - 13$	
10	...	...
11	...	...
12	...	...
...	...	...

2 $5p + 23 = 221$

Value of p	Value of $5p + 23$	
20	...	...
...	...	...

3 $12y - 14 = 156.4$

Value of y	Value of $12y - 14$	
...	...	...

Usually this method is used for harder equations. This is where it becomes even more useful.

Example Solve $x^2 = 1444$ *Remember:* $x^2 = x \times x$

Value of x	Value of x^2	
30	$30 \times 30 = 900$	too small
40	$40 \times 40 = 1600$	too big
38	1444	correct

x is between **30** and **40**

Answer: $x = 38$

This is only part of the answer! You may need to think about negative values!

Value of x	Value of x^2	
-30	900	too small
-40	1600	too big
-38	1444	correct

x is between -40 and -30

So $x = -38$ as well.

You can get two answers when you have to solve an equation with an x^2 term.

You need to find two answers in questions **4–6**.

4 $x^2 + 45 = 270$

Value of x	Value of $x^2 + 45$	
10	...	...
...	...	...

5 $p^2 - 50 = 311$

Value of p	Value of $p^2 - 50$	
...	...	...

6 $x^2 + x = 812$

Value of x	Value of $x^2 + x$	
...	...	...

Example   Solve $x^3 = 1728$ *Remember:* $x^3 = x \times x \times x$

 Key in: **1** **0** **y^x** **3** to do 10^3

 Key in: **1** **0** **x^y** **3** to do 10^3

Value of x	Value of x^3	
10	1000	too small
15	3375	too big
12	1728	correct

Answer: $x = 12$
This is the only answer this time.

There is only one answer for questions **7** and **8**.

7 $x^3 = 216$

Value of x	Value of x^3	
...	...	...

8 $m^3 - 3m = 488$

Value of m	Value of $m^3 - 3m$	
...	...	...

9 The length of this picture is
6 inches more than its width.
The area of the picture is 40 in².
The width is x inches.
The length is $x + 6$ inches.
So $x(x + 6) = 40$
Solve this equation by trial and
improvement to find the length
and width of the picture.

$x + 6$

x

Sometimes answers do not work out exactly.
When this happens, you may have to give your answer correct to 1 dp.
Start by trapping the answers between two consecutive whole numbers.
Then look at values to 1 dp.

Example   Solve $x^3 = 135$

Value of x	Value of x^3		
5	125	too small	
6	216	too big	x is between 5 and 6
5.5	166.375	too big	x is between 5 and 5.5
5.1	132.651	too small	x is between 5.1 and 5.5
5.2	140.608	too big	x is between 5.1 and 5.2
5.15	136.590 875	too big	x is between 5.1 and 5.15

This value is half-way between 5.1 and 5.2

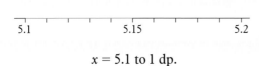

5.1   5.15   5.2

$x = 5.1$ to 1 dp.

x must be somewhere in the green part
of the number line.
Any number in the green part rounds
down to 5.1 to 1 dp.

Exercise 6:13

1 Solve these equations by trial and improvement.
Draw a table to help you find each solution.
When the equation has an x^2 term you need to find two answers.
The other equations only have one answer.
Give all of your answers to 1 dp.
   a $x^2 = 160$
   b $x^2 - 50 = 31$
   c $x^3 = 250$
   d $x^2 + x = 900$
   e $x^3 + x = 45$
   f $x^3 + 4x = 70$

2 Solve these equations using trial and improvement.
You need to rearrange the equations to get all the xs on the same side.
Part **a** has been rearranged for you.
All of these equations only have one answer.
Give your answers to 1 dp.

a $x^2 + 1 = \dfrac{1}{x}$ This is the same as $x^2 + 1 - \dfrac{1}{x} = 0$

b $x^3 = \dfrac{1}{x}$

c $x^2 = \dfrac{1}{x} + 5$

d $x^3 = \dfrac{1}{x} + 3$

You can give greater accuracy than 1 dp in your answers.

Example $x^2 = 135$ gives $x = 11.6$ to 1 dp but you can carry on to get the answer to 2 dp.

Value of x	Value of x^2		
11.6	134.56	too small	x is between 11.6 and 11.7
11.7	136.89	too big	x is between 11.6 and 11.65
11.65	135.7225	too big	x is between 11.6 and 11.65
11.61	134.7921	too small	x is between 11.61 and 11.65
11.62	135.0244	too big	x is between 11.61 and 11.62
11.615	134.908 225	too small	x is between 11.615 and 11.62

This value is half-way between 11.61 and 11.62

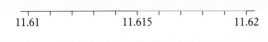

11.61   11.615   11.62

x must be somewhere in the green part of the number line.
Any number in the green part rounds up to 11.62 to 2 dp.

$x = 11.62$ to 2 dp.

---

3 Solve the equations in question **1** giving your answers to 2 dp.

4 Solve the equations in question **1** giving your answers to 3 dp.

Now you can solve the problem at the start of this section and other problems like it. You need to set up an equation that you solve by trial and improvement.

Exercise 6:14

1 This is Fred building his
rectangular fence.
The length of the fencing is 30 m.
He wants the area of the rectangle
to be 50 m².

This is a diagram of the final fenced area.
Let the width of the rectangle be x m.

a How long is the bottom side of the
rectangle?
b What is the area of the rectangle in terms of x?
c Fred wants the area to be 50 m².
Write down an equation that he needs to solve.
d Solve the equation to find the length and width of the rectangle.

2 The length of this picture is 10 cm more
than its width.
The area of the picture is 150 cm².
Call the width x cm.

a Write down the length in terms of x.
b Write down the area in terms of x.
c Write down an equation that tells
you that the area is 150 cm².
d Solve the equation by trial and
improvement to find the length and
width of the picture.
Give your answers to 1 dp.

3 The area of this square carpet is 10 m².
Call the side of the square x m.

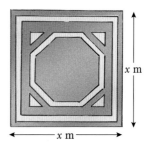

a Write down an equation that tells
you that the area is 10 m².
b Solve the equation by trial and
improvement to find the length of
each side of the carpet.
Give your answers to 1 dp.
● **c** Find the length of the side of the
square to the nearest centimetre.

1 Collect these by collecting terms where possible.
Where it is not possible to collect terms, give a reason.
- **a** $t + t + t$
- **b** $s + s + t + t$
- **c** $d + c + d + c - d + c$
- **d** $f^2 + 2f$
- **e** $3g^2 + 2g^2$

2 Simplify these by multiplying.
- **a** $f \times r$
- **b** $3 \times 6g$
- **c** $2z \times 3z$
- **d** $2s \times 3s \times 4s$
- **e** $-3c \times 4c$
- **f** $-3d \times -6d$

3 Multiply out these brackets.
- **a** $2(x + 3)$
- **b** $-3(2x + 6)$
- **c** $-4(3y - 2)$
- **d** $\frac{1}{2}(4x - 6)$

4 Multiply out these brackets.
- **a** $x(x + 2)$
- **b** $y(y^2 - 3)$
- **c** $3y(2y + x)$
- **d** $y^2(y + x)$

5 Solve these equations.
- **a** $2x + 3 = 15$
- **b** $3x - 6 = 12$
- **c** $5x + 3 = 2x - 6$
- **d** $3x - 4 = 8x - 29$

6 Solve these equations.
- **a** $\dfrac{x}{3} = 6$
- **b** $\dfrac{x}{4} = -7$
- **c** $\dfrac{x}{2} + 3 = 14$
- **d** $\dfrac{x}{4} + 3 = 10$
- **e** $\dfrac{y}{5} - 4 = 8$
- **f** $\dfrac{y}{6} - 6 = 12$

7 Solve these equations.
- **a** $4x + 4 = 13 + x$
- **b** $6 - x = 14 - 3x$
- **c** $2x + 1 = 7 - 4x$
- **d** $1 + 4x = 25 - 2x$
- **e** $17 - 3x = 11 - x$
- **f** $5 + 2x = 8 - 4x$

8 Solve these equations.

a $\dfrac{3x}{4} + 2 = 14$ **c** $\dfrac{x}{2} + 3 = \dfrac{x}{4} + 12$

b $\dfrac{2x}{3} + 4 = 16$ **d** $\dfrac{x}{4} + 1 = \dfrac{x}{3} - 3$

9 Solve these equations.

a $2(2x + 3) = 18$ **c** $4(3x - 7) = 32$
b $3(3x - 4) = 15$ **d** $3(3x - 4x) = -15$

10 Solve these equations by trial and improvement.
For each part:
(1) Copy the table.
(2) Fill it in.
(3) Add more rows until you find the answer.
There are two answers for each part.
a $x^2 + 56 = 681$

Value of x	Value of $x^2 + 56$	
20	...	...
...	...	...

b $x^2 - 51 = 2350$

Value of x	Value of $x^2 - 51$	
40	...	...
...	...	...

11 Solve these equations by trial and improvement.
Draw a table to help you find each solution.
When the equation has an x^2 term you need to find two answers.
The other equations only have one answer.
Give all of your answers to 1 dp.

a $x^2 = 190$ **c** $x^2 + x = 440$
b $x^3 - 26 = 37$ **d** $x^3 + x = 19$

12 Solve the equation $x^3 - 4 = \dfrac{1}{x}$ by trial and improvement.
You need to rearrange the equation so that all the xs are on the same side.
Give your answer to 1 dp.

1 Simplify these by collecting terms where possible.
When it is not possible to collect terms, give a reason.
  a $5x^2 + 3x^2 + 4y^2 - 3y^2$
  b $11x^2 - 13x^2 - 5z^2 - 2z^2$
  c $6t^2 - 2h^2 - 6t^3 + 2h^3$
  d $5a^2b + 8a^2b - 6a^2b$
  e $6xy^2 - 4xy - 9xy^2$
  f $12ab^2 - 8ab^2 + 3b^2a$

2 Jim is 5 years older than his brother Alan.
Their ages add up to 23.
  a Let Alan's age be x.
    Write down Jim's age in terms of x.
  b Write down an equation in x.
  c Solve your equation.
  d Write down the ages of the two boys.

3 Tina buys 6 m of fencing to make a run for her rabbit.
She wants to make the run 0.75 m wide.

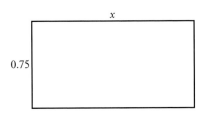

  a Write down an equation for the perimeter of the run.
  b Solve the equation to find the length of the run.

4 A square's sides are $3x$ m long.
A rectangle has a length of $4x$ m and a width of 2 m.
  a Write down the perimeter of the square in terms of x.
  b Write down the perimeter of the rectangle in terms of x.
  c The perimeters of the two shapes are equal.
    Write down an equation.
  d Find the perimeter of each shape.

5 The area of a field is 180 m².
The length of the field is 25 m more than the width of the field.
Call the width of the field x m.
  a Write down an equation that you need to solve to find the width of
    the field.
  b Solve the equation by trial and improvement.
    Give the width and the length of the field correct to the nearest
    centimetre.

1 Simplify these :

    a $2f + 6f - 7f$

    b $4x + 3x^2 - x + 5x^2$

    c $4t \times 2t$

    d $3q \times 6q$

2 Multiply out these brackets.

    a $5(4x - 1)$

    b $-3(8 - 5x^2)$

    c $7(a^2 - 2a + 9)$

    d $y(4y - 3)$

    e $m(m^2 + 4m)$

    f $3x(7 - 5x)$

3 Solve these equations.

    a $4g - 3 = 21$

    b $\dfrac{x}{5} + 6 = 10$

    c $8x = 5x - 12$

    d $3a + 13 = 5a$

    e $14s - 5 = 9s + 20$

    f $\dfrac{24}{x} = 8$

    g $6d + 8 = 29 - d$

    h $7(3x - 12) = 42$

4 Solve the equation $x^2 - 30 = 3151$ by trial and improvement.
There are two answers. One is a negative number.
Draw a table to help you find each solution.
Give both answers to 1 dp.

5 **a** Write down the perimeter of this
triangle in terms of x.
   b The perimeter of the triangle is 34 cm.
Write down an equation in x.
   c Use your equation to find the value of x.
   d Write down the length of the
three sides of the triangle.
   e What is the special name of the triangle?

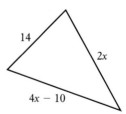

14

2x

4x − 10

7 Ratio and proportion

1 Ratio
Introducing ratio
Comparing objects
Simplifying ratios
Expressing ratios in the form $n:1$

2 Splitting up
Dividing into two parts
Dividing into more than two parts
Ratios and fractions

CORE

3 Value for money?
Comparing two sizes of the same product
Using the unitary method
Using direct proportion
Using direct proportion with more complex problems

QUESTIONS

EXTENSION

TEST YOURSELF

1 **Ratio**

Blackpool Tower was opened in 1893 and was the second tallest building in the world. It is a copy of the Eiffel Tower in Paris which was then the tallest structure in the world.
The Blackpool Tower is not an exact copy and it is only 0.53 of the height of the Eiffel Tower.

Ratios can be used to compare two measurements.

Example   The first building is twice the height of the second one.
The ratio of their heights is **2 : 1** (said two *to* one)

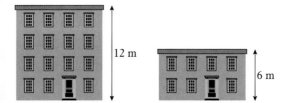

Exercise 7:1

1 Look at each of these pairs of pictures.
For each one, write down the ratio.

a

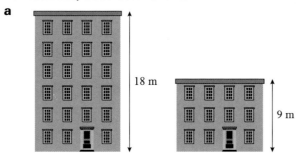

b

 9 coins

 3 coins

c

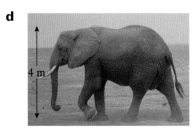 120 cm

 30 cm

d

 4 m

 1 m

2 Look at the weights of each of these objects.
Write down the ratio of their weights.

a

 500g

 100g

b

 16 pounds

 8 pounds

The order that you write the numbers down is important.

The ratio of the volumes of
these Coke bottles is **2 : 1**
The one on the left has **twice**
as much Coke as the one on
the right.

The ratio of the volumes of
these Coke bottles is **1 : 2**
The one on the left has **half**
as much Coke as the one on
the right.

Example   Write down the ratio of the number of pages in a writing pad with 100
pages compared with one of 300 pages.

The ratio is **1 : 3**
The second pad has 3 times the number of pages.

Exercise 7:2

1   Steve is half the weight of his father.
Copy and complete:
The ratio of Steve's weight to his father's is … : …

2   Dfer the Dalmatian eats twice as much food as Spanner the Spaniel.
Copy and complete:
The ratio of the amount Dfer eats to the amount Spanner eats is … : …

3   A large tin of paint contains 5 litres. A small tin contains $\frac{1}{2}$ litre.
What is the ratio of their contents?

4   A mouse weighs about 30 g. An elephant weighs about 6 000 000 g.
What is the ratio of their weights?

Ratios that look different can be the same.
Ratios will simplify like fractions.

Tom has three packs of tapes.
There are three tapes in each pack.
Mike has two packs of the tapes.

If you look at the ratio of tapes they
have it is **9 : 6**
If you look at the ratio of packs they
have it is **3 : 2**

These two ratios **must** be the same.

If you can find a number which divides
exactly into both parts of a ratio then
you can simplify it.

Example Simplify these ratios if possible.

     a 9 : 6   **b** 20 : 15   **c** 9 : 2

    a 3 divides into 9 and 6 exactly.
       9 ÷ 3 = 3 and 6 ÷ 3 = 2 so 9 : 6 = 3 : 2
    b 5 divides into 20 and 15 exactly.
       20 : 15 = 4 : 3
    c No whole number divides exactly into 9 and 2.
       9 : 2 can't be simplified.

Exercise 7:3

1 Simplify these ratios if possible.

    a 10 : 5   **f** 21 : 14
    b 12 : 4   **g** 18 : 6
    c 3 : 9   **h** 17 : 2
    d 12 : 6   **i** 9 : 15
    e 16 : 12   **j** 7 : 28

2 Simplify these ratios if possible.

    a 100 : 25   **d** 21 : 10
    b 36 : 10   **e** 18 : 72
    c 35 : 24   • **f** $\frac{1}{2} : \frac{1}{4}$

Because simplifying ratios is very similar to simplifying fractions, you can use the fraction button on your calculator.

Example   Simplify the ratio 72 : 24

Because of the way the calculator works, you must enter the **smaller** number first. You can swap them over later!

Key in: **2** **4** **aᵇ/c** **7** **2** **=**

You should see ⌐3 or ⌐3

Remember to write the ratio back around the right way.
So 72 : 24 = **3 : 1**

---

3   Simplify these ratios if possible.
Use a calculator to help you.

  a   52 : 39   **d**   45 : 54
  b   28 : 21   **e**   42 : 75
  c   34 : 85   **f**   28 : 39

4   Simplify these ratios.
Make sure they are in the same units first.

  a   5 kg : 100 g   **d**   500 kg : 3 tonnes
  b   2.5 m : 50 cm   **e**   50 ml : 6 *l*
  c   4 hrs : 30 mins   **f**   750 ml : 7 *l*

Sophie was looking at the *Guinness Book of Records*. She noticed the records for the tallest and smallest people.
The tallest was 272 cm and the smallest was 57 cm.

If you write these as a ratio 272 : 57 they will not simplify.

Sometimes it is useful to write ratios in the form *n* : 1 even if *n* is a decimal number.

Example   Write the ratio 272 : 57 in the form *n* : 1

To get the right-hand side of the ratio to be 1 you need to divide by 57.
This means that both parts of the ratio need to be divided by 57.
    272 ÷ 57 = 4.77 (2 dp)

The ratio 272 : 57 is the same as 4.77 : 1
This means that the tallest man was 4.77 times bigger than the smallest man!

Exercise 7:4

In this exercise, round your answers to 2 dp when you need to.

1 An average carrot weighs about 40 g.
The world's biggest ever carrot weighed 7000 g.
  a Calculate 7000 ÷ 40.
  b Write the ratio 7000 : 40 in the form *n* : 1.
  c Copy and complete:
     The world's biggest ever carrot weighed ... times more than an average carrot.

2 The following table has some more world records in it.
Copy the table and fill it in.

	Vegetable	Record weight (kg)	Average weight (kg)	Ratio	Ratio in the form *n* : 1
a	cabbage	56.24	2.3	56.24 : 2.3	
b	courgette	29.25	0.7		
c	leek	5.5	1.2		
d	pumpkin	449	8		
e	potato	3.5	0.3		
f	radish	17.2	0.1		

3 Write the following ratios in the form 1 : *n*.
  a 34 : 98
  b 21 : 54
  c 23 : 60
  d 0.5 : 17

2 Splitting up

Sharon is painting her lounge.
She wants a specific shade of green.
She is having the paint specially mixed at a DIY store.

Blue and yellow are mixed in the ratio 4 : 3

The machine puts 400 ml of blue paint and 300 ml of yellow paint in the mixture.

Ratios are used to describe how something is divided up.

Example   Tullis wants 1 litre of purple paint. For the shade of purple he wants he needs to mix blue and red paint in the ratio 3 : 1.
How much of each type of paint does he need?

1 litre is the same as 1000 ml.
The ratio 3 : 1 means 3 parts blue to 1 part red.
This is 4 parts altogether.

Divide 1000 by 4 $1000 \div 4 = 250$
So 1 part is 250 ml.

Tullis needs $3 \times 250 = 750$ ml of blue paint
and $1 \times 250 = 250$ ml of red paint.

Check: 750 ml + 250 ml = 1000 ml.

Exercise 7:5

1 Orange paint is made by mixing red and yellow paint.
Sunburst Orange is red and yellow in the ratio 4 : 2.
How much red and yellow paint is needed to make these amounts of Sunburst Orange?
    a 600 ml   **b** 6 litres   **c** 3 litres

2   Midnight Orange is red and yellow in the ratio 4 : 3.
How much red and yellow paint is needed to make these amounts of
Midnight Orange?
a   700 ml   **b**   7 litres   **c**   350 ml

3   A builder needs strong mortar for his
bricklaying.
He mixes sand and cement in the ratio 3 : 1.
How much sand and cement does he need
to make these amounts of mortar?
a   40 kg   **b**   100 kg   **c**   500 kg

4   ALT lemon drink is made by mixing lemonade and lemon juice in the
ratio 7 : 3.
How much lemonade and lemon juice is needed to make these amounts
of ALT?
a   1 litre   **b**   3 litres   **c**   500 ml

5   Linden and Alex are partners in a T shirt company.
To set up the company, Linden invested £7000 and Alex invested £3000.
a   Write their investments as a ratio.
b   Write your answer to part **a** as simply as possible.
c   The company makes £13 000 profit in its first year.
Linden and Alex split the profits in the same ratio as their
investments.
How much does each person get?

6   Banana milkshake is made by
mixing milk and flavouring in
the ratio 14 : 1.
How much milk and flavouring
is needed to make these amounts
of milkshake?
a   300 ml   **b**   900 ml   **c**   3 litres

It is possible to divide things up into more than two parts.

Example   A metal alloy is made from iron, copper and nickel in the ratio 7 : 4 : 1.
How much of each metal is needed to produce 300 kg of the alloy?

Find the total number of parts:
7 parts iron + 4 parts copper + 1 part nickel = 12 parts

Divide the total by 12 to find the size of 1 part:
300 ÷ 12 = 25 so 1 part = 25 kg

Metals needed: 7 × 25 = 175 kg of iron
4 × 25 = 100 kg of copper
1 × 25 = 25 kg of nickel

Check: 175 + 100 + 25 = 300

Exercise 7:6

1   The £10 000 profits of a company are shared out amongst the owners.
They are shared in the ratio 3 : 2 : 5.
Calculate how much each person gets.

2   Ned, Ben and Mary are in a lottery syndicate.
Each week, Ned pays £3, Ben pays £1 and Mary pays £4.
They agree to split any winnings in the same ratio.
Calculate how much each person receives if they win:
a £10   **b** £66   **c** £120 000

3   The three angles in a triangle are in the ratio 1 : 2 : 3.
Calculate the size of each angle.

4   St Aidan's school is ordering Key Maths GCSE books.
They order Foundation, Intermediate and Higher levels in the
ratio 4 : 5 : 2.
They order 176 books altogether.
How many of each type of book do they order?

5   A tin of paint is made by mixing red, yellow and white paints.
The three colours are mixed in the ratio 2 : 3 : 5.
300 ml of red paint is used.
Calculate how much of the other two paints is used.

6   Three sisters share out a Premium Bond win.
They share the money in the ratio of their ages, 12 : 14 : 16.
The middle sister gets £56.
Calculate how much each of the other two sisters get.

Ratios are really just another way of thinking about fractions.
You can easily swap between ratios and fractions.
It is **very** important to work out the total number of parts first.

Example   A concrete mix is made from sand and cement in the ratio 5 : 2.
What fraction of the concrete is sand and what fraction is cement?

5 parts sand + 2 parts cement = 7 parts altogether.
The fractions will be sevenths.

The sand makes up $\dfrac{5}{7}$ of the mix.

The cement makes up $\dfrac{2}{7}$ of the mix.

Exercise 7:7

1   A metal alloy contains iron and tungsten in the ratio 6 : 1.
What fraction of the alloy is iron?

2   Profits from a business are shared between three people.
They are shared in the ratio 7 : 2 : 3.
a   What fraction of the profits does each person get?
b   If the profits are £29 400, find out how much each person gets.

3   Boys make up $\frac{4}{11}$ of Class 10T.
What is the ratio of boys : girls in the class?

3　Value for money?

Washing powder is sold in lots of different sized containers.

It is often difficult to spot which is the best value for money.

Some shops put extra information on the ticket to help you.

To compare the value for money you need to work out the price for a fixed amount.

Example　　Brazen washing powder costs £4.30 for a 500 g box or £2.52 for a 300 g box. Which is better value?

It is easy to work out how much 100 g costs in each box.

　　　500 g box:　　£4.30 ÷ 5 = 86 p per 100 g
　　　300 g box:　　£2.52 ÷ 3 = 84 p per 100 g

The 300 g box is better value.
You pay less for each 100 g.

Exercise 7:8

1　Wizzo milkshake costs 66 p for a 300 ml bottle or £1.05 for a 500 ml bottle.
　a　Work out the cost per 100 ml in the small bottle.
　b　Work out the cost per 100 ml in the large bottle.
　c　Which size of bottle is better value?

2　Paws&Claws cat food costs 45 p for a 300 g tin or 70 p for a 500 g tin. Which size of tin is better value for money?

3 Woodhouse tea costs £1.56 for 80 bags and £1.98 for 120 bags.
   a Work out the cost of 10 bags in the 80 bag box.
   b Work out the cost of 10 bags in the 120 bag box.
   c Which is better value?

4 Choc pops breakfast cereal is sold in three sizes.
   The sizes and prices are: 300 g   £1.26
                              500 g   £1.95
                              800 g   £3.20
   a Work out the price of 100 g in each size of box.
   b Which size of box is the best value?

5 Sprinters crisps are sold in 3 ways.
   Single bags cost 24 p.
   A 6 pack costs £1.38
   An 8 pack costs £2.00 but has a special offer of one extra bag free.
   What is the cheapest way to buy 18 bags of crisps?

Sometimes sizes are not so easy to compare.
You may have to work out the cost of 1 g or 1 ml to compare the value
for money.

Example   Panine shampoo is sold in two sizes.
The 325 ml bottle costs £2.40 and the 412 ml bottle costs £3.16
Which is the better value?

Work out the amount of shampoo per £1 in each bottle. To do this divide
the volume by the price.
   325 ml bottle: 325 ÷ £2.40 = 135 ml for £1 (3 sf)
   412 ml bottle: 412 ÷ £3.16 = 130 ml for £1 (3 sf)

The smaller bottle is slightly better value for money.
You get slightly more shampoo for each £1.

Exercise 7:9

1 Goblin washing up liquid comes in two sizes.
525 ml costs £1.58 and 740 ml costs £2.12
  a Work out the amount of liquid you get for £1 in the small bottle.
  b Work out the amount of liquid you get for £1 in the large bottle.
  c Which bottle is better value?

2 Columbo Coffee costs £3.45 for 175 g and £4.58 for 260 g.
  a Work out the amount of coffee you get for £1 in the
    small jar. $(175 \div 3.45 = \quad)$
  b Work out the amount of coffee you get for £1 in the large jar.
  c Which jar is better value?

3 Tomato Ketchup comes in three sizes.
The sizes and costs are shown in this table.

Size	Cost
125 ml	£1.24
263 ml	£2.51
415 ml	£3.99

Which size is the best value for money?

4 Satellite washing powder comes in lots of different sizes.
Look at the following offers.
Decide which is the best value for money.
Show all of your working.

Size	Cost	Offers
1.5 kg	£2.54	
2.3 kg	£3.67	Buy 2 get 50 p off
3.7 kg	£5.68	
4.2 kg	£7.45	Extra 200 g free

Some products are sold in a way that makes it easy to compare.
For example, if you buy bananas, you would pay by the kilogram.
If 1 kg costs £1.20, you can guarantee that 2 kg would cost twice as
much, £2.40
Petrol is the same. Two litres will cost twice as much as 1 litre and
3 litres will cost 3 times as much.

This is called **direct proportion**.

Example   Copy this table showing petrol prices.
Fill in the gaps marked with letters.

Amount (litres)	1	2	6	c	d
Cost	70 p	a	b	£4.90	£6.30

a   2 litres cost twice as much as 1 litre.
2×70 p = **£1.40**
b   6 litres cost 6 times as much as 1 litre.
6×70 p = **£4.20**
c   Divide the cost by the price for 1 litre.
£4.90 ÷ 70 p = 7
7 litres cost £4.90
d   Divide the cost by the price for 1 litre.
£6.30 ÷ 70 p = 9
9 litres cost £6.30

Exercise 7:10

1   Copy this table.
It shows the price of different amounts of apples.

Amount (kg)	1	2	5	c	d
Price	38 p	a	b	£3.04	£5.32

Fill in the gaps marked with letters.
Show your working.

2 Copy this table.
It shows the price for different amounts of carpet.

Amount (m²)	2	6	11	c	d
Price (£)	35	a	b	245	472.50

Fill in the gaps marked with letters.
Show your working.

3 Pic 'n' Mix sweets cost 74 p per 100 g.
a Work out the cost for 300 g.
b Work out the cost of 150 g.
c What weight of sweets could you buy for £4.81?
d What weight of sweets could you buy for £1.11?

All the examples you have seen so far involve money.
This method can also be used to compare other quantities.
The two quantities must be in direct proportion.
If one doubles, the other must double as well.

Example　A car travels on a motorway at 70 mph.
Look at this table of distances.
Fill in the gaps marked with letters.

Time (hours)	1	2	$4\frac{1}{2}$	c	d
Distance (miles)	70	a	b	350	437.5

a In 2 hours the car will go twice as far as in 1 hour.
　　2×70 miles = **140 miles**

b In $4\frac{1}{2}$ hours the car will go $4\frac{1}{2}$ times as far as in 1 hour.
　　$4\frac{1}{2} \times 70$ miles = **315 miles**

c Divide the number of miles by the speed.
　　$350 \div 70 = 5$
　　The car will take **5 hours** to go 350 miles.

d Divide the number of miles by the speed.
　　$437.5 \div 70 = 6.25$
　　The car will take $6\frac{1}{4}$ **hours** to go 437.5 miles.

4 This table shows the area of wall covered by paint.

Area (m²)	5	15	**b**	55	**d**
Paint needed (litres)	1	**a**	7	**c**	9.5

Copy the table. Fill in the gaps marked with letters.

5 A recipe for 4 people needs 600 g of sugar.
   a How much sugar would be needed for 16 people?
   b How much sugar would be needed for 6 people?
   c How many people could be catered for with a 1.2 kg bag of sugar?

6 When a photograph is enlarged the shape of the photo has to stay the same, otherwise the picture will be distorted.
This means that the width and length have to stay in proportion.
Copy this table. It shows the width and length of different sizes of photos. Fill in the spaces **a** to **d**.

Length (cm)	10	15	20	35	50
Width (cm)	8	**a**	**b**	**c**	**d**

Sometimes the numbers are a little more difficult to compare.
You will need a calculator to do these questions.

Example The sizes of some photographs are shown in this table.
Fill in the missing lengths.

Photo	1	2	3
Length (cm)	6.4	8.8	13.6
Width (cm)	3.4	**a**	**b**

   a Divide the length of photo 2 by the length of photo 1.
         $8.8 \div 6.4 = 1.375$
      This means that the second photo is 1.375 times as long as the first one. The width must also be 1.375 times as big.
         $3.4 \times 1.375 = \textbf{4.675}$ cm
   b $13.6 \div 6.4 = 2.125$
      Photo 3 is 2.125 times as long as photo 1.
      The width is $\textbf{3.4} \times 2.125 = \textbf{7.225}$ cm

---

Exercise 7:11

1 The cost of gas is proportional to the amount used.
   a Copy this table.

Customer	1	2	3
Meter reading	240	522	783
Cost	£18.50		

   b Work out $522 \div 240$.
   c Copy this. Fill it in.
      Customer 2 has used ... more gas than customer 1.
   d Use part **c** to work out the cost of customer 2's gas.
   e Work out the cost of customer 3's gas.

2 The cost of electricity is also proportional to the amount used.
   a Copy this table.

Customer	1	2	3
Meter reading	324	567	923.4
Cost	£16.24		

   b Work out $567 \div 324$.
   c Copy this. Fill it in.
      Customer 2 has used ... more electricity than customer 1.
   d Use part **c** to work out the cost of customer 2's electricity.
   e Work out the cost of customer 3's electricity.

3 The energy content of food is proportional to the amount you eat.
   A 68 g pot of yoghurt provides 420 kJ of energy.
   a How many times more yoghurt is there in a 119 g pot?
   b How much energy would a 119 g pot provide?

4 The length of a shadow an object creates is directly proportional to its height.
   A tree of height 3.4 m casts a shadow of length 2.4 m at 4 p.m.
   a How many times bigger is a tree of height 4.8 m?
      Write your answer to 2 dp.
   b About how long would this tree's shadow be at 4 p.m.?

1   Stripes toothpaste is sold in two sizes.
    The small size contains 85 ml and costs 74 p.
    The large size contains 140 ml and costs £1.38.
    Which size gives better value for money?

2   A large tin of paint contains 6 litres. A small tin holds 2 litres.
    What is the ratio of their contents?
    Write your answer in its simplest form.

3   Joanne and Lucy are partners in a birthday card company.
    To set up the company, Joanne invested £6000 and Lucy invested £4000.
    a   Write their investments as a ratio in its simplest form.
    b   The company makes £23 000 profit in its first year.
          Joanne and Lucy split the profits in the same ratio as their
          investments.
          How much does each person get?

4   A tin of paint is made by mixing
    blue, yellow and white paints.
    The three colours are mixed in
    the ratio 1 : 3 : 4
    600 ml of yellow paint is used.
    Calculate how much of the other
    two paints is used.

5   Lisper washing up liquid comes in two sizes.
    520 ml costs £1.63 and 850 ml costs £2.24
    a   Work out the amount of liquid you get for £1 in the small bottle.
    b   Work out the amount of liquid you get for £1 in the large bottle.
    c   Which bottle is better value?

6   It takes 150 g of flour to make 4 scones.
    a   How many scones could you make with 900 g of flour?
    b   Calculate the weight of flour needed to make 22 scones.

7   The three angles in a triangle are in the ratio 2 : 3 : 4.
    Calculate the size of each angle.

1   Here are the ingredients for 18 rock buns.

> 285 g of flour
> 180 g of flour
> 180 g of margarine
> 2 eggs
> 240 g of fruit

a Write out the amount of each ingredient you would need to make 45 rock buns.

b If you had 135 g of margarine, what is the maximum number of rock buns you could make?

2   A prize of £6500 is to be shared between 4 people in the ratio of their ages.
Alan, Maggie, Andrew and Katy share the prize in the ratio
40 : 38 : 10 : 6.
Work out the amount each person receives to the nearest penny.

3   Kerry draws two squares.
The ratio of the lengths of their
sides is 3 : 1.
Calculate the ratio of the areas of the
two squares.

4   A piece of string is 36 cm long.
It is cut into two pieces in the ratio 3 : 1.
Work out the length of each piece.

5   A photocopier can make copies that are bigger or smaller than the original.
It has these ratios for length of original : length of copy:

> 1 : 0.5   1 : 0.7   1 : 1.5   1 : 2

a Which ratio will halve the lengths?

b Which ratio will double the lengths?

c Which ratio will about halve the area of the paper used?

1 Look at the heights of these trees.
Write down the ratio of the heights.

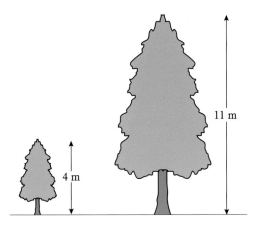

2 Simplify these ratios.

   a 21 : 14   **b** 16 : 24   **c** 250 : 375

3 Simplify these ratios.
Make sure they are in the same units first.

   a 1.5 m : 75 cm   **d** 2 h : 15 min

   b £2.40 : 60 p   **e** 2.4 km : 80 m

   c 250 ml : 3 l **f** 2 tonnes : 750 kg

4 **a** Write these ratios in the form $1 : n$.
      (1) 6 : 18   (2) 17 : 23
   b Write these ratios in the form $n : 1$.
      (1) 14 : 3   (2) 125 : 280

Give your answers to 2 dp when you need to round.

5 The areas of two triangles are in the ratio 1 : 8.
The smaller triangle has an area of 25 cm².
What is the area of the larger triangle?

6 Pele gets £40 birthday money. He spends some and saves the rest.
The ratio of money spent to money saved is 5 : 3.

   a How much money does he save?

   b What fraction of his money does he spend?

7   The three angles of a triangle are in the ratio 2 : 3 : 5.
    Find the size of each angle.
    (The angles of a triangle add up to 180°.)

8   A recipe for 1 litre of 'orange surprise' is

    300 ml orange juice
    450 ml lemonade
    250 ml grapefruit juice

    a   How much grapefruit juice would you need to make 5 litres of
        'orange surprise'?
    b   How much orange juice is needed if 1350 ml of lemonade is used?
    c   How much lemonade is needed if 150 ml of orange juice is used?

9   The ratio of cereal to meat in a pack of sausages is 3 : 4.
    a   What fraction is cereal?
    b   What fraction is meat?

10 An alloy is made from iron, copper and nickel in the ratio 6 : 3 : 1.
    What fraction of the alloy is
    a   copper   b   nickel   c   iron

11 Shinerite shampoo is made in three sizes.

    Small   150 ml   costing   £1.35
    Medium   250 ml   costing   £2.15
    Large   400 ml   costing   £3.50

    Which size of shampoo is the best value for money?
    Show your working clearly.

12 The cost of labels is proportional to the number ordered.
    a   Copy this table.

Number of labels ordered	50	90	180	340
Cost	...	£2.25	...	...

    b   Fill in the missing costs.

8 Graphs: a bit steep

1 Gradients
Looking at slopes of lines
Naming lines that go through the point (0, 0)
Lines that slope downwards

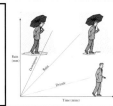

2 Straight lines
Naming lines that don't go through the point (0, 0)
Knowing when lines are parallel
Using graphs to solve problems

CORE

3 Linear equations
Spotting equations that make straight lines
Finding equations

QUESTIONS

EXTENSION

TEST YOURSELF

1 Gradients

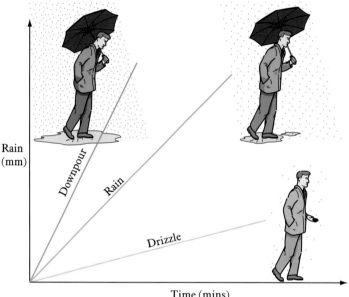

This graph shows different types of rainfall.
The heavier the rain, the steeper the line.

This graph shows the
number of pages in a
magazine and its cost.
The magazines are
Computer World, Your Car
and *Pop Scene*.

The steeper the line the
more pages you get per £1.

The best value magazine
is *Computer World*.
You get about 320 pages for £1.
This magazine gives the most pages per £1.

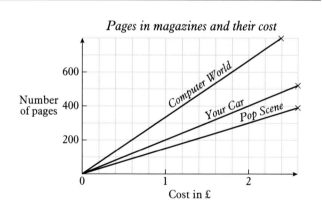

Exercise 8:1

1 Use the graph above to estimate the number of pages you get for £1 with:
  a *Pop Scene*   **b** *Your Car*

2 This graph shows the rates of climb on take off for some planes.

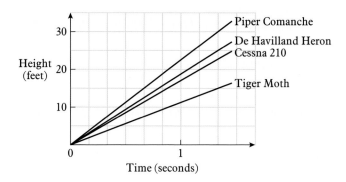

a Which plane takes off at a rate of 11 feet per second?
b Estimate the rate of climb for the other three planes.
c Which plane climbs the fastest?

Sometimes you need to know exactly how steep the line is.

Gradient

The **gradient** of a line tells you how steep the line is.

To find the gradient of a line choose two points on the line as far apart as possible.

You need to be able to read the co-ordinates of the points accurately.

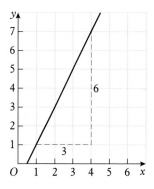

$$\text{Gradient} = \frac{\text{vertical change}}{\text{horizontal change}}$$

$$= \frac{7 - 1}{4 - 1}$$

$$= \frac{6}{3}$$

$$= 2$$

The gradient of the line is 2.

For each of these lines:

a Choose two points on the line whose co-ordinates you can read.
b Write down the vertical change between the two points.
c Write down the horizontal change between the two points.
d Find the gradient of the line.

3

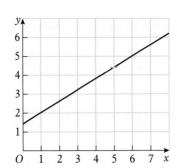

4

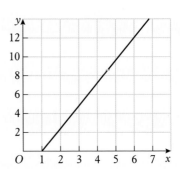

Work out the gradient of the line in questions **5–7**.

5

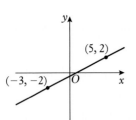

6

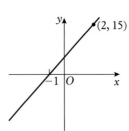

7

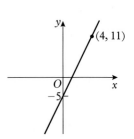

8 Find the gradient of the line passing through the points:
  a (2, 3) and (4, 11)
  b (5, 0) and (7, 14)
  c (1, 4) and (2, 5)
  d (0, 3) and (5, 28)

A shop expects to sell 5 computers per day on average.
If d is the number of days, the number of computers sold $= 5d$

If n is the number of computers sold then
$$n = 5d$$

$n = 5d$ is called a formula. You can draw a graph for this formula.

When $d = 1$, $n = 5 \times 1 = 5$
When $d = 2$, $n = 5 \times 2 = 10$
When $d = 3$, $n = 5 \times 3 = 15$

These values can be put into a table:

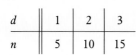

d	1	2	3
n	5	10	15

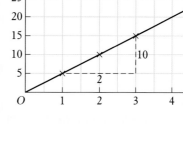

Plot the points $(1, 5)$ $(2, 10)$ $(3, 15)$
Join them up.
You get a straight line.

$$\text{gradient} = \frac{15 - 5}{3 - 1}$$
$$= \frac{10}{2}$$

$n = 5d$ is the equation of the straight line.
The gradient of the line is 5.

$$= 5$$

Exercise 8:2

1   This formula gives the average *number* of telephone calls received by a
firm each *hour*: $n = 8h$
   a   On average how many calls does
the firm get each hour?
   b   Copy this table.
Fill it in.
   c   Draw the straight line with
equation $n = 8h$
   d   What is the gradient of this line?
   e   Use your graph to find how many
calls the firm gets on average in 4 hours.
Draw a dotted line to show your method.

h	1	2	3
n	...	...	...

2 Ruth uses a graph to change £s into French Francs.
She knows that £1 is the same as 10 French Francs.

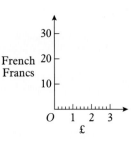

  a How many French Francs are the same as
    (1) £2   (2) £3?
  b Copy the axes.
  c Use your answers to part **a** to draw a line on the axes.
  d Write down the gradient of this line.
  e Use the graph to convert £2.80 into French Francs.

3 This table is for the formula $y = 2x$.

x	1	2	3
y	...	...	...

  a Copy the table.
    Fill it in.
  b Copy these axes.
  c Plot the graph of $y = 2x$.
  d Draw a triangle to find the gradient
    of the line.
  e What do you notice about the
    gradient and the formula?

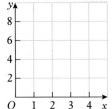

4 This table is for the formula $y = 3x$.

x	1	2	3
y	...	...	...

  a Copy the table.
    Fill it in.
  b Copy these axes.
  c Plot the graph of $y = 3x$.
  d Draw a triangle to find the gradient
    of the line.
  e What do you notice about the
    gradient and the formula?

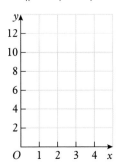

You sometimes use the word 'equation' instead of 'formula'.
If a line goes through the origin, there is an easy way to
get its equation.

This graph shows a straight line.
The gradient is 7.

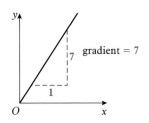

The equation of this line is $y = 7x$.
The number multiplying the x is the gradient.

Exercise 8:3

1 Write down the gradient of each of these lines.
    a $y = 5x$ **b** $y = 4x$ **c** $n = 7h$

2 Write down the equation of each of these lines.

a

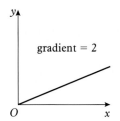

gradient = 2

b

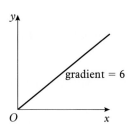

gradient = 6

c

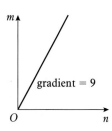

gradient = 9

This line has a negative gradient.
As you move along the line from A to B you go down 8.
The vertical change is negative. It is -8.

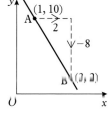

$$\text{Gradient} = \frac{\text{vertical change}}{\text{horizontal change}}$$

$$= \frac{8}{2}$$

$$= -4$$

The gradient is -4.

A line with a positive gradient
slopes uphill.

A line with a negative gradient
slopes downhill.

Exercise 8:4

1 These lines all have different gradients.

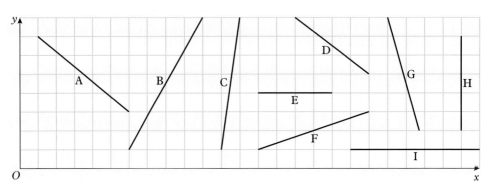

Write down the letters of lines
a with positive gradients
b with negative gradients
c which have neither positive nor negative gradients.

2 Find the gradient of each of these lines.

a

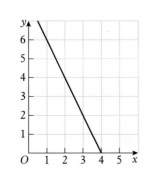

b

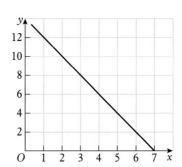

3 Work out the gradient of each of these lines.

a

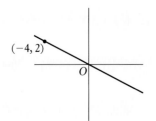

b

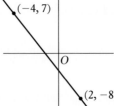

c

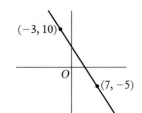

4   Find the gradient of each line.

a

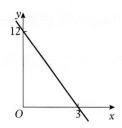

b

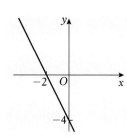

5   Find the gradient of the line passing through these pairs of points.
Draw a sketch to help you to see if the line has a positive or negative
gradient.
a (1, 1) and (6, 16)   **d** (−3, 0) and (0, 12)
b (2, 9) and (4, 5)   **e** (−5, 4) and (−3, 10)
c (−2, −12) and (4, 6)   **f** (−5, −14) and (−1, 4)

6   Write down the gradient of each of these lines.
a $y = -6x$ **b** $y = -3x$ **c** $y = -x$

7   These lines pass through the origin.
Find the equation of each line.

a

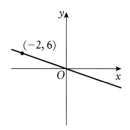

b

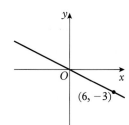

2 Straight lines

Both sides of this bridge are at the same angle.
As you travel from left to right the left side has a positive gradient and the right side has a negative gradient.

Exercise 8:5

1 **a** Copy this table for $y = 2x + 1$.
Fill it in.

x	1	2	3
y	...	...	...

b Copy these axes.
c Plot the line $y = 2x + 1$.
Label the line.
d Draw a table for $y = 2x + 2$.
Plot the line on the same set of axes.
Label the line.
e Draw a table for $y = 2x - 1$.
Plot the line on the same set of axes.
Label the line.
f What do you notice about all three lines?
g Can you see a link between the equations and where the lines cut the y axis?
Write down what you think it is.

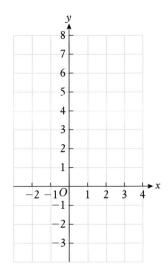

The equation of this line is $y = 4x - 2$.

The gradient of the line is 4.
The line crosses the y axis at -2.

If the equation of a straight line is $y = mx + c$ then the line has a gradient m and cuts the y axis at c.

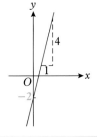

Parallel lines have the same gradient.

Exercise 8:6

1 Write down the gradient of each of these lines.
  a $y = 4x + 2$ **b** $y = 2x - 4$ **c** $y = 3x - 1$ **d** $y = -2x + 3$

2 Write down where each of the lines in question **1** crosses the y axis.

3 Write down the equations of the pairs of parallel lines from these:
  $y = 2x - 3$ $y = 3x + 2$ $y = 3x - 3$ $y = 2x + 1$

4 **a** Copy this table for $y = -2x + 2$.
   Fill it in.

x	1	2	3
y	...	...	...

  b Copy these axes.
  c Plot the line $y = -2x + 2$.
   Label the line.
  d Draw a table for $y = -2x$.
   Plot the line on the same set of axes.
   Label the line.
  e Draw a table for $y = -2x - 1$.
   Plot the line on the same set of axes.
   Label the line.
  f What do you notice about all
   three lines?

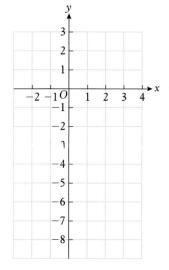

The equation of this line is $y = -3x + 2$.

The gradient of the line is -3.
The line crosses the y axis at 2.

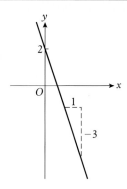

These are the lines $y = -2x + 4$
and $y = -2x - 2$.

These two lines have the same gradient -2.
They are parallel.

$y = -2x + 4$ can be written $y = 4 - 2x$.
The order of the last two terms has
been changed.
This makes no difference to the line.

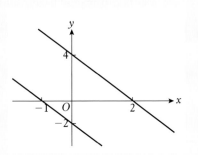

Exercise 8:7

1 Write down the gradients of each of these lines.
    a $y = -5x + 3$ **b** $y = -x - 4$ **c** $y = 6 - 3x$ **d** $y = 7 + x$

2 Write down where each of the lines in question **1** crosses the y axis.

3 Write down the equations of the pairs of parallel lines from these:
    $y = -x - 3$ $y = -2x + 2$ $y = 5 - x$ $y = 1 - 2x$

4 Write down the equation of the line with:
    a gradient 2 y intercept 5   **c** gradient -7 y intercept -2
    b gradient -5 y intercept 1   **d** gradient 1 y intercept -3

5 Write down the equations of these lines.

a

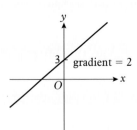

c

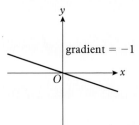

e

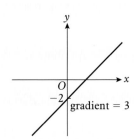

b

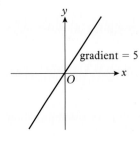

d

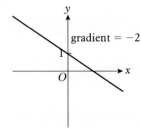

f

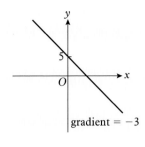

6 Write down the equation of the **red** line in each part.

a

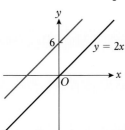

$y = 2x$

b

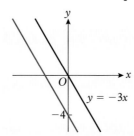

$y = -3x$

c

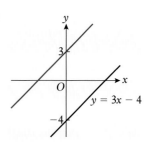

$y = 3x - 4$

Example

Does the point (5, 17) lie on the line $y = 3x + 4$?

Substitute the value of x into the equation
$y = 3 \times 5 + 4$
$\quad = 15 + 4$
$\quad = 19$

When $x = 5$ the value of y is 19 not 17.
The point (5, 17) does not lie on the line $y = 3x + 4$

---

7 Which of these points lie on the line $y = 2x - 3$?
  a (1, 5) **b** (2, 1) **c** (5, 7) **d** (−1, −5) **e** (0, 3)

8 These points lie on the line $y = 5x + 2$.
Copy the points and fill in the missing co-ordinates
  a (4, ...) **b** (..., 7) **c** (−3, ...) **d** (..., −3) **e** (..., −11)

The graph shows the cost of hiring a car.
The cost is made up of a fixed charge
and a daily rate.
The cost, C, is given by the formula

$\quad C = a + bn$

where n is the number of days.

You can use the graph to find
the values of a and b.

The fixed charge is the point
where the line cuts the vertical axis.
This is a.
The fixed charge is £30.
The daily rate is the gradient of the line.
This is b.
The daily rate is $\frac{60}{4} = £15$

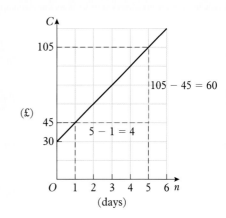

$105 - 45 = 60$

$5 - 1 = 4$

(£)

(days)

Exercise 8:8

1 This graph shows the cost, C, of a holiday.
The formula is $C = a + bn$
where n is the number of days.
a Find the values of a and b.
b Write down the fixed charge and the daily rate for the holiday.

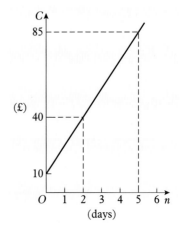

2 The graph shows how the speed of a car changes.

The formula for the speed is
$v = u + at$
where v is the speed and t is the time.
a Find the value of the acceleration a.
b Write down the value of u.

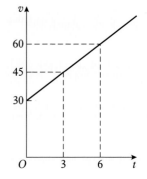

3 Chris is given a fixed amount of money to spend on holiday. He spends the same amount each day.
This is shown on the graph.
a Write down the equation of the line.
b Find the amount of money that he is given.
c How much does he spend each day?
d How many days did the holiday last?

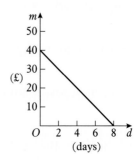

3 Linear equations

There are lots of different ways of spending your money at a fairground.

James has £10 to spend at the fair. He plans to spend it all on the dodgems and waltzers. Each ride costs £1. He spends £d on the dodgems and £w on the waltzers.

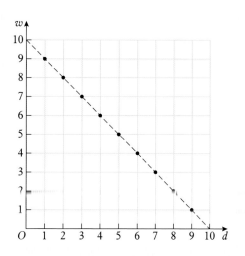

The plotted points show the different ways that James can spend his money. These points lie on a straight line.

The co-ordinates add up to 10 at each point. This means that $d + w$ is 10.

The equation of the line is $d + w = 10$.

Exercise 8:9

1 Vicky has £7 to spend on the waltzers and the dodgems.
  a Plot the points to show how she can spend her money.
  b Join the points with a straight line. Write down its equation.

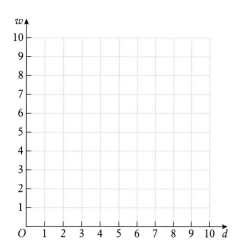

2 a Draw x and y axes labelled from 0 to 8.
  b Draw a straight line passing through 5 on each axis.
  c Write down the co-ordinates of three points on the line.
  d Find the value of $x + y$ at each of your three points.
  e Write down the equation of the line.

3 a Copy the diagram.
  b Draw a straight line through P, Q and R.
  c Where does this line cross the x axis?
  d Where does this line cross the y axis?
  e Add the x and y values together at:
    (1) P   (2) Q   (3) R
  f Write down the equation of the line.

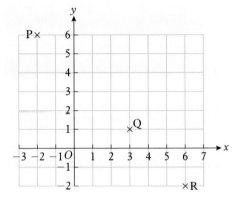

The line $x + y = 6$ crosses both axes at **6**.

The line $x + y = 2$ crosses both axes at **2**.

The line $x + y = -4$ crosses both axes at -4.

The line $x + y = a$ crosses both axes at **a**.

All of these lines are parallel.
They all have gradient -1.

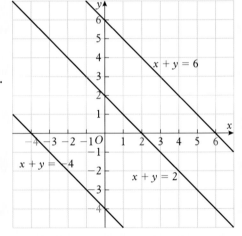

Exercise 8:10

1 A straight line crosses the x and y axes at 8.
  a Write down its equation.
  b Copy these co-ordinates of points on the line. Fill in the missing values.
    $(5, \dots)$ $(\dots, 7)$ $(-2, \dots)$ $(11, \dots)$
2 A straight line crosses the x and y axes at -5.
  a Write down its equation.
  b The point P $(3, \dots)$ lies on the line. Write down the co-ordinates of P.

3 **a** Find the value of $x + y$ at these points.

(1) A (4, 3)   (2) B (8, −1)

b Write down the equation of the straight line through A and B.

c Which of these points lie on the line AB?

P (2, 5)   Q (−2, 9)   R (−5, −2)   S (10, −3)   T (−6, 1)

d Copy these co-ordinates of points on AB. Fill in the spaces.

(1) (1, …)   (2) (2.5, …)   (3) (…, 3.5)   (4) (−3, …)   (5) (…, −1.5)

4 **a** Where does this line cross the x axis?

b Where does this line cross the y axis?

c Write down the equation of the line.

d Write down the equation of a parallel line passing through:

(1) (1, −5)   (2) (−8, 0)   (3) (−4, −6)

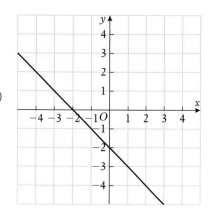

Linear equation An equation that can be written as $ax + by = c$ is called a **linear equation**; a, b and c are numbers.

$x + y = 4$ is a linear equation with $a = 1$, $b = 1$ and $c = 4$.

$x = 5$ is a linear equation with $a = 1$, $b = 0$ and $c = 5$.

$y = x^2 + 9$ and $y = \dfrac{4}{x} - 2$ are not linear.

If an equation is linear then you know that its graph will be a straight line.

Exercise 8:11

1 Look at these equations. Write down if each equation is linear or not linear.

a $y = x^2 + 3x$

b $y = 5x - 2$

c $y = 3 - 4x$

d $y = \dfrac{2}{x} + 7$

e $y = 1.4x + 2$

f $x + 3y = 10$

g $y = \dfrac{2x}{3} - 5$

h $x^2 + 3y = 12$

i $2y - 1.7x = 11$

Example Draw the graph of the equation $2x + 3y = 6$.

The equation is linear so the graph is a straight line.
This means that you only need to find the co-ordinates of two points on the line.

The easiest points to find are when x and y are zero.

When $x = 0$: $(2 \times 0) + 3y = 6$
                 so $3y = 6$
                 so $y = 2$

The point $(0, 2)$ lies on the line.

When $y = 0$: $2x + (3 \times 0) = 6$
                 so $2x = 6$
                 so $x = 3$

The point $(3, 0)$ lies on
the line.

The line goes through
$(0, 2)$ and $(3, 0)$:

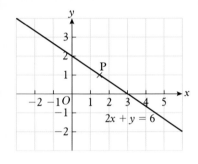

The equation $2x + 3y = 6$ works
for all points on the line.
Check: At P $(1.5, 1)$ $(2 \times 1.5) + (3 \times 1) = 6$ ✓

2 **a** Draw x and y axes from -5 to 5.
   b Find two points on the line $x + 2y = 7$.
   c Plot the points.
   d Draw the graph.
   e Check that the equation works for another point on the line.

3 **a** Draw x and y axes from -8 to 8.
   b Find two points on the line $2x - y = 6$.
   c Plot the points.
   d Draw the graph.
   e Check that the equation works for another point on the line.

4 The points, P, Q, R and S lie on the line $3x + y = 15$.
   Copy these co-ordinates. Fill in the spaces.
   P $(..., 0)$ Q $(2, ...)$ R $(6, ...)$ S $(..., -6)$

5 In the diagram, the line crosses the x and y axes at P and Q.
  a Write down their co-ordinates.
  b Find the value of $x + 2y$ at P.
  c Find the value of $x + 2y$ at Q.
  d Write down the equation of the line.

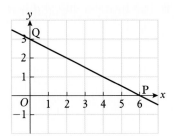

6 Match each of these equations with its graph.
  a $y = 2x - 1$ **b** $x + y = 5$ **c** $3x + y = 9$ **d** $\dfrac{x}{2} + 3y = 6$

(1)
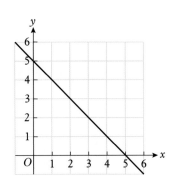

(3)
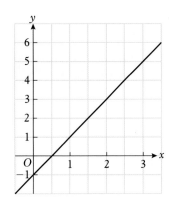

(2)
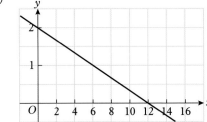

(4)
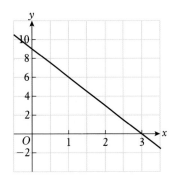

7 **a** Which of these points lie on the line $3x - y = 24$?
      P (10, 4)   Q (10, 6)   R (5, −9)   S (−7, −3)
  b Where does the line cross the x axis?
  c Where does the line cross the y axis?
  d Write down the co-ordinates of the point where the line $3x - y = 24$ crosses the line   (1) $x = 12$ (2) $y = 1.5$ (3) $x = 4$

1 Write down the gradient of each of these lines.
    a $c = 4d$ **b** $y = 3x$ **c** $d = -2t$

2 Find the gradient of each of these lines.

    a   **b**   **c**

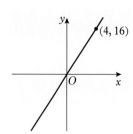 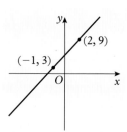 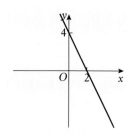

3 Where will these lines cross the y axis?
    a $y = 5x + 7$ **b** $y = 2x - 4$ **c** $y = 6x$

4 Which two of these lines are parallel?
    $y = 4x + 1$ $y = 3x - 4$ $y = 3x + 4$ $y = x - 4$

5 Which two of these lines are parallel?
    $x + 2y = 9$ $x + y = 9$ $2x + y = 11$ $x + y = 11$

6 The line PQ is parallel to the line $3x + y = 12$. The point $(6, 2)$ lies on PQ. Write down its equation.

7 A straight line passes through -4 on each axis. What is its equation?

8 L has co-ordinates $(0, 5)$ and M has co-ordinates $(3, 11)$
    a Draw a diagram to show the line LM.
    b Find the gradient of the line.
    c Write down its equation.
    d Find the equation of a parallel line passing through $(1, 10)$

9 Find the equation of the line passing through the points:
    a $(0, 7)$ and $(4, 11)$
    b $(0, -4)$ and $(4, 0)$
    c $(0, 8)$ and $(8, 0)$
    d $(0, 6)$ and $(3, 0)$

10 **a** Find the gradient of the line shown.
 b Write the equation of the line in the
     form $y = mx + c$
 c Use your equation to find the value
     of y when $x = 25$
 d What value of x gives a y value of -4?

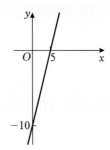

11 Ian is doing an experiment to find the value of m in the
     equation $F = ma$.

These are his results:

a	2.3	4.1	5.9	6.4
F	28	52	70	77.5

 a Plot the values of a and F as co-ordinates.

 b Join the points with a straight line through the origin.
 c Use the graph to find the value of m to the nearest whole number.

12 The table shows the co-ordinates of some points on a line.

x	1	3	5
y	5	11	17

The line has equation $y = mx + c$
 a Plot the points and join them up with a straight line.
 b Use your graph to find the values of m and c.
 c Use the equation of the line to find the value of y when $x = 20$.

1   The table shows the co-ordinates of some points on a line.

x	1	3	5
y	−5	−9	−13

The line has equation $y = mx + c$.
a   Plot the points and join them up with a straight line.
b   Use your graph to find the values of m and c.
c   Use the equation of the line to find the value of y when $x = 20$.

2   The graph shows the time taken
to cook a turkey.
The formula is $T = mw + c$.
w is the weight in pounds.
T is the time in minutes.
a   Find the value of m.
What does this value tell you?
b   Write down the value of c.
Explain what c is.

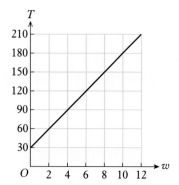

3   Dale uses a graph to change kilometres to miles.
He knows that 8 km is the same as 5 miles.
a   Copy the diagram.

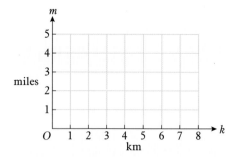

b   Use Dale's information to plot a point on the graph.
c   Explain why the graph must go through (0, 0). Draw the graph.
d   Dale travels 3.6 miles to work. How far is this in kilometres?
e   Write down the equation of the graph.
f   Use the equation to convert 400 miles to kilometres.

1   Find the gradient of each of these lines.

a

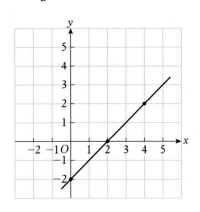

b

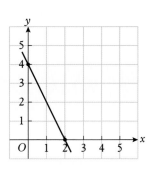

2   Find the gradient of the line passing through each pair of points.

   a $(2, 3)$ and $(4, 11)$ **b** $(0, 9)$ and $(2, 3)$

3   Write down the equation of each of these lines.

a

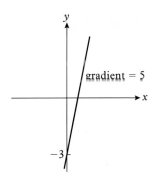

gradient $= 5$

b

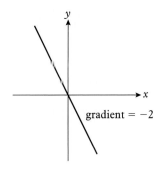

gradient $= -2$

4   Write down the gradients of these lines.
   a $y = 3x - 7$ **b** $y = x + 1$ **c** $y = -6x$

5   Write down where each line in question **4** crosses the y axis.

6   Write down the equation of a line that is parallel to $y = 7x - 8$.

7 Write down the equation of the **red** line in each part.

a

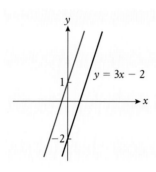

$y = 3x - 2$

b

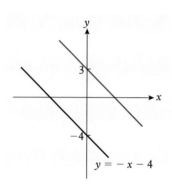

$y = -x - 4$

8 The graph shows the cost of printing posters.
The cost, C, is given by the formula

$$C = a + bn$$

where n is the number of posters.
C, a and b are all in £s.

Use the graph to find

a the fixed charge, a.
b the price per poster, b.

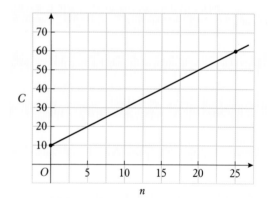

9 Draw the graph of $5x - 2y = 10$.

10 Write down whether each equation is linear or not linear.

a $y = x^2 - 5$ **b** $y = 7 - 2x$ **c** $y = \dfrac{4}{x} + 3$

9 Fractions, decimals and percentages

1 Halfway there!
Looking at fractions
Adding and subtracting fractions
Multiplying and dividing fractions
Using fractions
Cancelling algebraic fractions

2 Linking parts
Looking at percentage of possession in football
Linking percentages and fractions
Linking percentages and decimals
Linking ratio and percentage

CORE

3 Percentage of an amount
Finding simple percentages without a calculator
Finding VAT by adding 10%, 5% and 2.5%
Increasing and decreasing by a given percentage
Working with other percentages using a calculator

4 As a percentage of ...
Working out the percentage of first serves won in tennis
Writing **a** as a percentage of **b**
Working our percentage change
Working out percentage profit and loss

Henman
Points won on first serve 82%
Points won on second serve 43%

QUESTIONS

EXTENSION

TEST YOURSELF

1　Halfway there!

Jane is doing an exam.
She is reading these instructions.

Part 1	$\frac{3}{4}$ hour
Part 2	$\frac{3}{4}$ hour
Part 3	$\frac{1}{2}$ hour

Jane is puzzled.
She is trying to work out how long it is
before the end of the exam.
Jane wishes she had worked harder on
fractions!

In this section you are going to see how to
add, subtract, multiply and divide fractions
without using your calculator.

Alf is a chef.
He is looking at a pack of soup.
A pack contains 4 cartons.

Here are 4 cartons of soup:
This is one whole pack.

Here is 1 carton of soup:
This is $\frac{1}{4}$ of a pack.

Alf says there are $1\frac{1}{4}$ packs here altogether.

Exercise 9:1　

1　For each part:　(1) Copy the diagrams.
　　　　　　　　　(2) Write down how many cartons of soup there are.
　　　　　　　　　(3) Write down how many packs of soup there are.

　a 　**c** 　**e** 　**g**

　b 　**d** 　**f** 　• **h**

Look at the fraction $\frac{9}{4}$

The top number is bigger than the bottom.
The fraction is **'top heavy'**.

Look at Alf's packs of soup.
Nine quarters make two
wholes and one quarter: $\frac{9}{4} = 2\frac{1}{4}$

2 Write each of these diagrams as:
(1) A top heavy fraction.
(2) A whole number and a fraction.

a  **c**  **e**

b   **d**   **f**

Look at these cartons of soup.

 is the same number of cartons as

so half a pack.   is the same as   two quarter packs

You can write: $\frac{1}{2}$ $=$ $\frac{2}{4}$
These are called **equivalent fractions**.
They are the **same** fraction shown in different ways.

Look at this tray of strawberries in Alf's kitchen.

There are 8 cartons in a tray,
so each carton is $\frac{1}{8}$ of the tray.

 is the same number of cartons as

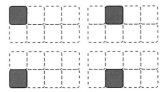

so half a tray   is the same as   four lots of one eighth of a tray
You can write: $\frac{1}{2} = \frac{4}{8}$
These are also equivalent fractions.

213

3 Copy these. Fill them in.

a 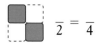 $\dfrac{}{2} = \dfrac{}{4}$

c  $\dfrac{}{4} = \dfrac{}{8}$

b  $\dfrac{}{4} = \dfrac{}{8}$

d  $\dfrac{}{2} = \dfrac{}{4}$

4 Amy delivers bottles of salad cream to Alf.
Bottles of salad cream are in packs of 16.
Copy these. Fill them in.

a 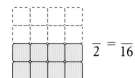 $\dfrac{}{2} = \dfrac{}{16}$

c  $\dfrac{}{8} = \dfrac{}{16}$

b 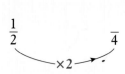 $\dfrac{}{4} = \dfrac{}{16}$

d 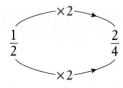 $\dfrac{}{8} = \dfrac{}{16}$

You can **make equivalent fractions** by multiplying.
To change $\frac{1}{2}$ into quarters, you need to make the bottom number 4.

$\dfrac{1}{2} \qquad \dfrac{}{4}$

$\dfrac{1}{2} \xrightarrow{\times 2} \dfrac{2}{4}$

You **multiply** the
bottom by 2 to get 4.

Then you **multiply**
the top by 2 to get 2.

To change $\frac{3}{4}$ into sixteenths, you need to make the bottom number 16.

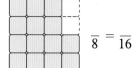

$\dfrac{3}{4} \qquad \dfrac{}{16}$

$\dfrac{3}{4} \xrightarrow{\times 4} \dfrac{12}{16}$

You **multiply** the
bottom by 4 to get 16.

Then you **multiply**
the top by 4 to get 12.

You always multiply the top and bottom **by the same number.**

Exercise 9:2

1   Change these fractions into eighths. Show your working.

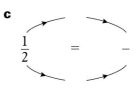

a $\frac{1}{4} = \frac{}{8}$ ×2

b $\frac{3}{4} = \frac{}{8}$

c $\frac{1}{2} = \frac{}{}$

2   Change these fractions into sixteenths. Show your working.

a $\frac{1}{8}$ c $\frac{3}{8}$ e $\frac{5}{8}$ g $\frac{7}{8}$

b $\frac{1}{4}$ d $\frac{3}{4}$ f $\frac{1}{2}$ • h $1\frac{1}{2}$

Adding fractions

To **add fractions,** the bottom numbers must be the same.
Alf knows this when he collects together different packs.

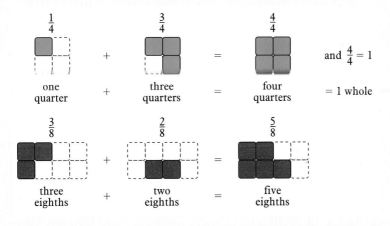

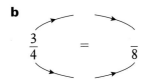

$\frac{1}{4}$ $\frac{3}{4}$ $\frac{4}{4}$

one   three   four   and $\frac{4}{4} = 1$
quarter   +   quarters   =   quarters   = 1 whole

$\frac{3}{8}$ $\frac{2}{8}$ $\frac{5}{8}$

three   two   five
eighths   +   eighths   =   eighths

Exercise 9:3

1   Work these out:

a $\frac{1}{4} + \frac{2}{4}$ b $\frac{2}{8} + \frac{3}{8}$ c $\frac{1}{8} + \frac{4}{8}$ d $\frac{5}{8} + \frac{2}{8}$

2   Work these out:

a $\frac{6}{8} + \frac{1}{8}$ b $\frac{3}{8} + \frac{4}{8}$ c $\frac{2}{4} + \frac{3}{4}$ d $\frac{4}{8} + \frac{5}{8}$

3 Work these out:

a $\frac{3}{8}+\frac{7}{8}$　　**b** $\frac{3}{16}+\frac{4}{16}$　● **c** $\frac{3}{16}+\frac{14}{16}$　● **d** $\frac{3}{8}+\frac{5}{8}+\frac{7}{8}$

Subtracting fractions

You can **subtract fractions** in the same way that you add fractions.

So $\frac{3}{8}$ − $\frac{2}{8}$ = $\frac{3}{8}$

4 Work these out:

a $\frac{3}{4}-\frac{2}{4}$　　**b** $\frac{5}{8}-\frac{4}{8}$　　**c** $\frac{5}{16}-\frac{4}{16}$　　**d** $\frac{9}{16}-\frac{2}{16}$

5 Work these out:

a $\frac{13}{16}-\frac{2}{16}$　　**b** $\frac{15}{16}-\frac{12}{16}$　　**c** $\frac{19}{16}-\frac{11}{16}$　　**d** $\frac{3}{8}-\frac{5}{8}+\frac{7}{8}$

Sometimes the bottom numbers in fractions are different.
To add or subtract these fractions you must make the bottom numbers the same.

Example　Find　**a** $\frac{3}{4}+\frac{1}{2}$　　　**b** $\frac{7}{8}-\frac{3}{4}$

a You need to change $\frac{1}{2}$ into quarters.

So $\frac{3}{4}+\frac{1}{2}=\frac{3}{4}+\frac{2}{4}$
$=\frac{5}{4}=1\frac{1}{4}$

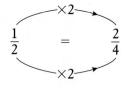

b You need to change $\frac{3}{4}$ into eighths.

So $\frac{7}{8}-\frac{3}{4}=\frac{7}{8}-\frac{6}{8}$
$=\frac{1}{8}$

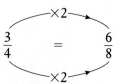

Exercise 9:4

1 Work these out:

a $\frac{1}{4} + \frac{1}{2}$ **c** $\frac{5}{8} + \frac{1}{4}$ **e** $\frac{5}{16} + \frac{1}{8}$ **g** $\frac{11}{16} + \frac{1}{2}$

b $\frac{3}{4} + \frac{1}{8}$ **d** $\frac{3}{4} + \frac{7}{8}$ **f** $\frac{9}{16} + \frac{3}{4}$ **h** $\frac{15}{16} + \frac{3}{4}$

2 Work these out:

a $\frac{1}{2} - \frac{1}{4}$ **c** $\frac{3}{8} - \frac{1}{4}$ **e** $\frac{15}{16} - \frac{3}{8}$ ● **g** $\frac{11}{16} - \frac{1}{2} + \frac{3}{4}$

b $\frac{3}{4} - \frac{1}{8}$ **d** $\frac{7}{8} - \frac{1}{2}$ **f** $\frac{13}{16} - \frac{3}{4}$ ● **h** $\frac{5}{16} - \frac{3}{4} + \frac{7}{8}$

Example   Which is bigger, $\frac{5}{8}$ or $\frac{11}{16}$?

You can tell which fraction is bigger when they have the same bottom number.

Change $\frac{5}{8}$ into sixteenths

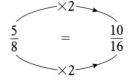

$$\frac{5}{8} = \frac{10}{16}$$

Now look at the fractions $\frac{10}{16}$ and $\frac{11}{16}$

$\frac{11}{16}$ is bigger than $\frac{10}{16}$ because 11 is bigger than 10.

You may need to change both fractions to see which is bigger. To do this look for the smallest number that both of the bottom numbers go into.

Example   Which is bigger, $\frac{2}{3}$ or $\frac{3}{5}$?

3 and 5 go into 15

Change $\frac{2}{3}$ so that
the bottom number is 15

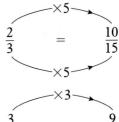

$$\frac{2}{3} = \frac{10}{15}$$

Change $\frac{3}{5}$ so that
the bottom number is 15

$$\frac{3}{5} = \frac{9}{15}$$

$\frac{10}{15}$ is bigger than $\frac{9}{15}$ so $\frac{2}{3}$ is bigger than $\frac{3}{5}$

3 Put these fractions in order of size. Start with the smallest.

a $\frac{3}{4}, \frac{5}{8}$ c $\frac{7}{8}, \frac{13}{16}$ e $\frac{3}{5}, \frac{3}{4}$ g $\frac{6}{7}, \frac{7}{8}$

b $\frac{7}{16}, \frac{1}{2}$ d $\frac{3}{4}, \frac{2}{3}$ f $\frac{2}{3}, \frac{4}{5}$ • h $\frac{1}{2}, \frac{2}{3}, \frac{4}{5}$

Adding fractions with whole numbers

To work out: $1\frac{3}{4} + 2\frac{7}{8}$

First add the whole numbers: $1 + 2 = 3$

Then add the fractions: $\frac{3}{4} + \frac{7}{8} = \frac{6}{8} + \frac{7}{8}$

$$= \frac{13}{8} = 1\frac{5}{8}$$

Now add your two answers together: $3 + 1\frac{5}{8} = 4\frac{5}{8}$

4 Work these out:

a $1\frac{1}{4} + \frac{1}{2}$ c $4\frac{3}{8} + 5\frac{7}{8}$ e $5\frac{5}{16} + 1\frac{3}{4}$ • g $8\frac{3}{4} + 4\frac{11}{16}$

b $2\frac{3}{4} + 3\frac{1}{8}$ d $2\frac{1}{16} + 6\frac{7}{8}$ f $1\frac{1}{2} + 4\frac{9}{16}$ • h $27\frac{7}{8} + 14\frac{15}{16}$

Subtracting fractions with whole numbers

To work out: $2\frac{3}{4} - 1\frac{7}{8}$

First write the fractions as top heavy fractions: $2\frac{3}{4} = \frac{11}{4}$ and $1\frac{7}{8} = \frac{15}{8}$

Next, get the bottom numbers the same.

Then you can subtract.

$$\frac{11}{4} - \frac{15}{8} = \frac{22}{8} - \frac{15}{8}$$

$$= \frac{7}{8}$$

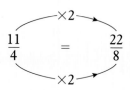

5 Work these out:

a $1\frac{1}{4} - \frac{1}{8}$ c $4\frac{3}{8} - 3\frac{1}{4}$ e $2\frac{1}{16} - 1\frac{3}{8}$ • g $6 - 2\frac{7}{8}$

b $2\frac{1}{4} - 1\frac{1}{8}$ d $1\frac{11}{16} - 1\frac{3}{8}$ f $5\frac{1}{2} - 1\frac{9}{16}$ • h $10\frac{7}{8} - 4\frac{15}{16}$

• **6** Laura has baked two large Christmas cakes. Each cake has 16 slices.
She gives $\frac{11}{16}$ of a cake to Jenny and $\frac{3}{4}$ of the other cake to Sam.
How much is left for Laura and her family to share?

Multiplying fractions

Alf is using half a carton of soup.

A carton is a quarter of a pack.
Alf wants to know what fraction of the pack he is using.
On the diagram you can see that half of a quarter is an eighth.
So Alf is using one eighth of a pack.

You can also see this by multiplying the fractions $\frac{1}{2} \times \frac{1}{4} = \frac{1}{8}$

You get $1 \times 1 = 1$ on the top
and $\quad 2 \times 4 = 8$ on the bottom.
You can multiply other fractions together like this.

Example

Work these out.

a $\frac{1}{14} \times 5$ **b** $\frac{2}{5}$ of $\frac{3}{4}$ **c** $1\frac{3}{4} \times 2\frac{3}{4}$

a $\frac{1}{14} \times \frac{5}{1} = \frac{5}{14}$ Write the whole number 5 as $\frac{5}{1}$.

b $\frac{2}{5}$ of $\frac{3}{4} = \frac{2}{5} \times \frac{3}{4} = \frac{6}{20}$ Of tells you to multiply.
$\qquad\qquad\qquad = \frac{3}{10}$ The top number and the bottom number both divide by 2.

c $1\frac{3}{5} \times 2\frac{3}{4} = \frac{8}{5} \times \frac{11}{4}$ Turn the fractions into top heavy fractions.

$\qquad\qquad = \frac{88}{20}$ The top number and the bottom number both divide by 4.

$\qquad\qquad = \frac{22}{5}$ Turn the answer back to a whole number and a fraction.

$\qquad\qquad = 4\frac{2}{5}$

Exercise 9:5

1 Work these out:

a $\frac{2}{3} \times 5$ **c** $\frac{3}{4} \times \frac{1}{6}$ **e** $\frac{5}{6}$ of $\frac{3}{4}$ **g** $1\frac{1}{3} \times 2\frac{3}{4}$

b $\frac{7}{10} \times \frac{2}{3}$ **d** $\frac{5}{7} \times \frac{3}{10}$ **f** $\frac{1}{6}$ of $\frac{3}{5}$ • **h** $3\frac{1}{2} \times 1\frac{2}{3}$

2 Use the formula $v = u + at$ to find v when $u = \frac{3}{4}$, $a = 1\frac{1}{2}$ and $t = \frac{3}{4}$

3 Use the formula $F = \frac{4}{5}x + \frac{3}{4}$ to find F when x is

   a $\frac{1}{2}$ **b** $\frac{3}{4}$ **c** $1\frac{2}{5}$ **d** $2\frac{4}{7}$

4 **a** Work out 20×4.
    b Multiply your answer to **a** by $\frac{1}{4}$.
    c What do you notice about your answer to **b**?

5 Write down the answer to each of these questions.

   a $18 \times 4 \times \frac{1}{4}$ **c** $120 \times 3 \times \frac{1}{3}$ **e** $11 \times 20 \times \frac{1}{20}$ **g** $\frac{1}{5} \times 6 \times \frac{1}{6}$

   b $17 \times 5 \times \frac{1}{5}$ **d** $20 \times 12 \times \frac{1}{12}$ **f** $\frac{1}{3} \times 4 \times \frac{1}{4}$ **h** $\frac{1}{12} \times 14 \times \frac{1}{14}$

Dividing fractions

Alf needs half a carton of soup for a recipe.
He has one and a half cartons.

You can see from the diagram that he has three half cartons.
So $\frac{1}{2}$ a carton fits into $1\frac{1}{2}$ cartons three times.

This is the same as $1\frac{1}{2} \div \frac{1}{2} = 3$

You can get this by turning the $\frac{1}{2}$ over and multiplying

$$1\frac{1}{2} \div \frac{1}{2} = \frac{3}{2} \div \frac{1}{2} = \frac{3}{2} \times \frac{2}{1} = \frac{6}{2} = 3$$

You can divide other fractions like this.
Turn the second fraction over and then multiply.

Example   Work these out.

       a $\frac{3}{4} \div \frac{5}{8}$ **b** $2\frac{2}{5} \div 1\frac{3}{4}$ **c** $\frac{4}{5} \div 2$

       a $\frac{3}{4} \div \frac{5}{8} = \frac{3}{4} \times \frac{8}{5} = \frac{24}{20} = \frac{6}{5} = 1\frac{1}{5}$

       b $2\frac{2}{5} \div 1\frac{3}{4} = \frac{12}{5} \div \frac{7}{4} = \frac{12}{5} \times \frac{4}{7} = \frac{48}{35} = 1\frac{13}{35}$

       c $\frac{4}{5} \div 2 = \frac{4}{5} \times \frac{1}{2} = \frac{4}{10} = \frac{2}{5}$

6 Work these out:

a $\dfrac{2}{3} \div \dfrac{5}{7}$ **c** $\dfrac{3}{4} \div \dfrac{1}{6}$ **e** $\dfrac{5}{6} \div 2$ **g** $1\dfrac{2}{3} \div 2\dfrac{3}{4}$

b $\dfrac{7}{10} \div \dfrac{2}{3}$ **d** $\dfrac{2}{5} \div \dfrac{3}{10}$ **f** $\dfrac{1}{6} \div 3$ **h** $3\dfrac{1}{2} \div 1\dfrac{2}{3}$

7 Use the formula $a = \dfrac{f}{m}$ to find a when $f = 2\dfrac{1}{2}$ and $m = \dfrac{3}{4}$.

A recipe for 4 people tells Alf to use 240 g of flour.
He wants to know how much flour to use for 3 people.

He writes 3 as a fraction of 4 to get $\dfrac{3}{4}$.

Then he works out $\dfrac{3}{4} \times 240$ g.

He works out $\dfrac{1}{4}$ first $240 \div 4 = 60$

Then he multiplies by 3 $60 \times 3 = 180$ g

So he needs 180 g of flour for 3 people.

Exercise 9:6

1 The amounts given are needed in recipes for meals for 4 people.
Work out the amounts you need for 3 people.

  a 360 g of flour   **c** 8 g of salt   **e** 4 eggs
  b 600 ml of milk   **d** 500 g of butter **f** 460 g of sugar

---

You can use a calculator to work out the amounts.
This is very useful when the answer needs to be left as a fraction.

Example   A recipe for 6 people needs 200 g of flour.
How much flour would you need for 5 people?

You need to work out $\dfrac{5}{6} \times 200$ g

Key in **5** **a^b/$_c$** **6** **×** **2** **0** **0** **=**

to get this display $166 \llcorner 2 \llcorner 3$ or $166 \llcorner 2 \lrcorner 3$

This means $166\dfrac{2}{3}$ g.

This is the exact answer.

You would not try to measure out exactly $166\dfrac{2}{3}$ g.

You would probably measure 167 g to the nearest gram.

---

2 The amounts given are needed in recipes for meals for 6 people.
Work out the exact amounts you need for 5 people.

a 400 g of flour   **c** 1 g of salt   **e** 350 g of water

b 700 ml of milk   **d** 310 g of butter   **f** 440 g of sugar

3 Look at your answers to question **2**.
These amounts would be very difficult to measure.
How much would you actually use in each part?

Algebraic fractions

Algebraic fractions work like normal fractions.
You can look at equivalent fractions.

Look at the fraction $\dfrac{5}{x}$

This is the same as the fraction $\dfrac{10}{2x}$

You can cancel fractions too.

The fraction $\dfrac{15}{3x}$ cancels down to give $\dfrac{5}{x}$

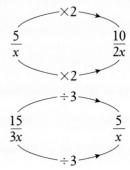

Exercise 9:7

1 Copy these. Fill in the gaps.

a $\dfrac{5}{x} = \dfrac{...}{4x}$

b $\dfrac{4}{x} = \dfrac{8}{...}$

c $\dfrac{7}{x} = \dfrac{...}{3x}$

d $\dfrac{8}{x} = \dfrac{...}{5x}$

e $\dfrac{3}{x} = \dfrac{21}{...}$

f $\dfrac{9}{x} = \dfrac{9x}{...}$

g $8 = \dfrac{...}{1} = \dfrac{...}{x}$

h $5 = \dfrac{...}{y}$

i $\dfrac{3x}{2} = \dfrac{...}{2y}$

2 Copy these. Fill in the gaps.

a $\dfrac{10}{15x} = \dfrac{...}{3x}$

b $\dfrac{12}{3x} = \dfrac{4}{...}$

c $\dfrac{21}{7x} = \dfrac{...}{x}$

d $\dfrac{25}{5x} = \dfrac{...}{x}$

e $\dfrac{3xy}{9y} = \dfrac{...}{3}$

f $\dfrac{(x-2)}{2(x-2)} = \dfrac{1}{...}$

g $\dfrac{(x+1)}{(x+1)^2} = \dfrac{1}{...}$

h $\dfrac{5(y+4)}{(y+4)^2} = \dfrac{...}{y+4}$

i $\dfrac{2(x-3)^2}{(x-3)} = \dfrac{...}{1} = ...$

2 Linking parts

In a football match the side that has the ball controls the game.

Football commentators use percentages to compare the amount of time that each side has possession of the ball. They show the information on the TV screen. They use a bar like this.

61%   39%

The percentages always add up to 100%.

The figures show that the red team has had more chance to control the game. Later in the game things have changed.

55%   45%

It is still true that the red team has had more possession but the blues are turning the game in their favour.

Exercise 9:8

1 Copy the diagrams for red and blue teams. Fill in the missing percentages.

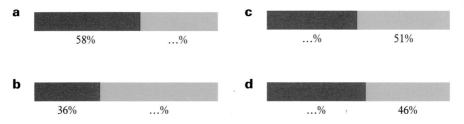

a

58%   ...%

c

...%   51%

b

36%   ...%

d

...%   46%

2 Copy the diagrams. Estimate the percentages shown.

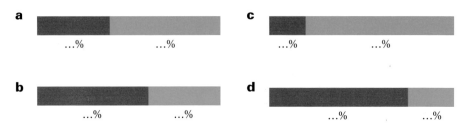

a ...%   ...%

c ...%   ...%

b ...%   ...%

d ...%   ...%

3 In a rugby match the players try to keep play out of their half of the field. Look at the information below.

Minutes played	Minutes in home team's half	% time in home team's half
35	15	43
55	21	38

a Is the home team doing better or worse as the game goes on?
b Which column of the table is easier to use when you compare the teams?

4 Mr Brown wants more of the students in Year 11 to stay on into the sixth form.

	Number in year	Number staying on
last year	143	67
this year	187	81

a How many more pupils are staying on this year?
b Mr Brown adds another column to the end of the table. Do you think that he will be happy? Explain your answer.

% staying on
47
43

5 Chris did a survey about Sport's Day. He found that 64% of his class took part in the 800 m race and 47% took part in the 200 m race.
a The percentages add up to more than 100%. Explain how this can happen.
b Chris said that 30% of the class ran in both races. Can this be true?

Percentages are another way of writing fractions.

Sharon has scored $\dfrac{68}{100}$ in a test. This means that she scored 68 marks out of 100.

The fraction $\dfrac{68}{100}$ can be written as **68%**.

This only works when the bottom number is 100.

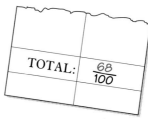

TOTAL: $\dfrac{68}{100}$

Sharon scored $\dfrac{32}{50}$ in another test.

You need to make the bottom number 100 to see the percentage: $\dfrac{32}{50} = \dfrac{64}{100}$

$\times 2$

$\times 2$

She scored 64% this time.

Exercise 9:9

1 Copy these and fill in the missing numbers.
   a 27% means 27 out of …
   b 19% means … out of …
   c 41 out of 50 is the same as … out of 100.
   d 23 out of 50 is the same as …%.
   e 20 out of 25 is the same as … out of 100.
   f 11 out of 25 is the same as …%.

2 Write each of these fractions as a percentage.

   a $\dfrac{91}{100}$ **c** $\dfrac{7}{20} = \dfrac{…}{…}$ **e** $\dfrac{15}{20}$

                         $\times 5$

   b $\dfrac{14}{50} = \dfrac{…}{100}$ **d** $\dfrac{9}{10}$ **f** $\dfrac{19}{25}$

      $\times 2$

3 Copy these. Fill in the gaps.
   a 68 out of 200 is the same as … out of 100.
   b 36 out of 300 is the same as … out of 100.
   c 88 out of 200 is the same as …%.
   d 27 out of 300 is the same as …%.
   e 55 out of 500 is the same as …%.

4 Barbara scored 21 out of 25 in a test. What percentage is this?

● **5** 80% of the guests at a wedding arrived by car. There were 50 guests. How many guests arrived by car?

You can write any percentage as a decimal. First you write it as a fraction.

Example Change these percentages to decimals.

  a 43%   **b** 9.4%

  a $43\% = \dfrac{43}{100}$ **b** $9.4\% = \dfrac{9.4}{100}$

    $= 43 \div 100$ $- 9.4 \div 100$

    $= 0.43$ $= 0.094$

Exercise 9:10

1 Copy these. Fill in the gaps.

  a $61\% = \dfrac{\cdots}{100} = 0.61$ **c** $10\% = \dfrac{\cdots}{100} = \cdots$ **e** $17.5\% = \dfrac{\cdots}{100} = \cdots$

  b $4\% = \dfrac{\cdots}{100} = \cdots$ **d** $20\% = \dfrac{\cdots}{100} = \cdots$ ● **f** $0.81\% = \dfrac{\cdots}{\cdots} = \cdots$

2 Write these percentages as decimals.
  a 12%   **d** 10.6%   **g** 8.623%
  b 83%   **e** 5%   **h** 12.5%
  c 3%   **f** 76.5%   **i** 0.74%

To change a decimal to a percentage you multiply by 100.

Example Change these to percentages.

  a 0.37   **b** 0.0812

  a 0.37×100 **b** 0.0812×100

    $= 37\%$ $= 8.12\%$

---

3 Change these decimals to percentages.
  a 0.49   **d** 0.06   **g** 0.0027
  b 0.732   **e** 0.074   **h** 0.0106
  c 0.1   **f** 0.403   **i** 0.9002

You can change a fraction to a percentage by turning it into a decimal first.

Example

Write $\dfrac{3}{8}$ as a percentage.

Using a calculator: $3 \div 8 = 0.375$ so $\dfrac{3}{8} = 0.375$

Multiply by 100% $0.375 \times 100\% = 37.5\%$

You can do the calculations in one key sequence.

Example

Write $\dfrac{17}{33}$ as a percentage correct to 1 dp.

Key in: **1** **7** **÷** **3** **3** **×** **1** **0** **0** **=**

$\dfrac{17}{33} = 51.515\ 151...\%$

$= 51.5\%$ to 1 dp.

Exercise 9:11

1 Write these fractions as percentages. Give your answers to 1 dp.

   a $\dfrac{11}{16}$ **c** $\dfrac{67}{128}$ **e** $\dfrac{4}{7}$ **g** $\dfrac{37}{1028}$

   b $\dfrac{29}{36}$ **d** $\dfrac{219}{245}$ **f** $\dfrac{5}{71}$ **h** $\dfrac{6}{4087}$

2 Write these in order of size. Start with the smallest.

   0.732   68.1% $\dfrac{43}{71}$ $\dfrac{89}{193}$

3 Gold purity is measured in carats.
Pure gold is 24 carat gold.
Debbie has a 14 carat gold bracelet.
This means that $\frac{14}{24}$ of the bracelet is pure gold.
   a Find the percentage of gold in Debbie's bracelet.
   b A catalogue sells 9 carat gold jewellery.
     What percentage of pure gold does the jewellery contain?

You may be given information as a ratio.
You can change it to a percentage.

Example

The number of votes for three candidates in an election were in the ratio 2 : 3 : 7. What percentage of the votes were for the winner? Give your answer to 1 dp.

2 shares + 3 shares + 7 shares = 12 shares

The winner had $\frac{7}{12}$ of the votes.

Key in: **7** **÷** **1** **2** **×** **1** **0** **0** **=**

= 58.3333...%

The winner had 58.3% of the votes to 1 dp.

Exercise 9:12

1 When Chris makes mortar he mixes water, sand and cement in the ratio 1 : 3 : 1. What percentage of the mixture is sand?

2 The pupil to teacher ratio on the school trip was 24 : 1
What percentage of the group were teachers?

3 At a disco girls outnumbered boys in the ratio 5 : 3.
What percentage of the people at the disco were boys?

4 When a biased coin is flipped it shows heads
60% of the time.
  a What percentage of the time does it show tails?
  b What is the ratio of heads to tails?

5 50% of the radiation that comes to the Earth is absorbed by the land and the sea. Another 15% is absorbed by the atmosphere and the rest is reflected back into space.
Write the amount of radiation absorbed to the amount reflected as a ratio.
Simplify your ratio as far as possible.

3 Percentage of an amount

VAT stands for Value Added Tax.

The rate of VAT is 17.5%.

This makes a big difference to the price that you pay.

Some percentages can be written very simply as fractions.
You can use them to find a percentage of an amount without a calculator.

$50\% = \dfrac{1}{2}$ 50% of 24 is the same as $24 \div 2 = 12$

$25\% = \dfrac{1}{4}$ 25% of 24 is the same as $24 \div 4 = 6$

$33\frac{1}{3}\% = \dfrac{1}{3}$ $33\frac{1}{3}\%$ of 24 is the same as $24 \div 3 = 8$

$10\% = \dfrac{1}{10}$ 10% of 24 is the same as $24 \div 10 = 2.4$

Exercise 9:13

1   Find the value of each of these.

   a   50% of 86   **e**   10% of 61   **i**   25% of 9.2
   b $33\frac{1}{3}\%$ of 12   **f** $33\frac{1}{3}\%$ of 45   **j**   10% of 3.7
   c   10% of 160   **g**   50% of 76   **k** $33\frac{1}{3}\%$ of 171
   d   25% of 32   **h**   25% of 92   **l**   50% of 29

2   Work these out. Remember to include the units in your answer.

   a $33\frac{1}{3}\%$ of 120 cm   **c**   25% of £12.32
   b   50% of £37   **d**   10% of 86 kg

3 A coat is reduced by 25% in a sale.
Before the sale the coat would have cost £84.
How much cheaper is the sale price?

4 Andy's garage has special offers on new cars.
You save money if you pay a deposit of $33\frac{1}{3}$%.
What deposit is needed on each of these prices?

a £9000   **d** £7500   **g** £19 200
b £9999   **e** £8100   **h** £14 250
c £4200   **f** £6120   **i** £11 229

Example   Find the value of   **a** 40% of £27   **b** $66\frac{2}{3}$% of 36 kg

a 40% is the same as 4 × 10%.

10% of £27 = £27 ÷ 10
= £2.70

40% of £27 = 4 × £2.70
= £10.80

b $66\frac{2}{3}$% is the same as 2 × $33\frac{1}{3}$%

$33\frac{1}{3}$% of 36 kg = 36 kg ÷ 3
= 12 kg

$66\frac{2}{3}$% of 36 kg = 2 × 12 kg
= 24 kg

Exercise 9:14

1 Find the value of each of these.
a 75% of 16 kg   **d** $66\frac{2}{3}$% of 27 miles   **g** 30% of £18.50
b 30% of £71   **e** 20% of £125   **h** 75% of £6
c 20% of £48   **f** 60% of 400 g   • **i** $12\frac{1}{2}$% of 240 volts

2 Barbara did a survey in the school canteen.
She found that 80% of pupils eat chips every day.
650 pupils took part in the survey.
How many eat chips every day?

3 Four years ago Chris bought a new car for £12 600.
It has now lost 60% of its original vaue.
a How much has the car's value fallen?
b What is the car worth now?

VAT is charged at 17.5%. This doesn't make a very simple fraction but there is an easy way to work it out.

$$17.5\% = 10\% + 5\% + 2.5\%$$

$\div 2 \qquad \div 2$

To find 17.5% of £56 find 10% first.	10% of £56 = £5.60
Divide by 2 to find 5%.	5% of £56 = £2.80
Divide by 2 again to find 2.5%.	2.5% of £56 = £1.40
Add your three answers together.	17.5% of £56 = £9.80

You can adapt this method to work out other percentages.

Exercise 9:15

1 Copy these calculations. Fill in the gaps.

a   10% of £84 = …
       5% of £84 = …
    2.5% of £84 = …
   17.5% of £84 = …

b   10% of £126 = …
       5% of £126 = …
    2.5% of £126 = …
   17.5% of £126 = …

2 Copy these calculations. Fill in the gaps.

a   10% of £43 = …
       5% of £43 = …
    15% of £43 = …

b   25% of £640 = …
     …% of £640 = …
   37.5% of £640 = …

3 A new computer costs £960 before VAT is added at 17.5%.
   a How much is the VAT on £960?
   b What is the total cost of the computer?

4 Rob makes an insurance claim of £560 for damage to his lounge carpet. The insurance company remind him that the carpet is 5 years old. They give him 62.5% of the claim. How much does the company pay?

To **increase** an amount by a percentage you work the percentage out as normal and then **add** it to the original amount.

To **decrease** an amount by a percentage you work out the percentage as normal and then **subtract** it from the original amount.

Exercise 9:16

1 Increase each of these amounts by 10%.

a	30 years	**d**	8.6 m	**g**	5.4 light years
b	420 kg	**e**	11.5 tonnes	**h**	£8 million
c	£6.80	**f**	0.9 cm	**i**	0.07 mm²

2

Reduce all of these prices by $33\frac{1}{3}$%.

a	£99	**d**	£135	**g**	£13.50
b	£75	**e**	£174	**h**	£249.99
c	£81	**f**	£6.99	**i**	£67.50

3 An iceberg weighing 6000 tonnes was spotted in the North Sea. Ten days later it had reduced in size by 30%. What did it weigh after ten days?

4 Robert Wadlow was the tallest man in history. He was 6 ft tall when he was 8 years old. By the time he was 17 years old his height had increased by another $33\frac{1}{3}$%. How tall was he when he was 17 years old?

You can find a percentage of an amount using a calculator.
To do this: (1) Change the percentage to a decimal.
(2) Multiply by the decimal.

Example   Find 23% of £160

Change 23% to a decimal $23\% = \dfrac{23}{100}$

$= 0.23$

Multiply the amount by 0.23 23% of £160 $= 0.23 \times £160$

This is what your calculator displays 36.8

You need 2 dp in the answer to $= £36.80$
show the number of pence.

Exercise 9:17

1 Copy these calculations. Fill in the gaps.

a $19\% = \dfrac{...}{100}$ **b** $17.5\% = \dfrac{17.5}{100}$

$= ...$ $= ...$

19% of $350 = ... \times 350$ 17.5% of £86 $= ,,, \times £86$

$= ...$ $= ...$

2 Find the value of each of these.
    a 37% of £49   **d** 9.6% of 48 m
    b 24% of $2300   **e** 11.9% of 3600 km
    c 17.5% of £64   **f** 0.63% of £1800

3 Dave took his car to the garage for a service. The cost of parts and labour
came to £64. VAT at 17.5% was added to the bill.
    a How much was the VAT?
    b What was the total bill?

4 The two highest mountains in the world are Mount Everest and K2.
The peak of Everest is 8848 m high. K2 is 8.16% lower than Everest.
    a What is the difference in height between Everest and K2?
    b How high is the peak of K2?
Give your answers to the nearest metre.

5 A wide-screen television with surround sound costs £899 + VAT.
  a Find the amount of VAT to pay at 17.5%.
  b Find the total cost of the television.
  Give your answers to the nearest penny.

6 Only 3% of people in the UK have blood group AB.
  The population of the UK is approximately 58 million.
  How many people in the UK have blood group AB?
  Give your answer to two significant figures.

7 In 1983 the land-speed record over
  a distance of one mile was broken
  by Richard Noble in Thrust 2.
  The record speed was 633.468 mph.
  In 1997 Thrust SSC driven by
  Andy Green increased the record
  by 20.4536%
  What was the new speed record?
  Give your answer to 3 dp.

8 The diameter of the Sun is about 864 000 miles.
  The diameter of the Earth is only 0.917% of the Sun's diameter.
  What is the diameter of the Earth?
  Give your answer to the nearest 1000 miles.

9 Peter owes £4360 on his credit card.
  Each month 1.1% interest is added
  to the amount he owes.

  a How much interest is added after 1 month?
  b Peter pays the credit card company £50.
    How much does he owe now?
  c How much interest is added for the next month?
  d Peter pays another £50.
    How much does he owe now?
  e Peter has paid £100 over two months.
    How much has he reduced the amount he owes?

4 As a percentage of ...

Henman
Points won on first serve 82%
Points won on second serve 43%

These figures show that Henman is more likely to win a point if his first serve is in. He is losing more than half the points when he has to play a second serve. These figures are for the match so far. They change as the match carries on. They are worked out from the start of the game.

In the first game of a tennis match, Greg got 4 first serves in. He won 3 of these 4 points. You can work out the percentage of points that Greg won on his first serve in this game. You need to work out 3 as a percentage of 4.
To do this:
(1) Write the numbers as a fraction.
(2) Turn the fraction into a percentage. Multiply by 100%.

Write 3 out of 4 as a fraction $\dfrac{3}{4}$

Multiply by 100% $= \dfrac{3}{4} \times 100\%$

Key in: **3** **÷** **4** **×** **1** **0** **0** **=**

$$= 75\%$$

Greg has won 75% of his first serves in this game.

Exercise 9:18

1 **a** In his second service game Greg got 5 first serves in.
He won 4 of these 5 points.
What percentage of points did Greg win on his first serve in this game?
b In his third service game Greg got 10 first serves in.
He won 9 of these 10 points.
What percentage of points did Greg win on his first serve in this game?

This table shows the number of first serves that Greg got in his next two service games. It also shows the number of these points that Greg won.

Service game	Number of first serves in	Number of these points won
4th	8	5
5th	8	7

c What percentage of points did Greg win on his first serve in
  (1) the 4th service game   (2) the 5th service game?

2 So far Greg has served for 5 games.
  a How many first serves has he got in altogether?
  b How many of these points has he won?
  c What percentage of points has Greg won on his first serve so far?

3 In the whole match, Greg served 82 first serves in.
  He won 67 of these points.
  a What fraction of first serves did he win?
  b What percentage of first serves did he win?
    Write your answer to the nearest whole number.

4 In the whole match, Greg served 65 second serves in.
  He won 28 of these points.
  a What fraction of second serves did he win?
  b What percentage of second serves did he win?
    Write your answer to the nearest whole number.

You can use this method to write any number as a percentage of another number.

Example   Jill asked 200 people to name their favourite breakfast cereal.
      130 said cornflakes.
      What percentage of people in Jill's survey said cornflakes?

Write 130 as a fraction of 200 $\dfrac{130}{200}$

Multiply by 100% $\dfrac{130}{200} \times 100\%$

Key in: **1** **3** **0** **÷** **2** **0** **0** **×** **1** **0** **0** **=**

          $= 65\%$

65% of the people in Jill's survey said cornflakes.

Exercise 9:19

1 Mrs Hamer spends £35 in Tesco's.
She spends £21 on food.
  a What fraction of the money
    does she spend on food?
  b What percentage of the money
    does she spend on food?

2 In one month 60 people took their
driving test with FastPass.
45 passed first time.
  a What fraction of the people who
    took their test passed first time?
  b What percentage of the people who
    took their test passed first time?

3 John scores 24 out of 60 in a maths test.
  a Write John's mark as a fraction.
  b Work out John's percentage for the test.

4 Helen is doing a sponsored walk.
She will walk 75 miles in 4 days.
The table shows the number of miles
that she will walk each day.

Day	1	2	3	4
Number of miles	20	22	18	15

  a Write down the fraction of the walk that Helen will do each day.
  b Write down the percentage of the walk that Helen will do each day.
    Write your answers to 1 dp.

5 Gary and Samira have a meal in a restaurant.
The bill is £32.
They leave a tip of £3.
  a What fraction of the bill is the tip?
  b What percentage of the bill is the tip?
    Give your answer to 1 dp.

You need to make sure that the numbers in the question are in the same units.
If you want to find 35 pence as a percentage of £2

you cannot do $\dfrac{35}{2} \times 100\%$ because the 35 is in pence and the 2 is in pounds.

It is usually easier to change everything into the smaller unit.
Pence are smaller than pounds.
Change the question. Find 35 pence as a percentage of 200 pence.

Work out $\dfrac{35}{200} \times 100\% = 17.5\%$

6 Find
   a 20 p as a percentage of £4   **c** 45 cm as a percentage of 3 metres
   b 30 mins as a percentage of 2 hours   **d** 60 g as a percentage of 2 kg

7 Lucy gets £6.50 pocket money.
   a She spends £5.10   **b** She has 34 p left at the end of the week.
      What percentage does   What percentage of her pocket
      she spend?   money is this?

W *Game – 100 pair cent*

You need the game worksheet.

Percentage change

You always work out a percentage change using the starting value.

$$\text{Percentage change} = \frac{\text{actual change}}{\text{starting value}} \times 100\%$$

Example   Find the percentage decrease when a shirt is reduced from £25 to £17.

The actual decrease is £25 − £17 = £8
The starting price was £25.
Now find the percentage change by finding £8 as a percentage of £25.

$\text{Percentage decrease} = \dfrac{8}{25} \times 100\%$ Key in:

$= 32\%$ $\boxed{8} \ \boxed{\div} \ \boxed{2} \ \boxed{5} \ \boxed{\times} \ \boxed{1} \ \boxed{0} \ \boxed{0} \ \boxed{=}$

Exercise 9:20

1 Harry is a market trader.
He has a sale to get rid of some stock.
The table shows his normal price
and his sale price for each item.
Work out the percentage reduction in
the sale for each item.

	Item	Normal price	Sale price
a	bracelet	£30	£25
b	earrings	£24	£18
c	portable stereo	£60	£45
d	book	£8	£6
e	clock	£50	£42
● **f**	porcelain figure	£120	£80

2 A new all-seater stadium is built.
The old stands could take 10 350 people.
The new all-seater stadium can take
5240 people.
Find the percentage reduction in the
capacity.
Give your answer to 1 dp.

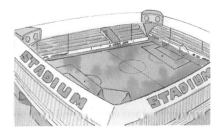

Harry is buying new stock for his stall. He buys a toaster and an antique table.

He pays £20 for the toaster.
He sells the toaster for £30.
He makes a profit of £10.

He pays £100 for the antique table.
He sells the table for £110.
He makes a profit of £10.

Harry realises that his profit on the table
isn't as good as his profit on the toaster.
He risked much more money on the table.

He can work out his percentage profit. This is just a percentage change.
Actual profit is the actual change.
Cost price is the starting price.

$$\text{Percentage profit} = \frac{\text{actual profit}}{\text{cost price}} \times 100\%$$

For the toaster:

$$\text{percentage profit} = \frac{10}{20} \times 100\%$$
$$= 50\%$$

For the table:

$$\text{percentage profit} = \frac{10}{100} \times 100\%$$
$$= 10\%$$

Harry has made a much bigger percentage profit on the toaster.

---

3 Harry buys lots of items and sells them at a profit.
The table shows how much each item cost him and his selling price.
Work out the percentage profit that he makes for each item.

	Item	Cost price	Selling price
a	watch	£15	£25
b	necklace	£12	£18
c	Discman	£60	£75
d	CD	£3	£6
e	diamond ring	£35	£75
f	Playstation	£25	£65

Harry bought a coat for £50. He sold it for £40. He has made a loss.

$$\text{Percentage loss} = \frac{\text{actual loss}}{\text{cost price}} \times 100\% = \frac{10}{50} \times 100\% = 20\%$$

---

4 Harry sells some items at a loss to get rid of them.
The table shows how much each item cost him and his selling price.
Work out the percentage loss for each item.

	Item	Normal price	Sale price
a	record player	£20	£15
b	camcorder	£100	£80
c	vase	£40	£30
d	kettle	£20	£12
e	Game Boy	£25	£15
f	socket set	£14	£8

1 Write each of these diagrams as:
(1) a top heavy fraction
(2) a whole number and a fraction

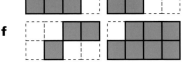
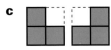

2 Copy these. Fill them in.

a $\overline{16} = \overline{8}$

b  $\overline{16} = \overline{8}$

3 Work these out.

a $2\frac{1}{4} + 1\frac{1}{2}$ **c** $3\frac{5}{8} + 4\frac{3}{4}$ **e** $6\frac{5}{16} + 2\frac{7}{8}$ **g** $8\frac{1}{2} + 7\frac{9}{16}$

b $2\frac{3}{4} - 2\frac{1}{8}$ **d** $7\frac{1}{16} - 6\frac{3}{8}$ **f** $11\frac{3}{4} - 9\frac{13}{16}$ **h** $40\frac{3}{4} - 9\frac{15}{16}$

4 Put these fractions in order of size. Start with the smallest.

a $\frac{2}{5}, \frac{3}{10}$ **b** $\frac{5}{8}, \frac{9}{16}$ **c** $\frac{4}{5}, \frac{3}{4}$ **d** $\frac{5}{6}, \frac{7}{8}, \frac{7}{12}$

5 Metrobuses have 32 seats.
One metrobus has 12 passengers when it breaks down.
The next metrobus has 15 passengers.
All of the passengers get on the second bus.
What fraction of the seats is empty?

6 Work these out.

a $\frac{3}{5} \times \frac{2}{7}$ **c** $\frac{3}{4} \div \frac{1}{8}$ **e** $2\frac{5}{6} \div \frac{1}{2}$ **g** $1\frac{2}{3} \div 2\frac{3}{4}$

b $\frac{7}{10} \div \frac{2}{3}$ **d** $1\frac{5}{7} \times \frac{3}{10}$ **f** $\frac{1}{6} \times 3\frac{3}{5}$ **h** $1\frac{1}{5} \times 1\frac{2}{7}$

7 Write each of these fractions as a percentage.

a $\dfrac{41}{100}$ b $\dfrac{18}{50}$ c $\dfrac{3}{20}$ d $\dfrac{7}{10}$ e $\dfrac{13}{25}$

8 Write each of these percentages as decimals.
a 14% b 45% c 34.6% d 2% e 0.34%

9 Change these decimals to percentages.
a 0.23 b 0.42 c 0.05 d 0.354 e 0.037

10 Write each of these fractions as percentages. Give your answers to 1 dp.

a $\dfrac{14}{17}$ b $\dfrac{19}{37}$ c $\dfrac{27}{144}$ d $\dfrac{204}{275}$ e $\dfrac{4}{73}$

11 2500 people were asked if they carry a donor card.
70% said yes. How many people said yes?

12 The ratio of boys to girls on a school trip is 2 : 3.
What percentage are boys?

13 Jenny's father won £840 in the lottery.
He shared the prize between his children
in the ratio 5 : 4 : 2
Jenny got the smallest share.
a How much did Jenny get?
Jenny saved $33\frac{1}{3}$% of her money.
b How much did she save?
c How much did she spend?

14 Find the value of each of these.

a 50% of 66 c 25% of 8.2 e $33\frac{1}{3}$% of £36 g 75% of 16 kg
b $33\frac{1}{3}$% of 15 d 10% of 61 f 60% of £400 h $66\frac{2}{3}$% of 42 m

15 Copy these calculations. Fill in the gaps.

a   10% of £124 = ...   b   10% of £236 = ...
    5% of £124 = ...   5% of £236 = ...
    2.5% of £124 = ...   2.5% of £236 = ...
    ──────────────   ──────────────
    17.5% of £124 = ...   17.5% of £236 = ...

16 A new camcorder costs £560 before
VAT is added at 17.5%.
  a How much is the VAT on £560?
  b What is the total cost of the camcorder?

17   **a** Reduce all of these prices by $33\frac{1}{3}$%.
      (1) £165   (2) £1650   (3) £16.50   (4) £1.65
  b Increase all of the prices in part **a** by 40%.

18 Phil scores 44 out of 60 in a maths test.
  a Write Phil's mark as a fraction.
  b Work out Phil's percentage for the test. Give your answer to 1 dp.

19

  a Pears cost 30% more than apples.
    How much is 1 kg of pears?
  b The oranges have gone up in price.
    Yesterday they were 17 pence each. Today they are 19 pence each.
    What is the percentage increase in price?
    Give your answer to 1 dp.

20 The usual charge for renting a TV is £9.25 per month.
John can get a discount.
He pays £8.14 per month.
What percentage discount does John get?

21 The table shows cost price and selling price.
Work out the percentage profit or loss for each part.

	Cost price	Selling price
a	£25	£15
b	£60	£90
c	£80	£50

1   Graham has £12 235 in a savings account.
    The annual rate of interest is 6.35%.
    a Find the interest on £12 235 over a year.
    Graham is a tax payer so 20% of this is deducted for tax.
    b How much does Graham get?
    c What rate of interest does he actually get?

2   In 1990, Mr Block bought this house for £88 000.
    In 1992, Mr Block sold the house to Mrs Garrity
    for £77 000.
    a What was Mr Block's percentage loss?
    In 1996, Mrs Garrity sold the house.
    She made a profit of 31% on what she had paid.
    b How much did she get for the house?
    c Work out the percentage change in the
    value of the house from 1990 to 1996.

3   A car loses 20% of its value each year.
    Barry buys a car for £12 000.
    a Work out how much the car will be worth after
        (1) 1 year   (2) 2 years   (3) 5 years.
    b Work out the value of the car after 5 years as
        a percentage of its original value.

4   Terry is changing the size of his rectangular club logo.
    He increases the length by 10%.
    He decreases the width by 10%.
    What has he done to the area of the logo?

5   A TV costs £330 now.
    The price of the TV has risen by 10% since 1995.
    How much was the TV in 1995?

1   Work these out. Cancel the fraction in the answer if you can.

    a $\frac{7}{12} - \frac{5}{12}$ **d** $3\frac{1}{4} + 4\frac{5}{8}$ **g** $2\frac{1}{6} \times 3\frac{1}{2}$

    b $\frac{1}{4} + \frac{3}{8}$ **e** $5\frac{3}{4} - 2\frac{1}{2}$ **h** $\frac{3}{8} \div \frac{1}{4}$

    c $\frac{1}{2} - \frac{1}{6}$ **f** $\frac{3}{5} \times \frac{1}{4}$ **i** $1\frac{3}{4} \div 2\frac{1}{3}$

2   Put these fractions in order of size. Start with the smaller.

    $\frac{3}{4}$ $\frac{5}{8}$

3   Brian needs 72 oz of pastry to make 6 flans.
    Work out how much pastry he needs to make 5 flans.

4   Copy these. Fill in the gaps.

    a $\dfrac{3}{x} = \dfrac{\ldots}{4x}$ **c** $\dfrac{30}{10x} = \dfrac{\ldots}{x}$

    b $\dfrac{5}{x} = \dfrac{15}{\ldots}$ **d** $\dfrac{18}{6x} = \dfrac{3}{\ldots}$

5   Use the formula $w = \dfrac{A}{l}$ to find w when $A = 3\frac{3}{4}$ and $l = \frac{5}{8}$.

6   Write

    a $\frac{33}{100}$ as a percentage   **d** 81% as a decimal

    b 12 out of 25 as a percentage   **e** $\frac{5}{8}$ as a percentage

    c 0.35 as a percentage   **f** 49% as a fraction

7 The men to women ratio of a running club is 16 : 9.
What percentage are men?

8 Work out
   a 25% of 360   **b** 40% of £375

9 A firm makes chocolate cakes. It is expected that 3% will be rejects.
Today the firm made 864 cakes.
How many rejects would you expect?

10 A camera costs £380 before VAT is added at 17.5%.
   a How much is the VAT on £380?
   b What is the total cost of the camera?

11 **a** Increase 560 by 20%.   **b** Decrease £250 by 30%.

12 A company sends 950 letters in one week.
They send 703 of these by first class post.
   a What fraction is sent first class?
   b What percentage is sent first class?

13 A garage buys a car for £1500 and then sells the car for £1920.
Find the percentage profit that the garage makes on the car.

14 The same type of TV is sold in three shops at different prices.

Davies Electricals	Buyrite	Discount TVs
£268	£390	£350
SALE	**SALE** $\frac{1}{3}$ OFF	SALE 25%
5% discount today only	this week!	off this price

   a Work out the price for each shop.
   b Which shop has the best price in the sale?

10 Basically probability

1 It all adds up to one
Drawing probability scales
Deciding whether an experiment is fair
Knowing that probabilities add up to one
Finding the probability of something not happening
Writing probabilities as fractions

CORE

2 Finding probabilities
Knowing the meaning of equally likely
Using equally likely events to find probabilities
Using data given in tables to find probabilities
Finding probabilities using an experiment
Knowing which method to use to find probabilities
Playing a game: Win or lose?

QUESTIONS

EXTENSION

TEST YOURSELF

1   It all adds up to one

Moses and Whitney are watching the weather forecast.
The presenter says that the probability of a hurricane is 40%.
Moses is worried.
Whitney is more cheerful.
She says the probability of the hurricane missing them is 60%.

You usually write probabilities as fractions.
40% is $\frac{40}{100}$ and 60% is $\frac{60}{100}$

Probability

Probability tells you how likely something is to happen.

Probabilities are often shown on a scale with 'impossible' at one end and 'certain' at the other.

This is a probability scale:

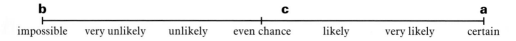

b		**c**		**a**
impossible	very unlikely unlikely	even chance	likely very likely	certain

These probabilities are shown on the scale:
a   the sun will rise tomorrow
b   ice will be found on the sun
c   the sun will shine on the first day of spring.

Exercise 10:1

For questions **1** and **2** draw a probability scale.
Mark points **a**, **b** and **c** to show how likely you think each one is.

1   **a**   You will be struck by lightning tomorrow.
   b   You will drink something tomorrow.
   c   You will eat chips tomorrow.

2   **a**   A £1 ticket will win the jackpot in the National Lottery.
    b   A £1 ticket will win £10 in the National Lottery.
    c   A £1 ticket will not win anything in the National Lottery.

A probability scale often has numbers on it instead of words.
Something which is impossible has a probability of 0
Something that is certain has a probability of 1

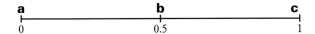

These probabilities are shown on the scale:
a   Great Britain will sink into the sea tomorrow
b   if I toss a coin it will land tail up
c   it will be a sunny day tomorrow in the Arizona desert.

The value of a probability can only be between 0 and 1.

---

3   Draw a probability scale with numbers.
Mark points **a**, **b** and **c** to show how likely you think each one of these is:
a   it will snow in Scotland in January
b   it will snow in Greece in August
c   it will snow in Wales in April.

4   **a**   Write down two things that have a probability close to 1.
    b   Write down two things that have a probability of 0.
    c   Write down two things that have a probability of 0.5

5   John says that the probability of Liverpool winning the cup is 1.5
Explain what is wrong with this.

6   Lucy says that the probability of her passing her music exam is −0.5
Explain what is wrong with this.

7   A coin is tossed.
Write down whether these statements are true or false.
a   There is a 50% chance of getting a head.
b   The chance of getting a tail on two tosses is about 1.2

You can use probability to decide whether something is fair or not.

John and Peter are deciding who is going to eat the last Rolo.

They are going to use this spinner.
John will eat the rolo if it lands on blue.
Peter will eat the rolo if it lands on yellow.
Why is this unfair?

There are more blue sections on the spinner than yellow.
There is a greater chance it will land on a blue section.
John has a better chance of getting the last Rolo!

Exercise 10:2

1 Katy and Laura only have one ticket for the football match.
They decide to roll a dice to see who gets the ticket.
Katy gets the ticket if the dice shows a 1, 2, 3 or 4.
Laura gets the ticket if the dice shows a 5 or 6.
Is this fair? Explain your answer.

2 Both David and Penel want the
last slice of chocolate fudge cake.
They both toss a coin.
If both the coins show heads then
Penel gets the cake. Otherwise
David gets to eat the cake.
Who is more likely to win?
Explain your answer.

3 Sam and Liam are playing a game with a dice.
They take turns to roll the dice.
If the dice shows an even number Liam writes it down.
If the dice shows an odd number Sam writes it down.
The winner is the first person whose numbers add up to 30.
Explain why the game is unfair.

Probabilities always add up to 1

There are 4 cubes in an envelope. There are 3 red and 1 blue.
One cube is chosen at random.
The probability of a red cube is $\frac{3}{4}$.
The probability of a blue cube is $\frac{1}{4}$.

$$\frac{3}{4} + \frac{1}{4} = 1$$

We can show this on a probability scale.

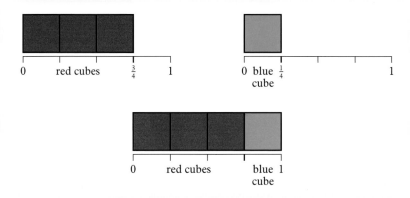

Exercise 10:3

1 This time 4 red cubes and 1 blue cube are put in the envelope.

    a What is the probability of picking a red cube?
    b What is the probability of picking a blue cube?
    c What do these probabilities add up to?

2 5 red cubes and 3 blue cubes are put in the envelope.
    a How many cubes are there altogether?
    b What is the probability of picking a red cube?
    c What is the probability of picking a blue cube?
    d What do these probabilities add up to?

3 7 black counters and 3 white counters are put in an envelope.
One counter is chosen at random.
- **a** How many counters are there altogether?
- **b** What is the probability of picking a black counter?
- **c** What is the probability of picking a white counter?
- **d** What do these probabilities add up to?

Ian puts 4 green cubes and 1 blue cube in an envelope.
There are 5 cubes altogether so you draw a scale using **fifths**.

The probability that he will pick a green cube is $\frac{4}{5}$.
You can colour the first four fifths of your scale in green.
The rest of the scale must be blue.

The probability of blue is $\frac{1}{5}$ This is written $P(\text{blue}) = \frac{1}{5}$.
This is also the probability of not getting a green.
So $P(\text{not green}) = \frac{1}{5}$

These probabilities add up to 1 so you can write
$$P(\text{not green}) = 1 - P(\text{green})$$
$$= 1 - \frac{4}{5}$$
$$= \frac{1}{5}$$

Example   Gareth picks a toffee at random from a bag of mixed toffees.
The probability that he gets a mint toffee is $\frac{2}{7}$.
What is the probability that he doesn't get a mint toffee?

$$P(\text{not mint toffee}) = 1 - P(\text{mint toffee})$$
$$= 1 - \frac{2}{7}$$
$$= \frac{5}{7}$$

Exercise 10:4

1 There are 4 red cubes and 2 blue cubes in an envelope.
Margaret picks out one at random.
- **a** What is the probability that she will pick a red cube?
- **b** What is the probability that she won't pick a red cube?

2 Sam has 10 friends. Four are female.
He rings one of his friends at random.
   a What is the probability that Sam rings a female friend?
   b Find the probability that Sam does not ring a female friend.

3 The probability of Joy being late is $\frac{1}{9}$.
Find the probability that she isn't late.

4 The probability that Karl reaches the
highest level on a computer game is $\frac{5}{8}$.
Find the probability that he won't reach
the highest level.

You can use decimals and percentages to give probabilities.

Example   The probability that Gemma will pass her accountancy exam is 0.8
Find the probability that she won't pass.

$$P\,(\text{not passing}) = 1 - P\,(\text{passing})$$
$$= 1 - 0.8$$
$$= 0.2$$

Example   The probability of Owen passing his exam is 85%.
Find the probability that he won't pass.

$$P\,(\text{not passing}) = 1 - P\,(\text{passing})$$
$$= 100\% - 85\%$$
$$= 15\%$$

---

5 Bella is very lucky at Bingo. The probability that she wins is 0.7
What is the probability that she won't win?

6 Nelson loves watching rugby. The probability that he is at a rugby match
on Saturday is 84%. What is the probability that he won't be there?

7 The weather forecast gives a 35% chance of rain.
What is the probability that it won't rain?

• **8** Kevin supports Dartmouth Argyle. The probability that they will win is 0.08
The probability they will draw is 0.66
What is the probability that they won't lose?

Event	The word event is often used in probability.

An **event** is one thing that can happen in a probability experiment.

When you choose a card at random from a pack of cards there are many different events that can happen.

Let A be the event 'getting a diamond'.

The probability of getting a diamond is $\frac{13}{52} = \frac{1}{4}$

You write $P(A) = \frac{1}{4}$

For an event A, the event 'not A' is written A'

$P(A') - 1 - P(A)$

The probability of 'not getting a diamond' is $P(A') = 1 - \frac{1}{4}$

$= \frac{3}{4}$

If B is the event 'getting the ace of spades' then

$P(B) = \frac{1}{52}$

So the probability of 'not getting the ace of spades' is

$P(B') = 1 - \frac{1}{52}$

$= \frac{51}{52}$

Exercise 10:5

1 The probability that Kay passes her driving test is 0.6
Let A be the event 'Kay passes her driving test'.
Find **a** $P(A)$ **b** $P(A')$

2 The probability that Kevin will be late for dinner is $\frac{3}{7}$.
Let B be the event 'Kevin is late for dinner'.
Find **a** $P(B)$ **b** $P(B')$

3 Sam has a 30% chance of being chosen for the hockey team.
Let C be the event 'Sam is chosen for the team'.
Find **a** $P(C)$ **b** $P(C')$

2 Finding probabilities

All the balls in the machine have an equal chance of being the first ball out.
The probability of one ticket matching the six numbers is 0.000 000 071 5

Equally likely

Two events are **equally likely** if they have the same chance of happening.

The chance of getting a red with this spinner is the same as the chance of getting a blue. Getting a red and getting a blue are equally likely.

You are more likely to get a red with this spinner than a blue. Getting a red and getting a blue are not equally likely with this spinner.

Exercise 10:6

1 Which of these spinners give equally likely events?

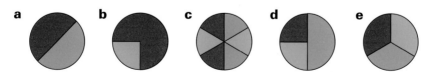

a   b   c   d   e

2 A person is chosen at random from a group of students.
It is equally likely that the person chosen will be male or female.
What does this tell you about the number of males and females in the group?

3　A gardener plants 200 bulbs. He knows that one bulb in twenty will not grow. He chooses one bulb at random. Are the events 'the bulb will grow' and 'the bulb will not grow' equally likely?
Explain your answer.

4　A box of chocolates contains 50% plain and 50% milk chocolates.
Judy chooses a chocolate at random.
Are the events 'she chooses a milk chocolate' and 'she chooses a plain chocolate' equally likely? Explain your answer.

5　John is given the choice of playing football or table tennis after school. Are the events 'he chooses football' and 'he chooses table tennis' equally likely?
Explain your answer.

You can use equally likely events to work out probabilities.

Danny uses this spinner.
There are five equal sections.
They are green, red, yellow, blue and red.
Red has two sections.

Probability of an event A

The **probability of an event A** is:

$$\frac{\text{the number of ways that the event A can happen}}{\text{the total number of things that can happen}}$$

The probability of getting a green $= \dfrac{1}{5}$　　only 1 of the 5 sections is green

The probability of getting a red $= \dfrac{2}{5}$　　2 of the 5 sections are red

---

Exercise 10:7

1　George spins this spinner.
Find the probability that the colour he gets is:
a　yellow
b　purple

2 A bag holds two red balls and three blue balls.
A ball is chosen at random. Find the probability that the ball is:
   a blue   **b** red

3 John buys a box of 12 eggs. Two of these are cracked.
John picks an egg at random from the box.
Find the probability that the egg is
   a cracked   **b** not cracked

4 This fair dice is rolled.

Find the probability of getting:
   a a 2   **c** an even number   **e** 3 or more
   b a 6   **d** 2 or less   **f** a prime number

5 Jim asks his friends where they are spending this Easter holiday.
Seven are staying at home, five are visiting relatives and three are
going abroad. Jim picks one of his friends at random.
Find the probability that, for Easter, they are:
   a staying at home   **c** not going abroad
   b going abroad   **d** not visiting relatives

6 Joggers crisps have a special offer. 8 bags in
every 100 contain a voucher for a free packet of
crisps. Sian buys a packet of crisps at random.
Find the probability that her packet contains a
voucher.

7 Look at these numbers: 4, 5, 7, 9, 10, 13, 15, 19, 20, 22, 27
A number is chosen from these at random.
Find the probability that the number is:
   a even   **c** a prime number   **e** a number greater than 10
   b a multiple of 5   **d** a square number   **f** a number less than 10

You can get data from tables to find probabilities.

Example   The table shows the people that took part in a survey.

	male	female
child	12	15
adult	5	8

a How many people took part in the survey?
b How many children took part in the survey?
A person is chosen at random from those in the survey.
Find the probability that the person is:
c a male adult   **d** a child

a You add up all the numbers to find the number of people.
   Number of people $= 12 + 15 + 5 + 8 = 40$
b To find the number of children you look at the row labelled child.
   Number of children $= 12 + 15 = 27$
c 5 male adults took part in the survey.
   The total number of people was 40.

   $$P(\text{the person is a male adult}) = \frac{5}{40}$$

d 27 children took part in the survey. The total number of people was 40.

   $$P(\text{the person is a child}) = \frac{27}{40}$$

Exercise 10:8

1   The table gives the membership of a bowling club.

	male	female
child	14	19
adult	46	55

a How many members does the bowling club have?
b How many children are members?
c How many members are female?
A member is chosen at random.
Find the probability that this member is:
d a child   **f** a male adult   **h** a female adult
e female   **g** a girl   **i** male

2 The table shows the shoe sizes of a class of 30 pupils.

Shoe size	4	5	6	7
Number of boys	1	3	7	5
Number of girls	2	5	6	1

A pupil is chosen at random from the class.
Find the probability that the pupil will be:
a a boy
b a girl
c a boy with shoe size 6
d a girl with shoe size 5

3 A store sells duvet covers of different sizes and colours.
The table shows how many of each size and colour they have in stock.

	Single	Double	King size
white	5	11	3
blue	2	6	1
green	8	5	1

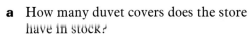

a How many duvet covers does the store have in stock?
A duvet cover is chosen at random.
Find the probability that it is:
b white
c double size
d blue king size
e green single size

4 A machine fills bags of sugar.
They should contain 2 kg sugar.
Rosemary tests the machine by
weighing 100 bags of sugar
chosen at random.
The table shows her results.

Weight of sugar	less than 2 kg	exactly 2 kg	more than 2 kg
Number of bags	5	64	31

Find the probability that a bag chosen at random will:
a contain exactly 2 kg
b not contain exactly 2 kg
c be underweight
d be overweight

Laura has made a tetrahedral dice.
She throws the dice 100 times and
records the number each time.
This table shows her results.

Number	Tally	Frequency
1	ЖІ ЖІ ЖІ ЖІ ІІ	22
2	ЖІ ЖІ ЖІ ЖІ ЖІ	25
3	ЖІ ЖІ ЖІ ЖІ ЖІ ІІІІ	29
4	ЖІ ЖІ ЖІ ЖІ ІІІІ	24

Frequency   The **frequency** of an event is the number of times that it
happens.

Relative   **Relative frequency** of an event $= \dfrac{\text{frequency of the event}}{\text{total frequency}}$
frequency

The relative frequency gives an estimate of the probability.

If the dice is fair the probability of getting each number is $\frac{1}{4}$.
Laura checks her data to see if the dice is fair.
She uses the relative frequency from her experiment.

The relative frequency of 1 is $\frac{22}{100}$.
Laura wants to see if $\frac{1}{4}$ and $\frac{22}{100}$ are about the same value.
She converts them both to decimals.
$\frac{1}{4} = 0.25$ $\frac{22}{100} = 0.22$
The two values are close. The dice is probably fair.

Laura can get a better estimate for the probability by repeating the experiment more
times.

Exercise 10:9

1   Darren tossed a coin 50 times.
This is his data.

Outcome	Tally	Frequency
Head	ЖІ ЖІ ЖІ ЖІ	20
Tail	ЖІ ЖІ ЖІ ЖІ ЖІ ЖІ	30

a   Find the relative frequency of
(1) a head
(2) a tail
b   Do you think the coin is fair?
Explain your answer.

2   Greg is playing in a tennis tournament. His coach is keeping a tally of
the points won and lost on his first serve. These are his results:

	points won	points lost
1st serve	35	15

Greg gets his next first serve in.
Estimate the probability that Greg will:
a   win the point
b   lose the point

3   Gemma is testing a biased spinner.
She has spun it 100 times.
The table shows her results.

Colour	Frequency
blue	20
green	45
yellow	35

Estimate the probability that on the next spin the colour Gemma will
get is:
a   blue   **b**   green   **c**   not yellow

4   A factory makes skirts. The waist sizes of 200 skirts were tested.
35 were smaller than the stated size. 62 were larger than the stated size.
Estimate the probability that a skirt made by this factory will have a
waist size that is:
a   larger than stated
b   smaller than stated
c   equal to the stated size

Methods of finding probability

There are three methods of finding probability.

Method 1   Use equally likely outcomes
e.g. to find the probability of getting a 6 with a fair dice.

Method 2   Use a survey or do an experiment
e.g. to find the probability that a drawing pin will land point up
when dropped.

Method 3   Look back at data
e.g. to find the probability that it will snow in Monaco this
winter, look at the records of snow for previous years.

Exercise 10:10

Look at each of these probabilities.
Write down which method you would use to find the probability.
State whether your answer would be the actual probability or an estimate.
If you say method 2 write down what experiment or survey you would do.

1   The probability that the next car to pass the school will be white.

2   The probability that a blue cube will be chosen at random from a box of 20 cubes.

3   The probability that there will be a flu epidemic this winter.

4   The probability that a coin will show a tail when tossed.

5   The probability of a person chosen at random voting Labour in the next General Election.

6   The probability of a biased dice giving a 5 when tossed.

7   The probability of a battery taken from the production line being faulty.

8   The probability of a cat living beyond 18 years.

9   The probability of Swansea winning their next football match.

Game: Win or lose?

This is a game for two players.
You need two dice.

Take it in turns to roll two dice.
Multiply the two numbers together.
Player 1 gets a point if the score is even.
Player 2 gets a point if the score is odd.

The first player to reach a score of 10 wins.
Play the game with a partner.

Investigating the game

Work with your partner.
You have to carry out an
experiment to see if the
game is fair.

Roll the dice.
Multiply the numbers and record whether the answer is odd or even.
Do this 50 times.

Work out the relative frequency of 'getting an odd number' and 'getting an
even number'.
Is the game fair? Explain your answer.
What happens if you roll the dice 100 times?

What happens if you add the numbers instead of multiplying?
Is this version of the game fair?

What happens if you subtract the numbers?

1   Copy this probability scale.

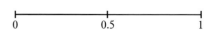

Mark points **a, b** and **c** to show how likely you think each one of these is.
   a   It will be the 30th February tomorrow.
   b   It will rain tomorrow.
   c   You will score a number less than 7 with a dice.

2   Robert says that the probability of him scoring full marks in a test is −0.2
    Explain what is wrong with his value for the probability.

3   You have 6 red cubes and 8 blue cubes in a bag.
    One cube is picked at random.
    Write down the probability that you will:
    a   pick a red
    b   pick a blue
    c   not pick a red
    d   not pick a blue

4   The probability of England winning their next cricket match is 0.36
    What is the probability that they will not win?

5   Helen says that her family has a 40% chance of having visitors to stay
    over the summer. Find the probability that they will not have visitors
    staying with them over the summer.

6   The probability that Emma and her brother argue over the weekend is $\frac{7}{12}$.
    Write down the probability that they will not argue over the weekend.

7   The probability that a new car is free of faults is 0.27
    Let A be the event 'a new car is free of faults'.
    Find   **a** $P(A)$ **b** $P(A')$

8   Rory has a 58% chance of finishing his coursework on time.
    Let F be the event 'Rory finishes his coursework on time'.
    Find   **a** $P(F)$ **b** $P(F')$

9   Fatima is given the chance of having chips or mashed potato with her
    sausages. Are the events 'she chooses chips' and 'she chooses mashed
    potato' equally likely? Explain your answer.

10 The letters of the word PARALLELOGRAM are written on cards.
The cards are put into a box and one card is then chosen at random.
What is the probability that the letter on the card chosen is:

    a A   **c** a vowel   **e** not an A

    b L   **d** not a vowel   **f** S

11 A card is chosen at random from a pack of 52 playing cards.
Write down the probability that the card is:

    a a black card   **c** a red ten   **e** a four

    b a king   **d** a heart   **f** the queen of spades

12 A purse contains 20 coins. Three are £1 coins, four are 50 p coins,
five are 20 p coins, two are 10 p coins, the rest are 2 p coins.
A coin is picked out at random.
Write down the probability that the coin is:

    a a 20 p   **c** either a 20 p or a 10 p   **e** worth less than 50 p

    b a 50 p   **d** worth more than 10 p

13 Deidre has carried out a survey on the main sport played by people
during the last month. These are her results.

	tennis	golf	swimming	squash
men	17	34	19	29
women	21	27	26	27

    a How many people took part in her survey?

Deidre chooses a person at random from her survey.
What is the probability that this person:

    b is male and swims   **e** plays tennis

    c is female and plays golf   **f** plays golf or squash

    d is female   **g** is a male squash player

14 In the last 40 matches the school chess team has won 26, lost 8 and
drawn the rest.
Estimate the probability that in their next match the team will

    a win   **b** lose   **c** not win

1   Ben has carried out a survey of cars in a supermarket car park.
He has drawn this bar chart to show his results.

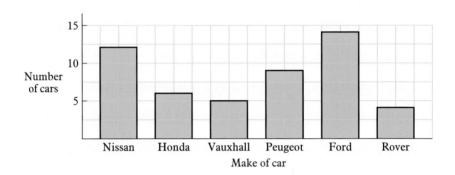

If a car is chosen at random from the survey, find the probability that
the make will be:

a Nissan   **b** Ford   **c** Peugeot

The next day a car is chosen at random from the same car park.
Estimate the probability that the car will be made by:

d Vauxhall   **e** Honda   **f** Rover

2   A bag contains 60 beads. There are four different colours.
A bead is chosen at random from the bag.
The table shows the probability of getting three of the colours.

Colour	red	blue	white
Probability	$\frac{1}{4}$	$\frac{1}{5}$	$\frac{1}{3}$

The fourth colour is black.
a Find the probability that a bead chosen at random is black.
b How many beads are there of each colour?

3   There are three events A, B and C. Here are some probabilities:

$P(A) = 0.16$ $P(B') = 0.42$
$P(A) + P(B) + P(C) = 1$

Find   **a** $P(A')$ **c** $P(C)$
          b $P(B)$ **d** $P(C')$

1 Sam and Gemma use this spinner to decide who takes the dog for a walk. Sam has to walk the dog if it lands on a multiple of 4, otherwise Gemma walks the dog.

Is this fair?

Explain your answer.

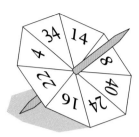

2 The probability that Zara will go to France for her holiday is 0.55
What is the probability that Zara will not go to France for her holiday?

3 Ivan says the probability that he will win his squash match is 67%.
What is the probability that he won't win?

4 A box contains 15 counters.

7 of the counters are black.

Jimmy picks a counter at random from the box.

Write down the probability that the counter is

   a black

   b not black

5 If $P(C) = 0.58$ find $P(C')$.

6 A box contains 8 plain chocolates and 12 milk chocolates.

Aslan picks a chocolate at random.

Are the events 'He picks a plain chocolate' and 'He picks a milk chocolate' equally likely? Explain your answer.

7 There are 8 girls and 5 boys in the school chess club.

One of these is chosen at random to receive a shield.

What is the probability that a girl is chosen?

8 Greg says that the probability of him passing his music exam is -0.8
Explain what is wrong with this statement.

9 Look at these numbers: 2, 3, 4, 6, 10, 18.

A number is chosen from these at random.
Find the probability that the number is
a odd
b a multiple of 6
c a triangle number
d a number less than 4

10 The table shows the favourite science of a group of pupils.

	Physics	Chemistry	Biology
Girls	7	11	12
Boys	13	8	9

a How many pupils are represented in the table?

A pupil is chosen at random.
Write down the probability that this pupil is:
b a girl who prefers Physics   **d** a boy who prefers Biology
c a pupil who prefers Biology   **e** a girl

11 Dana uses this spinner 80 times.
She records the colour she gets each time.
The table shows her data.

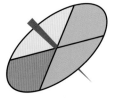

Colour	red	blue	green	yellow
Frequency	18	25	21	16

a Write down the relative frequency of the colour blue.
b Dana uses the spinner another 400 times.
What would you expect to happen to the relative frequency of the colour blue?

12 How would you estimate the probability that:
a you would get a 5 with a biased dice
b there will be a measles epidemic this winter?

11 The bigger picture

QUESTIONS

EXTENSION

TEST YOURSELF

1 Enlargements

Jo is visiting London.
She thinks the tube train looks
very small from a distance.
It is only when it is much closer
that she realises how big it is.
She thinks the railway lines are
like construction lines for an
enlargement.

This is how to enlarge a shape using a scale factor 2.

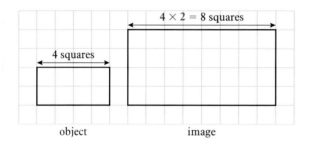

object   image

You multiply all the lengths by 2.
The enlargement is 2 times as long and 2 times as high as the object.

Exercise 11:1

1 Copy these shapes on to squared paper.
Enlarge each shape using a scale factor of 2.

a   **b**   **c**

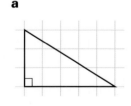
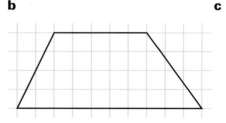
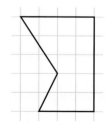

2 Enlarge the shapes in question **1** using a scale factor of 3.

If you have a centre of enlargement, you multiply distances from the centre of enlargement by the scale factor.

Example   Enlarge triangle RST with scale factor 2 and centre X.

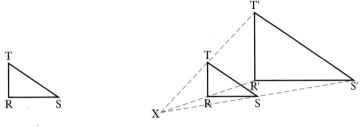

Draw lines from X through R, S and T.
Mark the point R' so that $XR' = 2 \times XR$
Mark the point S' so that $XS' = 2 \times XS$
Mark the point T' so that $XT' = 2 \times XT$
Draw triangle R'S'T'

3 Trace these shapes.
Use X as the centre of enlargement each time.
Enlarge each shape using a scale factor of 4.

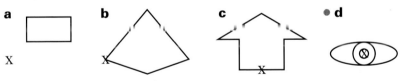

a   **b**   **c**   **• d**

The scale factor of an enlargement may be a fraction.
The diagram shows a parallelogram enlarged using a scale factor of $2\frac{1}{2}$

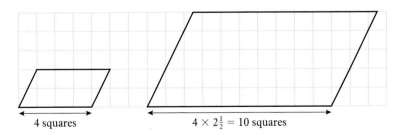

4 squares $4 \times 2\frac{1}{2} = 10$ squares

All the lengths are $2\frac{1}{2}$ times longer.

4 Enlarge each of the shapes in question **1** using a scale factor of $2\frac{1}{2}$.

5 Trace these shapes.

a Enlarge this shape using a scale factor of $1\frac{1}{2}$

● **b** Enlarge this shape using a scale factor of 1.6

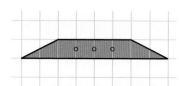

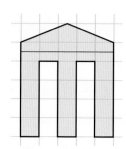

You can use enlargements to make shapes smaller.
These enlargements have a scale factor smaller than 1.
This diagram shows a rectangle enlarged using a scale factor of $\frac{1}{2}$

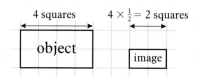

4 squares $4 \times \frac{1}{2} = 2$ squares

object lengths $\times \frac{1}{2} =$ image lengths

Exercise 11:2

1 For each pair of shapes write down the scale factor for the enlargement
from (1) P into Q   (2) Q into P.
Make any measurements that you need to do this.

a

c

b

d

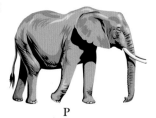

2 Copy these shapes on to squared paper.
Enlarge each shape using a scale factor of   (1) $\frac{1}{2}$ (2) $\frac{1}{4}$

a

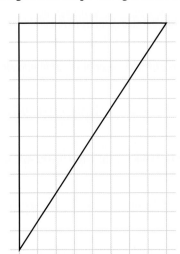

b

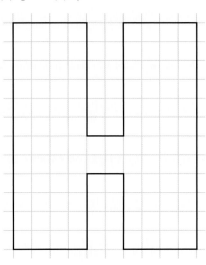

3 Trace these shapes. Use C as the centre of enlargement each time.
Enlarge each shape using a scale factor of $\frac{1}{3}$.

a

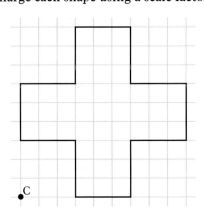

b

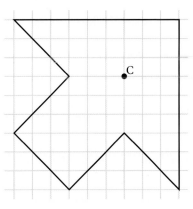

4 Trace these shapes. Use X as the centre of enlargement each time.
Enlarge each shape using a scale factor of   (1) $\frac{1}{5}$ (2) $\frac{2}{5}$

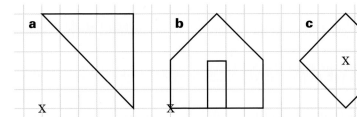

Enlargements with co-ordinates

If you have a centre of enlargement **at the origin** then:
co-ordinates of object × scale factor = co-ordinates of image

Example   Find the image of P (3, 6) after an enlargement with these scale factors, centre the origin: **a** 2   **b** $2\frac{1}{2}$ **c** $\frac{1}{3}$

   a   The image of P (3, 6) is (3 × 2, 6 × 2)   = (6, 12)
   b   The image of P (3, 6) is (3 × $2\frac{1}{2}$, 6 × $2\frac{1}{2}$) = ($7\frac{1}{2}$, 15)
   c   The image of P (3, 6) is (3 × $\frac{1}{3}$, 6 × $\frac{1}{3}$)   = (1, 2)

When you enlarge a shape, you always join up the vertices of the image.

Exercise 11:3

1   Find the image of these points using an enlargement with scale factor 2, centre the origin.

  a (1, 2)   **c** (3, 8)   **e** ($2\frac{1}{2}$, 4)   **g** (−1, 4)
  b (2, 2)   **d** (0, 6)   **f** (0, 0)   **h** (−2, −5)

2   Find the image of these points using an enlargement with scale factor $\frac{1}{3}$, centre the origin.

  a (3, 3)   **c** (9, 12)   **e** ($1\frac{1}{2}$, $7\frac{1}{2}$)   **g** (−9, 15)
  b (6, 6)   **d** (0, 9)   **f** (0, 0)   **h** (−12, −3)

3   The points A, B, C have co-ordinates A (1, 1), B (2, 1) and C (1, 2).

  a   Copy these axes.
     Plot the points A, B and C.
     Join them up to get a triangle.
  b   Measure the lengths of AB, BC and AC.
  c   Find the new co-ordinates if the
     triangle is enlarged using a scale factor
     of 4, centre the origin.

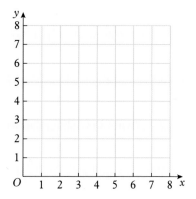

  d   Check these new co-ordinates are
     correct by drawing the enlargement.
     Show your construction lines.
     Label the image A' B' C'.
  e   Measure the lengths of A'B', B'C' and A'C'.
     How do these lengths show if your
     enlargement is correct?
  f   Measure all the angles on the object.
  g   Measure all the angles on the image.
  h   Write down what you notice about angles in corresponding positions
     on the object and the image.

4 The points Q, R, S, T have co-ordinates:
Q (4, 4), R (4, 8), S (12, 8) and T (12, 4).

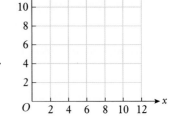

a Copy these axes. Plot the points Q, R, S and T.
Join them up to get a rectangle.

b Measure the lengths of QR and RS.

c Find the new co-ordinates if the rectangle is
enlarged using a scale factor of $\frac{1}{4}$, centre the origin.

d Check these new co-ordinates are correct by
drawing the enlargement.
Show your construction lines.
Label the image Q'R'S'T'.

e Measure the lengths of Q'R', R'S', S'T' and T'Q'.
How do these lengths show if your enlargement is correct?

f Measure all the angles on the object.

g Measure all the angles on the image.

h Write down what you notice about these angles.

Similar

Two diagrams are **similar,** if one is an enlargement of the other.
They have the same shape but different sizes.

If an object and its image are the same shape, all their angles in
corresponding positions will be equal.
You can use the scale factor to find missing lengths.

Flags A and B are similar. Find the missing lengths.

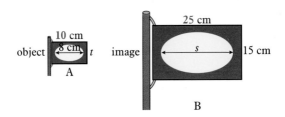

Now use common sense. Flag B is bigger than flag A so the scale
factor going from left to right is **more than 1.**

So from flag A to flag B,　the scale factor $= \dfrac{25}{10} = 2.5$

So the length s is $8 \times 2.5 = 20$ cm

Flag A is smaller than flag B,
so the scale factor going from right to left is **less than 1.**

So from flag B to flag A,　the scale factor $= \dfrac{10}{25} = 0.4$

So the width t is $15 \times 0.4 = 6$ cm

Exercise 11:4

Each question in this exercise has a pair of similar shapes.
a Write down the corresponding lengths on the object and image.
   These lengths are shown in red in questions **1** and **2**.
b Use these lengths in each part to work out the scale factor.
c Use the scale factor to find the sides marked with letters.

1

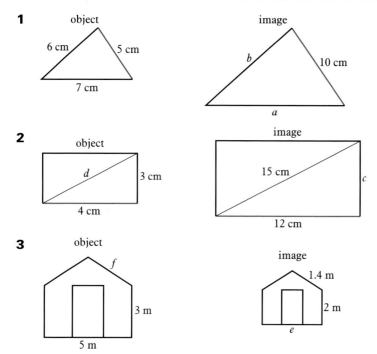

2

3

4 The picture shows a section from a bridge with a model alongside.

5

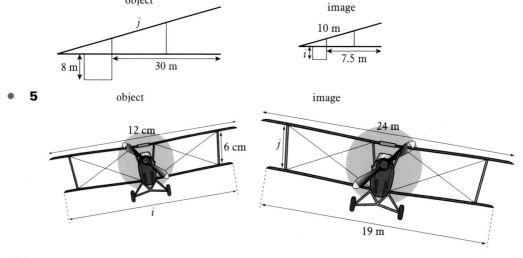

Exercise 11:5

1 **a** Copy this shape onto squared paper.
   b Work out the perimeter of the shape.
   c Enlarge the shape using a scale factor 2. Use C as the centre of enlargement.
   d Work out the perimeter of the new shape.
   e Write down what has happened to the perimeter of the shape when it has been enlarged

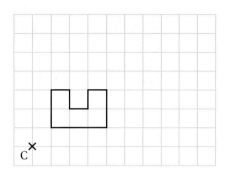

2 **a** Copy this shape onto squared paper.
   b Work out the perimeter of the shape.
   c Enlarge the shape using a scale factor 0.5 Use C as the centre of enlargement.
   d Work out the perimeter of the new shape.
   e Write down what has happened to the perimeter of the shape when it has been enlarged.

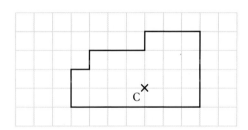

If a shape is enlarged by a scale factor n then the perimeter will also be enlarged by a factor of n.

---

3 A shape has a perimeter of 12 cm.
   The shape is enlarged by a scale factor of 4.5
   Write down the perimeter of the new shape.

4 A shape is enlarged by a scale factor of 2.5
   The perimeter of the enlarged shape is 46.25 cm.
   What is the perimeter of the original shape?

If the centre of enlargement of an object is not at the origin then the easiest way to find the co-ordinates of the image is by drawing.

Exercise 11:6

1 **a** Copy the diagram.

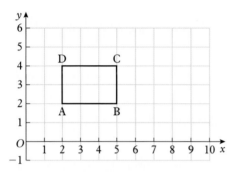

    b Find the new co-ordinates by drawing if the shape is enlarged using a scale factor of 2, centre (1, 3).
    c Show your construction lines.
    d Label your image $A_1B_1C_1D_1$.
    e Is the image similar to the object? Write down your reasons.

2 The points V, W, X, Y, Z have co-ordinates:
V (3, 1), W (5, 1), X (6, 3), Y (4, 4) and Z (2, 3).
    a Copy these axes. Plot the points.
       Join them up to get a pentagon.
    b Find the new co-ordinates by drawing
       if the pentagon is enlarged using a
       scale factor of 3, centre (1, 2).
    c Show your construction lines.
    d Label your image $V_1W_1X_1Y_1Z_1$.
    e Is the image similar to the object?
       Write down your reasons.

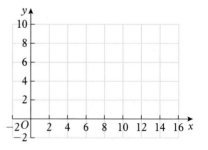

3 **a** Repeat question **2a**. Use another copy of the same set of axes.
    b Find the new co-ordinates by drawing if the pentagon is enlarged
       using a scale factor of $1\frac{1}{2}$, centre (4, 2).
    c Show your construction lines.
    d Label your image $V_2W_2X_2Y_2Z_2$.
    e Is the image similar to the object? Write down your reasons.

Finding the centre of enlargement

To find the centre of enlargement:
(1) Join points on the image to their corresponding points on the object.
(2) Extend all the lines so that they meet at the centre.

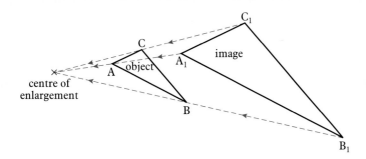

4 Trace these shapes.
Find the centre of enlargement. Show your construction lines.

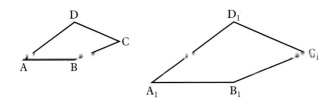

5 Copy the diagrams on to squared paper.
Find the centres of enlargement. Show your construction lines.

a

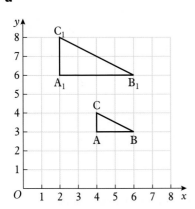

b

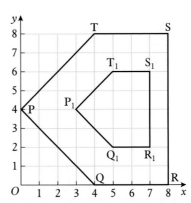

Inverse of an enlargement	The **inverse of an enlargement** with scale factor k is an enlargement with scale factor $\frac{1}{k}$.

To find the inverse of an enlargement:
(1) Write the scale factor as a fraction.
(2) Turn the fraction upside down.
The centre of enlargement does not change.

You can write scale factor 2 as scale factor $\frac{2}{1}$.
So the inverse of an enlargement with scale factor 2 is an enlargement with scale factor $\frac{1}{2}$

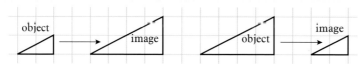

This is an enlargement scale factor 2   This is an enlargement scale factor $\frac{1}{2}$

So you get back to the shape you started with by using the inverse.

Example

An enlargement has scale factor **a** 4   **b** $\frac{1}{3}$
Find the scale factor of the inverse for each one.

a 4 is $\frac{4}{1}$, so turn it upside down to get $\frac{1}{4}$
The scale factor of the inverse is $\frac{1}{4}$
b Turn $\frac{1}{3}$ upside down to get $\frac{3}{1}$
The scale factor of the inverse is 3

---

6 These numbers are the scale factors of enlargements.
Write down the scale factor of the inverse of each one.

  a 2   **c** 5   **e** $\frac{1}{4}$ ● **g** 1.6
  b 3   **d** $\frac{1}{2}$ **f** $2\frac{1}{2}$ ● **h** $\frac{a}{b}$

7 **a** Find the scale factor of the enlargement
       from A to B.
    b Write down the scale factor of the inverse.

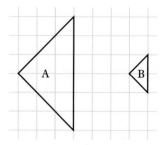

● **8** Find the scale factors for the inverses of each part of question **5**.

2   Scale drawing

This is a photo of the model village at Torquay.

The model village is an exact copy of the real village but it is much smaller!

The scale of the model is 1 to 12.

Models, scale drawings, plans and maps are all exact copies of something drawn to a smaller scale.
Maps can be used to find distances. Plans can be used to find lengths of rooms in a building or to plan the layout of houses or whole housing estates.

| Scale | A **scale** tells you what the length on a map or plan represents in real life. |

The scale on a house plan could be 1 cm = 1 m.
The scale on a road map could be 1 inch = 1 mile.

Exercise 11:7

1   Read through this list of plans and the list of scales.
Match up the plan with the correct scale.
Write down the correct pairs.

Plan	Scale
Plan of a bedroom	1 cm = 10 m
Plan of a housing estate	2 cm = 1 mile
Walkers' map showing footpaths	1 cm = 100 miles
Road atlas	1 cm = 1 m
Plans for a house	1 cm = 5 m
Map of Europe	5 cm = 1 km

This map of a theme park is drawn to scale.
The scale is 1 cm = 100 m.

Example

How far is it from the Rollercoaster to the Log Flume?

On the map the distance is 6 cm.
The scale is 1 cm = 100 m.
So in the park it is 6 × 100 m = 600 m.

---

2 **a** How far is it on the map from the Rollercoaster to the Runaway Train?
   b How far is it in the park from the Rollercoaster to the Runaway Train?
   c How far is it on the map from the Rapids to the Café?
   d How far is it in the park?
   e How far is it in the park from the Café to the Ghost Train?
   f William has a day out at the theme park.
      He walks from the entrance to the Log Flume and then to the
      Runaway Train. He then walks to the Rollercoaster.
      How far has William walked altogether?

3 Mark's bedroom is a rectangle 6.5 m long and 4.5 m wide.
   a Draw a scale plan of Mark's bedroom. Use a scale of 1 cm = 1 m.
      Mark has a wardrobe which is 2.5 m long and 1 m wide.
      He also has a desk which is 1.2 m long and 0.8 m wide.
   b Mark these in on your diagram. It does not matter where you put
      them.

4 This is part of a Derby street map.
The scale is 4 inches = 1 mile.

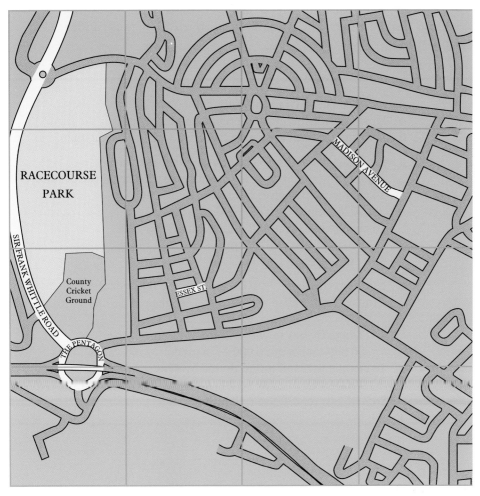

   a What distance does 2 inches on the map represent?
   b What distance does 1 inch represent?
   c About how long is Racecourse Park on the map?
   d About how long is the real Racecourse Park?
   e How long is Madison Avenue on the map?
   f How long is the real Madison Avenue?
   g How long is the real Essex Street?
   h What is the diameter of the Pentagon roundabout?
   i Estimate the length of Sir Frank Whittle Road.
   j The width of this section of map is about 5 inches.
      What length does this represent?
   k The map shown is a square.
      What area of Derby is shown on the map?

You can write a map scale as a ratio.
You do not put any units in when you do this.
The ratio tells you what 1 unit on the map represents in the real world.
A scale of 1 : 1000 means that 1 unit on the map is 1000 of those units in the real world.

Example

A road map is drawn to the scale 1 : 30 000
a   How many kilometres are represented by 3 cm on the map?
b   How many miles are represented by 3 inches on the map?

a   1 unit on the map = 30 000 units in the real world.
3 cm on the map = 3 × 30 000 cm = 90 000 cm on the ground.
To change centimetres to metres, divide by 100:
90 000 cm = 90 000 ÷ 100 m = 900 m
To change metres to kilometres, divide by 1000:
900 m = 900 ÷ 1000 km = 0.9 km
So 3 cm represents 0.9 km.

b   1 unit on the map = 30 000 units in the real world.
3 inches on the map = 3 × 30 000 inches
= 90 000 inches
To change inches to yards, divide by 36:
90 000 inches = 90 000 ÷ 36 yards = 2500 yards
To change yards to miles, divide by 1760:
2500 yards = 2500 ÷ 1760 miles = 1.42 miles (2 dp)
So 3 inches represents 1.42 miles.

Exercise 11:8

1   A map is drawn to the scale 1 : 30 000.
a   How many kilometres are represented by 1 cm on the map?
b   How many kilometres are represented by 5 cm on the map?

2   A map is drawn to the scale 1 : 20 000.
a   How many kilometres are represented by 1 cm on the map?
b   How many kilometres are represented by 3 cm on the map?

3   Canfield School has a rectangular playing field.
The field measures 800 m by 700 m.
The Deputy Head draws a plan of the field. He uses a scale of 1 : 25 000.
What size should the field be on the plan?

4 The scale of this map is 1 : 316 800

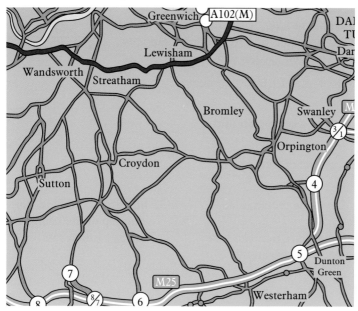

a What distance does 1 inch on the map represent?
b About how far is it between junctions 5 and 6 on the M25?
c About how far is it from Lewisham to Swanley along the A20?

5 The scale of this map is 1 inch = 250 yards.

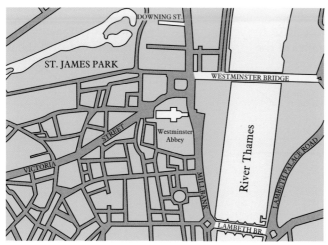

a Convert 250 yards into inches.
b Write the scale of the map as a ratio.
c About how far is it down the river from Westminster Bridge to Lambeth Bridge?
d About how far is it from Downing Street to Westminster Abbey?

There are other types of scale drawing.
Lots of people draw plans so that they can see what
the real thing will look like.
Lizzy is a garden designer. She runs a busy company.
She draws a plan of each garden before she plants it.

Here is a sketch of one of Lizzy's gardens.

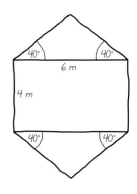

Lizzy wants to draw a scale plan of the
garden.

She decides on a scale of 1 cm = 1 m.

(1) First she draws the rectangular
    section.
    She uses a set square to make sure
    that the corners are exactly 90°.

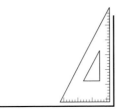

(3) She draws one line from each side.
    The top of the triangle is where
    the two lines cross.

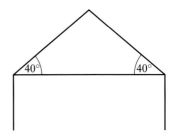

(2) Lizzy uses a protractor to
    measure the angles of the
    triangle.

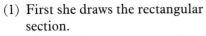
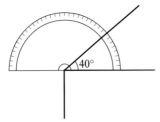

(4) She does the same for the other
    triangle to finish the plan.

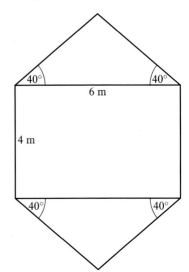

Exercise 11:9

1 Make a copy of Lizzy's plan.
Use a scale of 1 cm = 1 m.

2 Here is a sketch of another garden that Lizzy is designing.

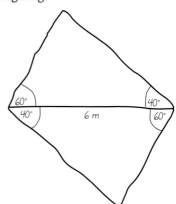

   a Draw the centre line.
      Use a scale of 1 cm = 1 m.

   b Draw the top triangle.
      Use a protractor to measure the angles.

   c Turn your diagram upside down.
      Draw the other triangle to finish the plan.

3 This is a sketch of a school playing field.
   a Make a scale drawing of the field.
      Use a scale of 1 cm = 5 m.
   b Measure the sides of your drawing in centimetres.
   c What is the perimeter of your drawing?
   d What is the perimeter of the real field?

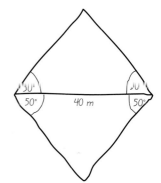

4 Lee is building a bird table with a nesting box on top.
Here is the sketch that he has made for it.

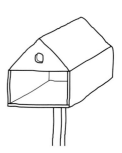

The end pieces look like this.
Make a scale drawing of the end piece.
Use a scale of 1 cm = 5 cm.

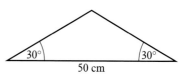

You can also draw triangles using compasses and a ruler.
To do this you need to know the lengths of all three sides.

Example   Draw a triangle with sides 8 cm, 6 cm and 4 cm.

(1) Draw the 8 cm side with a ruler.
Leave space above it for the other sides.

8 cm

(2) Set your compasses to 6 cm.
Draw an arc from one end of your line.

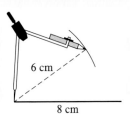

(3) Set your compasses to 4 cm.
Draw an arc from the other end of
your line.
The two arcs should cross.
This is the third corner of the triangle.

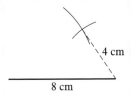

(4) Join the ends of your line to the
crossing point.

(5) Do not rub out your construction lines.
In an exam, these show your method.

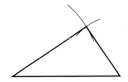

Exercise 11:10

1   Use compasses to draw a triangle with sides 8 cm, 5 cm and 6 cm.

2   Draw an equilateral triangle with sides of 6 cm.

3   Construct each of these shapes.

a

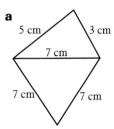

5 cm   3 cm
7 cm
7 cm   7 cm

b

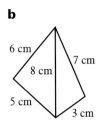

6 cm   7 cm
8 cm
5 cm
3 cm

c

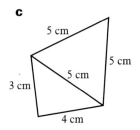

5 cm
5 cm
3 cm   5 cm
4 cm

288

1 **a** Copy these shapes on to squared paper.
    b Enlarge each shape using a scale factor of 3.

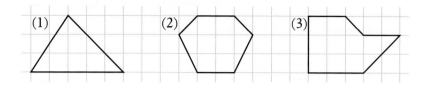

2 **a** Trace these shapes.
        Use the red dot as the centre of enlargement each time.
    b Enlarge each shape using a scale factor of $\frac{1}{2}$.

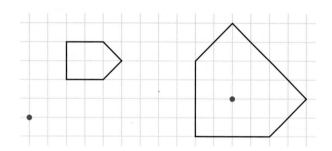

3 ABCD is a kite.
    a Copy the diagram. Write down the
        co-ordinates of A, B, C and D.
    b Measure the lengths of AC and BD.
    c Find the new co-ordinates if the kite is
        enlarged by scale factor 3, centre (0, 0).
    d Check these new co-ordinates are
        correct by drawing the enlargement.
        Show your construction lines.
        Label the image $A_1B_1C_1D_1$.
    e Measure the lengths of A_1C_1 and B_1D_1.
        How do these lengths show if your
        enlargement is correct?
    f Draw the new shape if $A_1B_1C_1D_1$ is
        enlarged by scale factor $\frac{1}{3}$, centre (0, 9).
        Label the image $A_2B_2C_2D_2$.
    g Write down the scale factor of the
        inverse of the last enlargement.
    h Is $A_1B_1C_1D_1$ similar to $A_2B_2C_2D_2$?
        Write down your reasons.

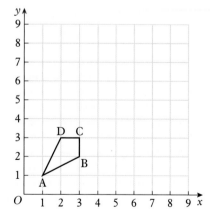

4 Sophie's bedroom is a rectangle 5.3 m long and 5.2 m wide.
  a Draw a scale plan of Sophie's bedroom. Use a scale of 1 cm = 1 m.
  b Sophie has a dressing table which is 1.8 m long and 1 m wide.
  She also has a computer desk which is 1.4 m long and 1.1 m wide.
  Mark these in on your diagram. It does not matter where you put them.

5 A map is drawn to the scale 1 : 25 000.
  a How many kilometres are represented by 1 cm on the map?
  b How many kilometres are represented by 4 cm on the map?

6 A map is drawn to the scale 1 : 30 000.
  a How many miles are represented by 1 inch on the map?
  b How many miles are represented by 6 inches on the map?
  Round your answers to 2 dp when necessary.

7 This is a sketch of a park.
  a Make a scale drawing of the park.
  Use a scale of 1 cm = 5 m.
  b What is the perimeter of the real park?

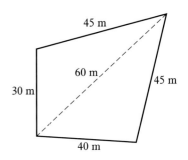

45 m

60 m

45 m

30 m

40 m

8 This is the sketch of part of a net of a square based pyramid.
Draw an accurate net for this pyramid.

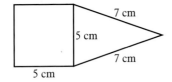

7 cm

5 cm

7 cm

5 cm

9 A model steam train is built to a scale
of 1 : 150.
  a The height of the funnel on the model
  is 0.5 cm.
  What is the height of the real funnel?
  b The length of the real train is 12 m.
  What is the length of the model train?

1 A map is drawn to a scale of 1 : 25 000.
  a Find the length represented by 1 cm on the map.
  b Find the area represented by 1 cm^2 on the map.

2 The diagram shows a sketch of a map. It is not to scale.
  When the map is drawn to scale, the distance between A and B is 28 cm.
  Work out the scale of the map.
  Give your answer in the form 1 : n where n is an integer.

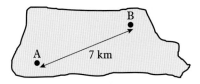

3 Howard wants to work out how far away a tower is on the other side of the river.
  He measures a distance of 100 m along the side of the river.
  He then measures the angles from the ends of his lines to the base of the tower.

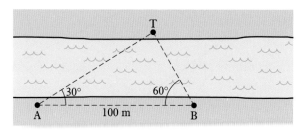

  a Draw an accurate scale plan of this situation.
  b Find the shortest distance from the tower to the bank of the river where Howard is standing.

4 An alien spaceship is able to shrink when under attack. When it shrinks all its angles stay the same. These are plan views of the ship before and after attack.

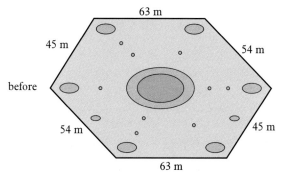

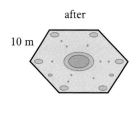

  a Work out the scale factor of the enlargement.
  b Find the lengths of the missing sides.

1 Copy these shapes onto squared paper. Enlarge each shape with the scale factor given. Use C as the centre of enlargement.

a   **b**

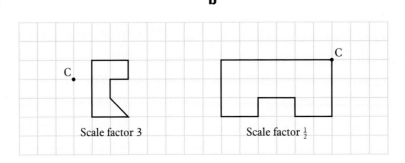

Scale factor 3   Scale factor $\frac{1}{2}$

2 These two shapes are similar.
Find the missing lengths marked with letters.

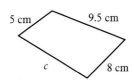

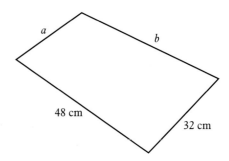

3 A triangle has a perimeter of 8.5 cm. The triangle is enlarged by a scale factor of 5. Write down the perimeter of the new triangle.

4 A map is drawn to the scale 1 : 30 000.
   a How many kilometres are represented by 1 cm on the map?
   b How many kilometres are represented by 7 cm on the map?

5 Construct these triangles.

a   **b**

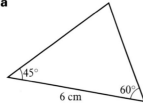

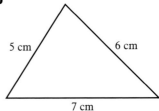

292

12 Power rules

CORE

No Steven, it does NOT stand for boring old division, multiplication, addition and subtraction.

BODMAS

QUESTIONS

EXTENSION

TEST YOURSELF

1 Properties of numbers

You can find many patterns of numbers in Pascal's triangle. The triangle numbers are highlighted.

The sums of pairs of the triangle numbers are square numbers.
$1 + 3 = 4$, $3 + 6 = 9$, $6 + 10 = 16$ ...
The first square number is 1.

You can use the x^2 key on the calculator to work out square numbers.

Example Work out 45^2

Key in:

Answer: 2025

Exercise 12:1

1 Use x^2 to work out:
   a 15^2 **b** 21^2 **c** 33^2 **d** 47^2

2 Use x^2 to work out:
   a 20^2 **b** 30^2 **c** 60^2 **d** 80^2
Without using your calculator, write down the answers to:
   e 40^2 **f** 50^2 **g** 70^2 **h** 90^2

3 Use x^2 to work out:
   a 0.2^2 **b** 0.3^2 **c** 0.4^2 **d** 0.5^2
Without using your calculator, write down the answers to:
   e 0.6^2 **f** 0.7^2 **g** 0.8^2 **h** 0.9^2

4 Find the area of these squares:

a
19 cm

b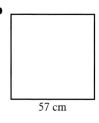
57 cm

c
3.5 cm

d
12.6 cm

Example

The area of this square is 36 cm².
What is the length of a side?

36 cm²

You know that $6 \times 6 = 36$
So the length of the side is 6 cm.

---

5 Write down the length of a side of a square with area:

   a 16 cm²   b 64 cm²   c 100 cm²   d 81 cm²

Square root

There is a $\sqrt{\ }$ key on the calculator.
This is called the **square root** key.
This key will undo what the x^2 key does.
It will find the length of a side of a square for you.

Example

A square has an area of 30 cm².
Find the length of a side correct to 1 dp.

The length of the side is $\sqrt{30}$.

Key in: $\sqrt{\ }$ **3** **0** **=**

Answer: 5.5 cm to 1 dp.

6 Work out:

    a $\sqrt{48}$ **b** $\sqrt{55}$ **c** $\sqrt{90}$ **d** $\sqrt{172}$

    Give your answers to 1 dp.

7 Write down the length of a side of a square whose area is:

    a 40 cm^2 **b** 82 cm^2 **c** 492 cm^2 **d** 200 cm^2

    Give your answers to 1 dp.

8 Find the square root of:

    a 85   **b** 381   **c** 0.08   **d** 0.008 64

    Give your answers to 1 dp.

There is a $\boxed{x^y}$ or $\boxed{y^x}$ key on your calculator. This is called the power key.

You can use it to work out cube numbers.

Example   Work out   **a** 6^3 **b** the cube of 2.5

a To find the value of 6^3 press these keys:

Remember $6^3 = 6 \times 6 \times 6$

Answer = 216

b To find the cube of 2.5 press these keys:

Answer = 15.625

Exercise 12:2

1 Use the power key to work out:

    a 7^3 **b** 2^3 **c** 5^3 **d** 9.2^3

2 Find the cube of:

    a 11   **b** 5.6   **c** 1.1   **d** 0.2

3 Find the volume of these cubes:

a
3 cm

b
8 cm

c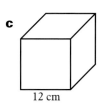
12 cm

d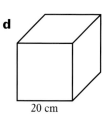
20 cm

There is a $\sqrt{}$ key on the calculator.
This is called the **root** key.
This key will undo what the x^y or y^y key does.
You can use it to find the length of a side of a cube.

Example

A cube has volume 40 cm³.
Find the length of a side of
the cube to 1 dp.

The length of a side is the cube root of 40.
This is written $\sqrt[3]{40}$.

40 cm³

Key in: **3** **4** **0**

Answer 3.4 cm to 1 dp.

---

4 Use the root key to work out:
   a $\sqrt[3]{27}$ **b** $\sqrt[3]{343}$ **c** $\sqrt[3]{1728}$ **d** $\sqrt[3]{0.027}$

5 Find the cube root of:
   a 3.375   **b** 10.648   **c** 2744   **d** 27 000

6 Find the length of a side of a cube with volume:
   a 512 cm³   **b** 2197 cm³   **c** 12 167 cm³   **d** 91.125 cm³

You sometimes have to multiply a number by itself lots of times.

$$3 \times 3 \times 3 \times 3 \times 3 \times 3$$

There are six 3s multiplied together.
A quick way of writing this is 3^6.

The small number ^{6} is called a power.

$$3^6 = 3 \times 3 \times 3 \times 3 \times 3 \times 3$$

Power

In 3^6 the **power** 6 tells you how many threes are multiplied together.

Examples

1 Write $5 \times 5 \times 5 \times 5$ using a power.
2 Find the value of 3^6.

1 $5 \times 5 \times 5 \times 5 = 5^4$

2 Key in:

$3^6 = 729$

---

7 Write these using powers:
a $6 \times 6 \times 6$
b $7 \times 7 \times 7 \times 7 \times 7$
c $2 \times 2 \times 2 \times 2$
d $1 \times 1 \times 1 \times 1 \times 1 \times 1 \times 1$

8 Write down the value of these.
Do not use a calculator.
a 2^5
b 3^4
c 1^5
d 10^6

9 Use your calculator to find the value of:
a 4^3
b 6^5
c 9^3
d 2^8
e 7^5
f 11^4
g 1^4
h 1^{12}

2 Indices

You are given a pair of baby rabbits for Christmas. They start having baby rabbits themselves in two months. They have a pair of babies every month. Every pair of babies also starts having babies when they are two months old and so on. How many pairs of rabbits will you have by next Christmas?

This puzzle comes from a book written by Fibonacci in 1202.
The answers to various stages of the puzzle give the Fibonacci numbers.

You have already used powers.
2^4 means there are 4 twos multiplied together.
So $2^4 = 2 \times 2 \times 2 \times 2 = 16$

Base

In x^n the number x is called the **base**.
In 2^4 the base is 2.

Index

In x^n the number n is called the **index** or power.
In 2^4 the index is 4.
The plural of index is **indices**.

Exercise 12:3

1 Copy this table.
a Fill in the missing numbers.

2^4	2^3	2^2	2^1
16	...	...	...

b Write down the pattern for the numbers in the second row.

c Add an extra column to your table, like this.

2^4	2^3	2^2	2^1	2^0
...	...	...	...	...

d Use the pattern of numbers in the second row to fill in the value for 2^0.

2 Copy these. Fill in the spaces.

a

3^4	3^3	3^2	3^1	3^0
...	...	...	...	...

b

4^4	4^3	4^2	4^1	4^0
...	...	...	...	...

Index of 0   Any number with an **index of 0** is equal to 1.
x^0 always equals 1 no matter what the value of x is.

You can extend your table further.
In question **1** the numbers in the
bottom line were divided by 2
each time.

2^4	2^3	2^2	2^1	2^0	2^{-1}
16	8	4	2	1	$\frac{1}{2}$

$1 \div 2 = \dfrac{1}{2}$ So $2^{-1} = \dfrac{1}{2}$

You can write this rule using letters: $x^{-1} = \dfrac{1}{x}$

Example   Find the values of   **a** 12^0 **b** 7^{-1} **c** 9^{-1}

   a $12^0 = 1$ Any number to the power 0 is equal to 1.
   b $7^{-1} = \frac{1}{7}$
   c $9^{-1} = \frac{1}{9}$

---

3 Write down the values of:
   a 11^{-1} **c** 14^{-1} **e** 27^{-1} **g** 20^{-1}
   b 8^0 **d** 4^{-1} **f** 15^0 **h** 10^0

Reciprocal $x^{-1} = \dfrac{1}{x}$ $\dfrac{1}{x}$ is called the **reciprocal** of x.

Example   Write down the reciprocal of   **a** 6   **b** $\frac{3}{5}$ **c** $2\frac{1}{2}$

     a $\frac{1}{6}$ **b** $\frac{5}{3}$ **c** $2\frac{1}{2} = \frac{5}{2}$ so the reciprocal is $\frac{2}{5}$

---

4 Write down the reciprocal of:
   a 8   **b** 2   **c** 11   **d** 100   **e** 20

5 Write down the reciprocal of:
   a $\frac{1}{5}$ **b** $\frac{1}{2}$ **c** $\frac{3}{4}$ **d** $\frac{3}{5}$ **e** $\frac{7}{8}$

6 Write down the reciprocal of:

a $3\frac{1}{2}$ **b** $5\frac{1}{2}$ **c** $1\frac{1}{4}$ **d** $5\frac{1}{4}$ **e** $2\frac{3}{4}$

7 Write down the value of:

a 6^{-1} **b** 24^{-1} **c** $\left(\frac{1}{5}\right)^{-1}$ **d** $\left(\frac{4}{9}\right)^{-1}$ **e** $\left(2\frac{1}{4}\right)^{-1}$

8 (1) Find the reciprocal of each of these numbers.
(2) Multiply each number by its reciprocal.

a 8   **b** 3   **c** $\frac{1}{2}$ **d** $\frac{2}{3}$ ● **e** $1\frac{1}{4}$

Multiplying numbers with powers

You have already simplified expressions like $3^2 \times 3^4$
$3^2 \times 3^4 = 3 \times 3 \quad \times \quad 3 \times 3 \times 3 \times 3 \quad = 3^6$
The indices are added together like this: $3^{2+4} = 3^6$
This can only be done when the base numbers are the same.
You cannot simplify $3^2 \times 5^4$ because the base numbers 3 and 5 are not the same.

You can write the rule using letters: $\quad x^m \times x^n = x^{m+n}$

Example

Simplify these:
a $x^4 \times x^7$ **b** $2a^3 \times a^5$ **c** $3d^2 \times 5d^4$ **d** $4x^3 \times 5y^2$

a x^{11} You add the indices 4 and 7 to give 11.
b $2a^8$ You add the indices 3 and 5 to give 8.
c $15d^6$ You multiply the numbers $3 \times 5 = 15$.
           You add the indices 2 and 4 to give 6.
d $20x^3y^2$ $4 \times 5 = 20$ You cannot simplify the x^3 and y^2
             because they have different bases.

Exercise 12:4

1 Simplify:

a $a^5 \times a^6$ **c** $d^3 \times d^6$ **e** $c^5 \times c$ **g** $b^3 \times b^5$
b $b^4 \times b^2$ **d** $g^4 \times h^5$ **f** $x^2 \times x^7$ **h** $h^4 \times h$

2 Simplify:

a $4a^3 \times a^2$ **c** $3d^4 \times d^9$ **e** $b^3 \times 7a^5$ **g** $h^3 \times 4h^4$
b $7b^6 \times b^2$ **d** $c^4 \times 5d^2$ **f** $6x^2 \times x$ **h** $r^8 \times 9r$

3 Simplify:

a $4a^5 \times 2a^3$ **c** $3d^4 \times 8d^5$ **e** $10c^4 \times 5c^3$ **g** $2p^3 \times 4q^4$
b $7b^2 \times 2b^2$ **d** $2m^3 \times 7m^5$ **f** $6x^7 \times 2x^3$ **h** $5h^4 \times 9k$

● **4** **a** Copy this. Fill it in.

$(3x^4)^2 = \ldots \times \ldots = \ldots$

b Simplify:

(1) $(2x^3)^2$ (3) $(6a^5)^2$ (5) $(5c^4)^2$ ● (7) $(3a^2b)^2$
(2) $(5x^2)^3$ (4) $(3y^6)^3$ (6) $(2y^4)^5$ ● (8) $(4x^3y^4)^3$

Dividing numbers with powers

You can simplify $2^5 \div 2^3$ by cancelling pairs of 2s.

$$\frac{2^5}{2^3} = \frac{2 \times 2 \times \cancel{2} \times \cancel{2} \times \cancel{2}}{\cancel{2} \times \cancel{2} \times \cancel{2}} = 2^2$$

The indices are subtracted like this: $2^5 \div 2^3 = 2^{5-3} = 2^2$

You can write the rule using letters: $x^m \div x^n = x^{m-n}$

Example   Simplify   **a** $5^6 \div 5^4$ **b** $4^5 \div 4^5$ **c** $y^8 \div y^5$

a $5^{6-4} = 5^2$ **b** $4^{5-5} = 4^0 = 1$ **c** $y^{8-5} = y^3$

If the question has more than one letter then you deal with each letter in turn.

Example   Simplify   **a** $d^6e^5 \div de^3$ **b** $8a^2b^6c \div 16ab^2c$

a $d^{6-1}e^{5-3} = d^5e^2$

b $\dfrac{8a^{2-1}b^{6-2}c^{1-1}}{16} = \dfrac{ab^4c^0}{2} = \dfrac{ab^4}{2}$ since $c^0 = 1$

Exercise 12:5

1 Simplify:

a $2^7 \div 2^3$ **b** $7^8 \div 7^5$ **c** $3^{11} \div 3^9$ **d** $8^4 \div 8^4$

2 Simplify:

a $y^8 \div y^6$ **b** $w^5 \div w^4$ **c** $p^4 \div p^2$ **d** $m^7 \div m^7$

3 Simplify:

a $10x^4 \div 5x^3$ **d** $7m^5 \div m^2$ **g** $p^6q^5 \div p^5q$ **j** $12p^5q^3 \div 2p^2q$
b $6w^6 \div 2w$ **e** $x^5y^4 \div x^2y$ **h** $r^5s^4t^2 \div r^2s^4t$ **k** $3a^3b^2 \div 6a^2b^2$
c $4m^7 \div 8m^3$ **f** $a^4b^4 \div ab^2$ **i** $6c^5d^3 \div 3c^2d$ **l** $4x^4y^7z^3 \div 12xy^3z^2$

You can sometimes end up with indices that are negative.

If you simplify $5^2 \div 5^5$ you have $\dfrac{\cancel{5} \times \cancel{5}}{5 \times 5 \times 5 \times \cancel{5} \times \cancel{5}} = \dfrac{1}{5 \times 5 \times 5} = \dfrac{1}{5^3}$

But $5^2 \div 5^5 = 5^{2-5} = 5^{-3}$ so $5^{-3} = \dfrac{1}{5^3}$

Similarly $6^{-2} = \dfrac{1}{6^2}$ and $8^{-4} = \dfrac{1}{8^4}$

You can write the rule using letters: $x^{-m} = \dfrac{1}{x^m}$

Exercise 12:6

1 Write these as fractions:
  a 2^{-3} **b** 8^{-5} **c** a^{-4} **d** y^{-2}

2 Write these using negative powers:
  a $\dfrac{1}{5^3}$ **b** $\dfrac{1}{4^6}$ **c** $\dfrac{1}{7^2}$ **d** $\dfrac{1}{9^4}$

3 Simplify:
  a $k^3 \div k^5$ **c** $s^2 \div s^3$ **e** $d^4e^2 \div de^5$ **g** $a^2b^4c^5 \div a^3b$
  b $y^4 \div y^7$ **d** $b \div b^3$ **f** $xy^2 \div xy^8$ **h** $pq^4 \div p^3q^4$

If you see negative indices in multiplication or division questions you still add or subtract the indices.

Example   Simplify   **a** $s^5t^{-2} \times s^{-1}t^{-4}$ **b** $a^{-3}b^5 \div a^6b^{-1}$

  a $s^{5+(-1)}t^{-2-4} = s^4t^{-6}$ **b** $a^{-3-6}b^{5+1} = a^{-9}b^6$ $\quad(--1 = +1)$

---

4 Simplify:
  a $f^{-3} \times f^7$ **e** $z^{-5} \div z^2$ **i** $6a^{-3}b^7 \div 5a^2b^{-5}$
  b $r^3s^{-4} \times r^{-2}s^4$ **f** $g^{-5} \div g^{-3}$ **j** $10x^{-3}yz^6 \div 5x^2y^3z^4$
  c $k^{-2}m^4 \times k^{-1}m^{-5}$ **g** $x^{-3}y^{-1} \div x^{-4}y^{-5}$ **k** $5r^3s^{-2}t \div 15r^3s^2t^{-4}$
  d $a^{-3}b^{-2} \times ab$ **h** $p^3q^{-4} \div p^{-3}q^{-4}$ **l** $15p^{-3}qr^4 \div 3p^{-4}q^{-1}r^{-4}$

Indices which are fractions

You have already met square roots.
$$\sqrt{2} \times \sqrt{2} = 2$$

If you write $\sqrt{2}$ as $2^?$ this means $2^? \times 2^? = 2^1$
You need $? + ? = 1$ so ? must equal $\frac{1}{2}$.
So $\sqrt{2}$ is the same as $2^{\frac{1}{2}}$

You can write the rule using letters:
$\sqrt{x}$ means the same as $x^{\frac{1}{2}}$.

Exercise 12:7

1 Write down the value of:

    a $49^{\frac{1}{2}}$ **b** $100^{\frac{1}{2}}$ **c** $256^{\frac{1}{2}}$ **d** $16^{\frac{1}{2}}$

● **2** 32 can be written as 2^5.
    This is in the form 2^p where $p = 5$
    Find the value of p in each of these:

    a $16 = 2^p$ **b** $25^p = 5$ **c** $20^p = 1$

$\sqrt[3]{2}$ means the cube root of 2.
So $\sqrt[3]{2} \times \sqrt[3]{2} \times \sqrt[3]{2} = 2$

If you write $\sqrt[3]{2}$ as $2^?$ this means $2^? \times 2^? \times 2^? = 2^1$.
You need $? + ? + ? = 1$ so ? must equal $\frac{1}{3}$.
So $\sqrt[3]{2}$ is the same as $2^{\frac{1}{3}}$.

You can write the rule using letters:
$\sqrt[3]{x}$ means the same as $x^{\frac{1}{3}}$.

---

3 Write down the value of:

    a $\sqrt[3]{8}$ **c** $\sqrt[3]{125}$ **e** $1000^{\frac{1}{3}}$ **g** $729^{\frac{1}{3}}$

    b $27^{\frac{1}{3}}$ **d** $216^{\frac{1}{3}}$ **f** $\sqrt[3]{64}$ **h** $1^{\frac{1}{3}}$

4 Find the values of f, g and h in these:

    a $2^f = \frac{1}{2}$ **b** $49^h = 7$ **c** $343^g = 7$

You can have two powers in the same expression.
For example $(x^2)^3$ or $(8^{\frac{1}{3}})^2$.

To work out the rule for this think about $(x^2)^3$.
The power 3 tells you to multiply three of the brackets together.
This means that $(x^2)^3 = (x^2) \times (x^2) \times (x^2)$
But each x^2 is made up of $x \times x$.
So $(x^2)^3 = (x \times x) \times (x \times x) \times (x \times x)$
This is 6 xs multiplied together so $(x^2)^3 = x^6$.

You will notice that $2 \times 3 = 6$
This shows that the rule is $(x^m)^n = x^{mn}$

Example   Simplify: **a** $(x^3)^4$ **b** $(p^2)^{\frac{1}{3}}$

a When you have one power raised to another power, you
multiply the powers.
This means that $(x^3)^4 = x^{3 \times 4} = x^{12}$.

b Again, multiply the powers. $2 \times \frac{1}{3} = \frac{2}{3}$
This means that $(p^2)^{\frac{1}{3}} = p^{\frac{2}{3}}$.

Exercise 12:8

1   Simplify

a $(x^2)^4$	**e** $(x^{-1})^5$	**i** $(y^{\frac{2}{3}})^{-1}$
b $(y^3)^5$	**f** $(t^2)^4$	**j** $(x^{\frac{2}{3}})^{\frac{1}{3}}$
c $(p^2)^{-3}$	**g** $(x^{\frac{1}{3}})^4$	● **k** $(x^{-2})^{-4}$
d $(z^2)^{0.5}$	**h** $(d^{\frac{2}{3}})^3$	● **l** $(x^{-2})^{-\frac{1}{2}}$

2   Work these out.

a $(3^2)^4$	**c** $(2^{-1})^5$	● **e** $(8^3)^{-1}$
b $(2^3)^5$	**d** $(1^2)^4$	● **f** $(8^2)^{-2}$

3   You can work out $8^{\frac{2}{3}}$ by thinking of it as $(8^{\frac{1}{3}})^2$

Work out $8^{\frac{2}{3}}$.

3 BODMAS

You need to know the rules of BODMAS to use your calculator properly.

Scientific calculators use the rules of BODMAS. Basic calculators do not.

Exercise 12:9

1 Do these questions without a calculator.
Work out the red parts first.
   a 3 × 4 + 5   **b** 3 × 4 + 5
   c Use your calculator to work out 3 × 4 + 5.
     Which of the two answers does your calculator get, **a** or **b**?

Your calculator worked out the multiplication first. This is part of the BODMAS rule.

BODMAS	First do	**Brackets**
	then powers	**Of**
	next do	**Division**
	and	**Multiplication**
	then	**Addition**
	and	**Subtraction**

Example   Work these out using the BODMAS rule.
    a 8 + 6 × 4   **b** 24 − 18 ÷ 6

    a 8 + 6 × 4   BOD**MA**S   Multiply comes before Add
       = 8 + 24
       = 32

    b 24 − 12 ÷ 6   BO**D**Ma**S**   Divide comes before Subtract
       = 24 − 2
       = 22

2 Work these out without using your calculator:

a $6 \times 4 + 3$ **c** $15 + 7 \times 3$ **e** $4.2 - 1.3 \times 2$

b $8 - 8 \div 2$ **d** $35 \div 5 - 4$ **f** $5.6 \div 4 - 2$

Brackets **always** come first. They overrule any other operation.

Example Work these out using the BODMAS rule:

a $(8 + 4) \times 3$ **b** $14 \div (8 - 6)$

a $(8 + 4) \times 3$ BODMAS   Brackets come before Multiply

   $= 12 \times 3$

   $= 36$

b $14 \div (8 - 6)$ BODMAS   Brackets come before Divide

   $= 14 \div 2$

   $= 7$

---

3 Work these out without using a calculator:

a $6 \times (4 + 3)$ **c** $(15 + 7) \times 3$ **e** $(5.7 - 3.2) \times 2$

b $(14 - 9) \div 2$ **d** $(100 - 10) \times 10$ • **f** $(18.7 - 5.7) \div 0.1$

Powers come before everything except brackets

Example Work these out using the BODMAS rule:

a $5 \times 6^2 - 7$ **b** $(9 + 3)^2$

a $5 \times 6^2 - 7$ BODMAS   power Of, then Multiply then Subtract

   $= 5 \times 36 - 7$

   $= 180 - 7$

   $= 173$

b $(9 + 3)^2$ BODMAS   Brackets then power Of

   $= 12^2$

   $= 144$

---

4 Work these out without using a calculator:

a $7^2 \times 5$ **d** $10^3 - 10^2 \div 5$ **g** $(5 - 1)^3$

b $8^2 - 24$ **e** $(3^2 - 2^2) \times 5$ **h** $(4^2 - 5)^2$

c $(3 + 5) - 2^3$ **f** $99 \div 3^2 - (3.6 + 2.8)$ **i** $15 + (5.3 - 2.3)^2$

5 Work these out using a calculator:

a $(2.56 - 1.06)^2$ **b** $(28 + 35)^3$ **c** $(7.68 \div 2.56)^4$

Some problems can be written without brackets.

A calculation like $(30 - 12.6) \div (4.2 + 1.6)$ can be written $\dfrac{30 - 12.6}{4.2 + 1.6}$

The brackets have gone.

If you use a calculator to work this out you **put the brackets back in**.

Keys to press:

$$\boxed{(}\ \boxed{3}\ \boxed{0}\ \boxed{-}\ \boxed{1}\ \boxed{2}\ \boxed{.}\ \boxed{6}\ \boxed{)}\ \boxed{\div}$$

$$\boxed{(}\ \boxed{4}\ \boxed{.}\ \boxed{2}\ \boxed{+}\ \boxed{1}\ \boxed{.}\ \boxed{6}\ \boxed{)}\ \boxed{=}$$

The answer is 3.

Example   Use your calculator to find the value of $\sqrt{56.9 + 153.35}$

Keys to press:

$$\boxed{\sqrt{}}\ \boxed{(}\ \boxed{5}\ \boxed{6}\ \boxed{.}\ \boxed{9}\ \boxed{+}\ \boxed{1}\ \boxed{5}\ \boxed{3}\ \boxed{.}\ \boxed{3}\ \boxed{5}\ \boxed{)}\ \boxed{=}$$

The answer is 14.5

Exercise 12:10

Work these out using a calculator:

1 **a** $\dfrac{2.84 + 9.61}{5}$ **b** $\dfrac{3.56 - 1.31}{0.82 - 0.67}$ **c** $\dfrac{4^3 + 21.5}{5.24 - 2.39}$

2 **a** $\sqrt{5^3 + 71}$ **b** $\sqrt{6 \times 9 - 5}$ **c** $\sqrt{4^3 + 5^2 - 8}$

3 Give the answers to these correct to 1 dp.

a $\dfrac{5.38 - 3.72}{1.73 + 0.96}$ **d** $5.38 - \dfrac{3.72}{1.73 + 0.96}$

b $\dfrac{5.38 - 3.72}{1.73} + 0.96$ **e** $2.97^3 - \dfrac{3.68}{\sqrt{0.08}} - 7.23$

c $5.38 - \dfrac{3.72}{1.73} + 0.96$ **f** $\dfrac{8.39^3 - 5.27^2}{3.97^2 - \sqrt{2.82}}$

1 Use your calculator to work these out:

a 23^2 **c** $\sqrt{1225}$ **e** 7^3 **g** $\sqrt[3]{5832}$

b 75^2 **d** $\sqrt{2.25}$ **f** 11^3 **h** $\sqrt[3]{0.001}$

2 s km/h is the maximum speed at which a train can travel around a circular arc of track. r is the radius of the track in metres. You can use the formula

$s = \dfrac{7}{2}\sqrt{r}$ to work out s.

Find the maximum speed on a circular track of radius:

a 676 m   **b** 961 m   **c** 2916 m

3 Write these using powers:

a $3 \times 3 \times 3 \times 3$ **c** $6 \times 6 \times 6$

b $4 \times 4 \times 4 \times 4 \times 4 \times 4$ **d** $9 \times 9 \times 9 \times 9 \times 9$

4 Use your calculator to find the value of:

a 3^5 **b** 8^3 **c** 9^2 **d** 6^4

5 Write down the value of:

a 14^0 **b** 12^{-1} **c** 25^0 **d** 19^{-1}

6 Write down the reciprocal of:

a 4 **c** 9 **e** $\frac{1}{6}$ **g** $\frac{1}{9}$

b 17 **d** 45 **f** $\frac{1}{4}$ **h** $\frac{1}{12}$

7 Write down the reciprocal of:

a $\frac{3}{5}$ **c** $\frac{5}{4}$ **e** $3\frac{1}{4}$ **g** $5\frac{3}{4}$

b $\frac{2}{3}$ **d** $\frac{3}{8}$ **f** $7\frac{1}{2}$ **h** $4\frac{2}{3}$

8 Simplify:

a $c^3 \times b^6$ **c** $4x^2 \times x^3$ **e** $3f^2 \times 5f^4$ **g** $9z^2 \times 2z$

b $m^2 \times m^5$ **d** $y^6 \times 7y$ **f** $2g^6 \times 8g^3$ **h** $5w^4 \times 2$

9 Simplify:

a $7^8 \div 7^3$ **d** $t^9 \div t^7$ **g** $8f^4 \div 4f^2$

b $4^6 \div 4$ **e** $5d^3 \div d^2$ **h** $2b^5 \div 6b$

c $r^7 \div r^2$ **f** $7x^6 \div x$ **i** $5a^4b^6 \div 15a^2b^3$

10 Write each of these as a fraction:

    a 5^{-3} **b** 2^{-4} **c** 3^{-2} **d** 7^{-6}

11 Simplify:

    a $b^{-3} \times b^6$ **c** $4m^{-2} \times 3m^{-3}$ **e** $(g^7)^3$ **g** $8x^3y^{-3} \div 2xy^{-4}$

    b $5f^3 \times 3f^{-2}$ **d** $a^2b^{-4} \times ab^{-3}$ **f** $(d^2)^{-4}$ **h** $r^{-3}s^3t^{-1} \div rs^2$

12 Write down the value of:

    a $25^{\frac{1}{2}}$ **c** $\sqrt{0.16}$ **e** $\sqrt[3]{512}$ **g** $0.027^{\frac{1}{3}}$

    b $64^{\frac{1}{2}}$ **d** $10\,000^{\frac{1}{2}}$ **f** $0.125^{\frac{1}{3}}$ **h** $\sqrt[3]{1728}$

13 Find the value of each letter:

    a $5^a = 125$ **c** $8^c = 64$ **e** $2^e = 128$ **g** $6^g = 1$

    b $7^b = \frac{1}{7}$ **d** $4^d = \frac{1}{16}$ **f** $3^f = \frac{1}{27}$ **h** $64^h = 8$

14 Work these out without using your calculator:

    a $2 + 5 \times 3$ **c** $15 - 10 \div 2$ **e** $2 + 3^2$ **g** $3^2 - 1^4$

    b $8 \div 4 - 3$ **d** $12 \div (7 - 4)$ **f** $15 - 2^3$ **h** $5^3 + 4^2$

15 Work these out using a calculator:

    a $(3.56 + 2.99)^2$ **c** $(17^2 - 15^2)^2$ **e** $\dfrac{72 - 18}{44 - 26}$

    b $(4.37 - 2.87)^2$ **d** $\dfrac{25 + 6.5}{4.7 - 1.2}$ **f** $\dfrac{7^3 - 181.8}{5.6 - 4.3}$

16 The formula for the volume of this pyramid is

$$V = \frac{1}{3}x^2h$$

where x is the length of the side of the square base and h is the height.

Calculate the volume of this pyramid.

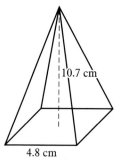

10.7 cm

4.8 cm

17 Use the formula $P = \dfrac{x}{5}\sqrt{3y^2 - z^2}$

to calculate the value of P to 1 dp when

    a $x = 24$, $y = 5$, $z = 3.1$ **b** $x = 120$, $y = 7.8$, $z = 2.54$

1 Find the value of y so that:

    a $5 \times 6^y = 180$ **b** $81^{2y} = 9$ **c** $2^{y+2} = 64$

2 The first four terms of a sequence are:

    5   5^2 5^3 5^4

    a Write down the fourth term as a number.
    b Write down the fifth term using a power of 5.
    c Write down an expression for the nth term of the sequence.

3 The first four terms of a sequence are:

    (1×3) (2×3^2) (3×3^3) (4×3^4)

    a Write down the fourth term as a number.
    b Write down the fifth term using a power of 3.
    c Write down an expression for the nth term of the sequence.

4 The formula for the nth term of a sequence is 5^{n+1}.
    Find the first four terms of the sequence.

5 Use the formula $s = ut + \frac{1}{2}at^2$ to find the value of s when
    a $u = 5$, $a = 3$ and $t = 6$
    b $u = 7$, $a = 14$ and $t = 8$

6 Use the formula $x = \dfrac{-b + \sqrt{b^2 - 4ac}}{2a}$ to find the value of x to 1 dp when

    a $b = 26$, $a = 2.5$ and $c = 1.9$
    b $b = 32$, $a = 7$ and $c = 2.5$

7 The formula $A = x^2 + x\sqrt{(4y^2 - x^2)}$ gives the surface area, A, of a square based pyramid.
    x cm is the length of the base and y cm is the length of the slant height.
    Find the value of A when $x = 9.8$ cm and $y = 7.5$ cm.
    Give your answer to 1 dp.

1   Write these as powers.

    a $7 \times 7 \times 7 \times 7 \times 7$ **b** $4 \times 4 \times 4$

2   Use your calculator to find the value of:

    a 12^3 **c** 23^2 **e** 10^5

    b $\sqrt{361}$ **d** $\sqrt[3]{1331}$ **f** $\sqrt[3]{1\,000\,000}$

3   Write down the reciprocal of:

    a   8   **b** $\frac{1}{5}$ **c** $\frac{2}{3}$

4   Write down the value of:

    a 11^0 **b** 4^{-1} **c** $\left(\frac{3}{4}\right)^{-1}$

5   Write each of these as a fraction.

    a 5^{-4} **b** 7^{-1} **c** a^{-1}

6   Simplify:

    a $y^4 \times y^3$ **e** $8x^7 \div 4x$ **i** $3x^3y^{-4} \times x^{-1}y$

    b $c^2 \times 6c$ **f** $a^5b \div a^2b^4$ **j** $(a^3)^5$

    c $5t^2 \times 7t^3$ **g** $h^4 \times h^{-2}$ **k** $(t^{\frac{1}{2}})^6$

    d $s^4 \div s^3$ **h** $w^8 \div w^{-1}$ **l** $(x^3)^0$

7   Write down the value of:

    a $25^{\frac{1}{2}}$ **b** $27^{\frac{1}{3}}$ **c** $(2^3)^2$ **d** $1^{\frac{1}{2}}$

8   Work these out using a calculator.

    a $\dfrac{53.6 - 11.8}{13.2 - 9.4}$ **c** $\dfrac{40^2}{16 \times 25}$

    b $(3.9 + 2.8)^2$ **d** $\dfrac{\sqrt{328} \times 62 - 736}{3.2^2 - 7.74}$

13 Graphs: moving on

1 Travel graphs
Measuring time
Using a calculator to work out times
Finding distances, speeds and times
Looking at compound units
Going on a journey

CORE

2 Line graphs
Deciding when to join points up
Going up in steps
Using graphs to change currencies

3 Graph sketching
Plotting points
Sketching graphs
Looking at slopes
Going round go-kart tracks
Designing water tanks

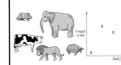

QUESTIONS

EXTENSION

TEST YOURSELF

1 Travel graphs

The scientists who did this learnt about this topic at school. Look where it landed them!

Terry is a taxi driver.
He has to pick up Richard by 10.18 a.m.
He leaves at 9.32 a.m. The journey takes 45 minutes.
When does Terry reach Richard?

You can work this out using the clock.
From 9.32 a.m. it is 28 minutes to 10 a.m.
This uses 28 minutes of the 45 minutes.
So there are 45 − 28 = 17 minutes left.
These 17 minutes are after 10 a.m.
So Terry arrives at 10.17 a.m.

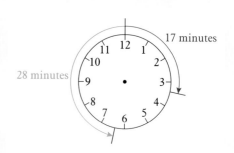

Exercise 13:1

1 Work out the time that Terry arrives to pick up these passengers.
   a Terry sets off at 8.27 a.m. He takes 46 minutes to reach Fred.
   b Terry sets off at 11.30 a.m. He takes 52 minutes to get to Ethel.
   c Terry sets off at 2.26 p.m. He takes 48 minutes to reach Abigail.
   d Terry sets off at 10.32 p.m. He takes 29 minutes to get to Nathan.
   e Terry sets off at 9.35 a.m. He takes 2 hours 56 minutes to reach Amanda.
   f Terry sets off at 14:12 He takes 30 minutes to get to Alan.
   g Terry sets off at 06:32 He takes 4 hours 51 minutes to reach Chloe.
   h Terry sets off at 22:48 He takes 2 hours 39 minutes to get to Mike.

There is another way of measuring time taken.

To find the length of time between time A and time B:
(1) **Find how long in minutes to the next hour from time A.**
(2) Find how many whole hours are taken.
(3) **Find how many minutes past the hour for time B.**
(4) Add all these times together.

So to find how long it is from 10.43 a.m. to 2.29 p.m.:

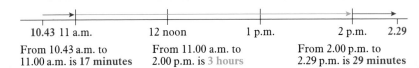

From 10.43 a.m. to 11.00 a.m. is **17 minutes**

From 11.00 a.m. to 2.00 p.m. is 3 hours

From 2.00 p.m. to 2.29 p.m. is 29 minutes

The total time is **17 minutes** + 3 hours + **29 minutes** = **3 hours 46 minutes**

2 How long is it between these times?
a 2.20 p.m. and 3.40 p.m.
b 7.32 a.m. and 1.07 p.m.
c 21:35 and 23:42
d 22:49 and 06:38

Using a calculator to work out times

You can use these keys to work with times **DMS**

The keys stand for degrees minutes and seconds. They are used for calculations with angles, but you can use them for time.

If you want to enter 2 h 45 min on the calculator:

Key in: **2** **DMS** **4** **5**

your calculator shows $2°45$
This means 2 h 45 min.

Key in: **2nd F** **DMS** to give 2.75

This is 2 h 45 min as a decimal.

Key in: **2** °'" **4** **5** °'" **=**

your calculator shows $2°45°0$
This means 2 h 45 min.

Key in: **Shift** °'" to give 2.75

This is 2 h 45 min as a decimal.

3 Copy this table. Enter each time into your calculator and fill in what your calculator shows.

Time	h min display	decimal display
2 h 30 min		
5 h 15 min		
01:40		
14:24		

You can use your calculator to work out lengths of times if you put the time in using the 24 hour clock.

If you want to find how long it is from 7.36 a.m. to 4.09 p.m.:

4.09 p.m. is 16:09 in 24 hour time and 7.36 a.m. is 07:36 in 24 hour time

Key in: $\boxed{1}\ \boxed{6}\ \boxed{\text{DMS}}\ \boxed{0}\ \boxed{9}\ \boxed{-}\ \boxed{0}\ \boxed{7}\ \boxed{\text{DMS}}\ \boxed{3}\ \boxed{6}\ \boxed{=}$

or: $\boxed{1}\ \boxed{6}\ \boxed{°\,'\,''}\ \boxed{0}\ \boxed{9}\ \boxed{°\,'\,''}\ \boxed{-}\ \boxed{0}\ \boxed{7}\ \boxed{°\,'\,''}\ \boxed{3}\ \boxed{6}\ \boxed{°\,'\,''}\ \boxed{=}$

This gives the answer of 8 h 33 min.

---

4 Use a calculator to find how long it is between these times.

a 7.40 a.m. to 8.20 a.m.	**e** 07:49 to 14:06
b 9.15 a.m. to 10.52 a.m.	**f** 11.42 a.m. to 1.18 p.m.
c 3.41 a.m. to 11.09 a.m.	**g** 9.37 a.m. to 7.04 p.m.
d 4.29 a.m. to noon	**h** 1.51 a.m. to midnight

Working with distances, speeds and times

Terry drives from Oxford to Southampton.

This is a distance of 100 km. It takes Terry 2 hours.

His average speed is 100 ÷ 2 = 50 km per hour.

So average speed = $\dfrac{\text{total distance}}{\text{total time}}$

There is a triangle that can help you to remember how to use this formula.

You remember $S = \dfrac{D}{T}$ then write out this triangle.

Cover up the letter you want. Then what you see is the rule.

Example   Terry drives 150 km in 2 hours 30 minutes.
Find his average speed.

You need the formula for speed:

If you cover S you see $\dfrac{D}{T}$    so $S = \dfrac{D}{T}$

$D = 150$ km, $T = 2$ h 30 min

30 minutes $= \frac{1}{2}$ an hour $= 0.5$ hours, so 2 h 30 min $= 2.5$ hours.

Put these values in the formula. $S = \dfrac{150}{2.5}$ so $S = 60$ km/h.

If you have a **DMS** key, you can key in hours and minutes.

Key in: **1** **5** **0** **÷** **2** **DMS** **3** **0** **=**

 1 **5** **0** **÷** **2** **°'"** **3** **0** **°'"** **=**

to get 60 km/h

Exercise 13:2

1 Find the average speeds in km/h for each distance and time.

	distance	time			distance	time
a	120 km	2 h		**d**	189 km	2 h 15 min
b	270 km	6 h		**e**	270 km	15 min
c	330 km	5 h 30 min		**f**	720 km	2 days

2 Robert drives a van for a removal company.
He sets off from the depot at 10.48 a.m.
He drives 12 km.
He arrives at Alice's old house at 10.58 a.m.
He completes the removals in 44 minutes.
Then Robert sets off for Alice's new house.
He drives 8 km. He arrives at 11.48 a.m.
Which journey does he drive at the greatest
average speed?

Example   Vanessa drives 243 km at an average speed of 54 km per hour. Find how long this journey takes.

You need the formula for time:

If you cover T you see $\dfrac{D}{S}$    so $T = \dfrac{D}{S}$

$D = 243$ km, $S = 54$ km/h

So put these values in the formula. $T = \dfrac{243}{50}$

Key in: **2** **4** **3** **÷** **5** **4** **=** **2nd F** **DMS**

  2 **4** **3** **÷** **5** **4** **−** **Shift** **°' ''**

to get 4 h 30 min.

---

3   Find the time for each of these journeys. Give your answer in hours.

	distance	average speed		distance	average speed
a	20 km	5 km/h	**d**	4 km	8 km/h
b	280 km	35 km/h	**e**	186 km	279 km/h
c	6000 km	800 km/h	**• f**	4500 km	36 000 km/h

Example   Franz skis for 2 hours 15 minutes at an average speed of 32 km/h. Find how far Franz skis.

You need the formula for distance:

If you cover D you see ST so $D = ST$

$S = 32$ km/h, $T = 2$ h 15 min

Key in: **2** **DMS** **1** **5** **2nd F** **DMS**   or   **2** **°' ''** **1** **5** **°' ''**

= **Shift** **°' ''**

to give 2 h 15 min = 2.25 h.

Then put these values in the formula: $D = 32 \times 2.25 = 72$ km

---

4   Find the distance for each of these journeys.

	time	average speed		time	average speed
a	2 h	15 km/h	**d**	2 h 12 min	12 miles/h
b	4 h	15 km/h	**e**	3 h 24 min	1870 km/h
c	19 seconds	11 m/s	**• f**	202 days	36 000 km/h

Compound units You can measure speed in lots of different units, metres per second, miles per hour, kilometres per day ...
Speed is an example of a quantity which has **compound units**. This is because it is a combination of two separate measures: distance *and* time.

There are other quantities that have compound units.
A drill where the speed is measured in revolutions per minute, filling an oil tank where the rate of flow is measured in litres per second.
Measuring the rate a car uses petrol in miles per gallon.

Exercise 13:3

1 An antique turntable spins 312 times to play an old 4 minute record. How many revolutions per minute is this?

2 Reg is a runner bean picker. He picks 1008 pounds in 9 hours 20 minutes. Work out his rate of picking in pounds per hour.

3 A petrol pump fills a car with 33 litres of petrol in 2 minutes 0 seconds. Give this as a rate in:
   a litres per second   **b** litres per minute   **c** litres per hour

4 A concert hall fills at an average rate of 142 people per minute. It takes 42 minutes to completely fill the hall. How many people does the hall hold?

5 Carolyn drives a thirsty car. She puts in 11 gallons of petrol and drives it 242 miles when it needs filling again. Work out its consumption in miles per gallon.

6 Dennis the farmer grows 14 kg of potatoes per square metre. He grows these in a field 80 m long by 120 metres wide. If he bags his potatoes in 50 kg bags, how many bags does he need?

7 In East Yorkshire, part of the coast is eroded at the rate of 40 centimetres per year. If this continues at this rate, how far inland will the coastline be in the year 4200? Give your answer in kilometres.

Travel graphs

Travel graphs are used to show distance and time. They show you the distance that something has moved away from a starting point. Time always goes on the horizontal axis. You can also work out speeds from travel graphs.

This graph shows Terry's journey from Oxford to Southampton.

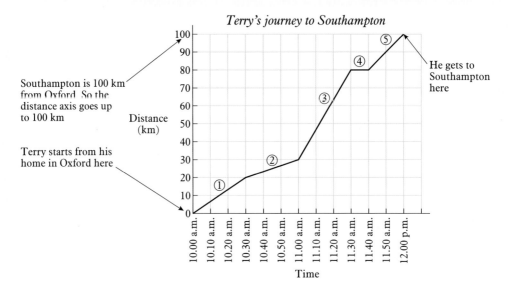

Terry's journey to Southampton

Southampton is 100 km from Oxford. So the distance axis goes up to 100 km

Terry starts from his home in Oxford here

He gets to Southampton here

This is part ① of Terry's journey. The graph is sloping upwards. This means that Terry is driving away from his house.

He drives 20 km in half an hour.
Speed = Distance ÷ Time
So his speed for this part is given by

$$S = \frac{20}{0.5} = 40 \text{ km/h}$$

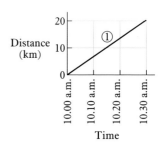

In part ② of the graph, Terry is still travelling away from his house. He only moves 10 km in 30 minutes. He is probably stuck in slow moving traffic.
His speed here is

$$S = \frac{10}{0.5} = 20 \text{ km/h}$$

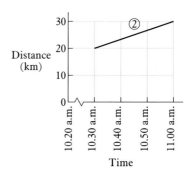

In part ③ of the graph, the graph has its
steepest slope.
Terry travels 50 km in 30 minutes.
He is going much faster in this part.
His speed here is

$$S = \frac{50}{0.5} = 100 \text{ km/h}$$

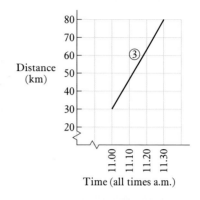

Part ④ of the graph looks like this.
The graph is horizontal.
This means that Terry is not moving.
He has stopped somewhere for 10 minutes.
His speed here is zero.

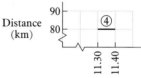

The last part of the graph looks like this.
The graph is sloping upwards again.
He travels 20 km in 20 minutes.
His speed here is

$$S = \frac{20}{0.3} = 60 \text{ km/h}$$

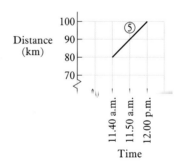

Look at the whole graph again.
The dotted red line covers the total distance. It also covers the total time.
You can use the red line to work out the average speed for the *whole* journey.

Terry's journey to Southampton

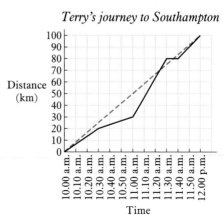

$$\text{Average speed} = \frac{\text{total distance}}{\text{total time}}$$

Terry travels 100 km in 2 hours.
So for this journey

$$\text{average speed} = \frac{100}{2} = 50 \text{ km/h}$$

Exercise 13:4

1 This is a graph of John's trip to Wembley Stadium.
He is travelling to see Newcastle United in the F.A. Cup.

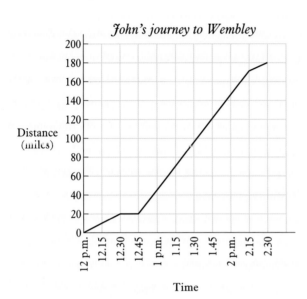

John's journey to Wembley

He starts by driving from his home in Sheffield to the station.
a How long does this take?
b How far is the station from his house?
c Work out his speed in miles per hour for this part of the journey.
John has to wait at the station for his train.
d How long does he have to wait?
John then catches a fast train to London.
e How far does the train travel until John gets off at 2.15 p.m.?
f Work out the speed of this train.
John then catches an underground train. He doesn't have to wait.
The underground train travels the last 10 miles in 15 minutes.
g Work out the speed of this train.
● **h** Work out John's average speed for the entire journey.

2 Sarah walks at 4 km/h for 30 minutes.
Then she waits for a bus for
30 minutes.
Then she travels for an hour on the
bus at 40 km/h.
  a Copy these axes on to squared paper.
  b Show Sarah's journey on your graph.
  c Work out Sarah's average speed
  for the whole journey.

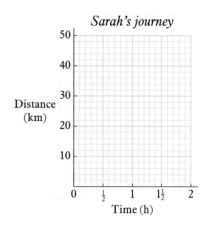

Some travel graphs show journeys that go back to where they started.
You work out the average speed of the entire journey in a different way for these.

Mrs Shipley drives to Dover to catch a ferry. The ferry is cancelled because of
storms. She has a cup of tea, then she drives back home to New Cross.
The graph shows her journey.

Her speed on the outward

journey is $\dfrac{100}{1} = 100$ km/h.

Her speed on the return

journey is $\dfrac{100}{1.25} = 80$ km/h.

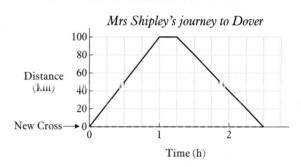

She has travelled a total
distance of 200 km in a
total time of $2\frac{1}{2}$ hours.

So her average speed for the entire journey is $\dfrac{200}{2.5} = 80$ km/h.

You use each distance from the graph and add them together to give the total
distance. You do not use the red dotted line!

3 George walks to the local shop. The
graph shows his journey.
He buys a loaf and chats with the
shopkeeper. Then he walks home.
Work out his average speed:
  a going to the shop
  b going back home
  c for the entire journey

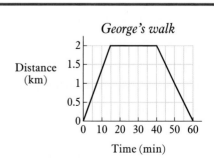

2 Line graphs

When you draw graphs you usually plot some points then join them with lines.

Sometimes you can't join the points. The lines in between the points may not have a meaning.

This happens a lot in statistics.
If you are plotting data about numbers of people, you can't join the points.
You can't have 2.8 people for example!

These two graphs show the number of people in a supermarket queue between 12:00 and 13:00.

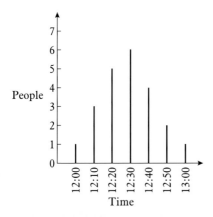

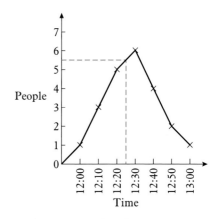

This is a **vertical line graph.**
It is like a bar chart with very thin bars!
This is the correct type of graph for this data.

This is a **line graph.**
You can join the points together with straight lines.
This is the wrong type of graph for this data. It shows that there were 5.5 people in the queue at 12:25!

Exercise 13:5

1 Write down whether you would draw a line graph or a vertical line
graph to show each of these:
a the number of bicycles sold each month by a shop
b the number of Smarties in 10 tubes
c the temperature of a cup of coffee as it cools down
d the number of people on a train during its journey
e the weight of a baby over a period of 8 weeks

2 Mr Jiwa has oil-fired central heating.
He records the amount of oil left in the tank every hour one afternoon.

Time	13:00	14:00	15:00	16:00	17:00
Oil left (litres)	155	148	140	132	125

a Draw a suitable graph of this data.
b Estimate the amount of oil left at 15:30.

3 The following data shows the number of people in a casualty waiting
room every hour one afternoon.

Time	13:00	14:00	15:00	16:00	17:00
Number of people	16	21	23	19	31

Draw a suitable graph of this data.

Some graphs have their points joined up but also have gaps in them!
These graphs are called **step graphs**.

Example   The current costs for first class mail are shown in this table.

Weight up to ...	60 g	100 g	150 g	200 g	250 g
Cost	27 p	41 p	57 p	72 p	84 p

Show this data on a graph.
All letters up to 60 g cost 27 p.
This produces the first horizontal line.
As soon as a letter goes over 60 g the cost jumps to 41 p.
This produces the second horizontal line.
The two lines are not joined together.
The graph continues in the same way and produces a series of steps.

The finished graph looks like this.

Postage costs

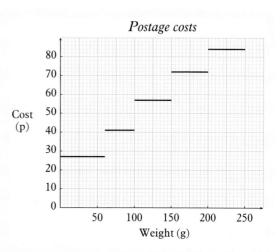

Cost (p)

Weight (g)

---

4 This table shows the costs for second class mail.

Weight up to ...	60 g	100 g	150 g	200 g	250 g
Cost	19 p	33 p	44 p	54 p	66 p

Draw a graph to show these costs.

5 The costs for special delivery are much higher.

Weight up to ...	100 g	500 g	1 kg	2 kg	10 kg
Cost	£3.50	£3.80	£4.95	£6.20	£17.80

Draw a graph to show these costs.

6 Radicomms is a new telephone company. Their prices for long distance calls are shown in the table.

RADICOMMS

Call time up to ...	1 min	3 min	5 min	10 min	20 min
Daytime cost	6 p	15 p	25 p	45 p	80 p
Evening cost	3 p	8 p	12 p	30 p	30 p

a Show both sets of data on the same graph.
   Use different colours for each rate.

● **b** Radnet is Radicomms' main rival.
   Their prices work differently. They charge 4.5 p per minute during the day and 2.5 p per minute in the evening. They charge by the second so their charges produce a straight line graph.
   Draw Radnet's charges on your graph.

● **c** Radnet is cheaper than Radicomms in each charge rate at the start.
   Write down the length of the call when Radicomms becomes cheaper than Radnet at each rate.

Conversion graphs

A conversion graph is a graph that you can use to change from one unit to another.
Conversion graphs are always straight lines.

Example   **a** Draw a conversion graph to change from miles to kilometres.
5 miles = 8 kilometres.
b Use your graph to convert 18 miles to kilometres.
c Use your graph to convert 32 km to miles.

a It does not matter which unit goes on which axis.
Plot the point (5 miles, 8 km) and the point (0 miles, 0 km).
Join the points with a straight line and extend the line upwards.

b Follow the blue line on the graph.
18 miles is 28.8 km.

c Follow the red line on the graph.
32 km is 20 miles.

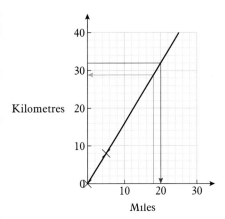

Exercise 13:6

1 Jaswinder is going on holiday to the USA. He needs to exchange his money into dollars ($).
£1 will buy $1.60
The bank has a graph to help customers.
a Draw axes from £0 to £50 and $0 to $80
b Mark the points (£0, $0) and (£50, $80).
c Join the points to make a conversion graph.
d Convert the following amounts into $.
(1) £20   (2) £35   (3) £42
e Convert the following amounts into £.
(1) $32   (2) $50   (3) $61

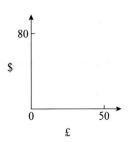

2 The graph to convert temperature from °C to °F is a straight line but it does not go through (0, 0).
This is because 0 °C = 32 °F.
The boiling point of water is 100 °C = 212 °F.
  a Draw a conversion graph to convert temperature from °C to °F.
  b Convert the following into °C   (1) 41 °F   (2) 59 °F   (3) 140 °F
  c Convert the following into °F   (1) 30 °C   (2) 75 °C   (3) 81 °C

3 Last year Lindsey went to Austria on a skiing holiday.
She converted her £ into Austrian Schillings.
The rate was £1 = 20 Schillings.
  a Draw axes from £0 to £100 and 0 Schillings to 2000 Schillings.
  b Draw a conversion graph.
  c Lindsey took £75. How many Schillings did she get?
  d This year, the rate is £1 = 19.5 Schillings.
    Put a new line on your graph to show this year's rate.
  e How many £ will Lindsey have to convert to get the same number of Schillings as she did last year?

4 Banks actually buy and sell foreign currency at different rates.
If you sell foreign currency back to the bank when you return from your holidays, they will not give you such a good rate for your money.
Here are some examples of a bank's rates.

Currency	Bank sells at (for £1)	Bank buys at (for £1)
French Francs F	9.2	9.6
German Marks DM	3.7	3.9
Spanish Pesetas Pta	230	250

  a For each currency draw a conversion graph showing both the buying and selling rates. Use different colours.
  b Dave exchanges £40 into Francs. How many Francs does he get?
  c Dave returns half his Francs to the bank and exchanges them for £. How much does he get back?
  d What is his percentage loss?
  e Anne returns from holiday with 600 pesetas. How much will she get for them?
  f If you exchanged £50 into DM and exchanged your DM straight back into £, how much would you lose?

3 Graph sketching

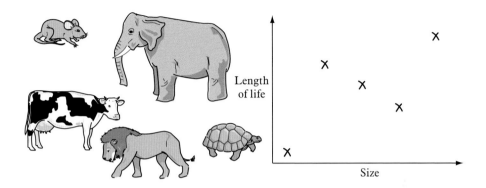

The graph shows the size and the length of life of the 5 animals in the picture. Can you decide which point represents each animal?

The graph does not have any scales on the axes. It is just a sketch graph. It is used to show a general pattern rather than to give accurate readings.

Exercise 13:7

1 Look at these pictures of cars.
Copy the axes shown and mark a point for each car.

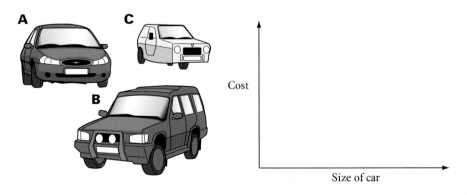

2 **a** Copy these axes.

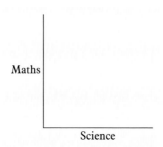

Six people took a Maths test and a Science test.
Here are some descriptions of how they did in their tests.
David: Did well in both Maths and Science.
Kirsty: Did well in Science but poorly in Maths.
Richard: Was ill when he took the tests. He did badly in both subjects.
Anisha: Did very well in Maths but only about average in Science.
Nathan: Got an average mark in both tests.
Catherine: Did well in Science but missed the Maths test and so scored 0.

b Mark a point on your graph to show each person's test results.

3 Look at this graph. It shows the cost of some boxes of chocolates and the number in each box.

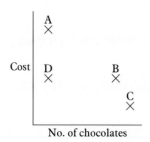

a Which box is the most expensive?
b Which box is the best value for money?
c Which boxes cost the same?
d Which boxes have the same number of chocolates in them?

Sketch graph   A **sketch graph** can show a pattern or trend.

Example   Paul cycles to school. After a while he goes uphill so he slows down. Later he goes downhill so he can speed up.

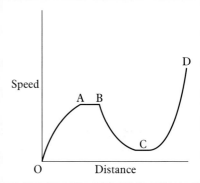

The graph shows the main features of the journey. It shows where Paul is speeding up or slowing down. It also shows if he is going faster at one point than another. You cannot tell his actual speed.
Between O and A Paul is speeding up.
From A to B he is going at a steady speed.
From B to C he is slowing down, he's going uphill.
From C to D he is speeding up, he's going downhill.

Gradient   The **gradient** measures how steep a line or curve is.
The gradient of a straight line is the same all the way along.
The gradient of a curve changes

Example   A car accelerates rapidly to 30 mph. It continues to accelerate up to 60 mph but less rapidly. When it reaches 60 mph it travels at a steady speed.
Sketch a graph to show the car's acceleration.

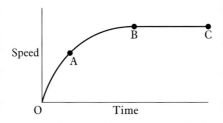

The gradient from O to A is steeper than from A to B as the car is accelerating more rapidly at first. The line from B to C is horizontal because the car is not accelerating. It is travelling at a steady speed. The gradient is 0.

Exercise 13:8

For each of these questions:
a Copy the axes.
b Draw a sketch of the graph from the description.
c Mark letters at important points and describe each section of the graph.

1 Howard cycles to school. The first part of his journey is along a level road. He then speeds up as he goes downhill. He slows down as he arrives at the school gate.

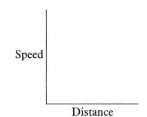

2 Lindsey jogs for the first part of her journey along a level road. The next part is uphill and she walks quite slowly.
She stops at the shops at the top of the hill.

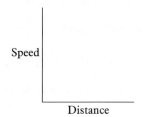

3 Kirsty made a jelly with boiling water. She put it in the fridge to cool. At first, it cooled very quickly, and then gradually settled down to a steady temperature.

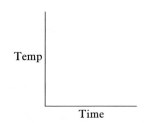

4 Andy is running a computer games stall at the school Christmas Fayre. He thinks that if the games are too cheap he will not make much money. If they are too expensive, very few people will want to pay.

Anna is very keen on go-karting.
She likes to visit different tracks to
practise.
It takes time to get used to a track and
find out how quickly you can go on
different parts of it.

Here is the diagram of Anna's home track.
She can go faster on the straights and slows down for the corners.
The graph shows Anna's speed as she goes around the track.

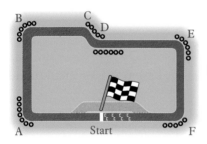

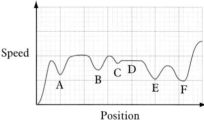

Look at the track and the graph together.
Read these notes that help to explain the graph.

From Start to A	Anna accelerates from the start. The graph goes up steeply.
A	Anna brakes into the corner and then accelerates out of it. The graph goes down and then back up again.
A to B	After Anna has accelerated out of the corner, she maintains a steady speed along the straight. The graph is horizontal.
B	Another corner like A.
B to E	This section is fairly straight so the graph is roughly horizontal. There are odd dips where Anna slows down for the gentle bends.
E to F	This section is almost the same as **A** to **B**.

Exercise 13:9

1 Look at this go-kart track.

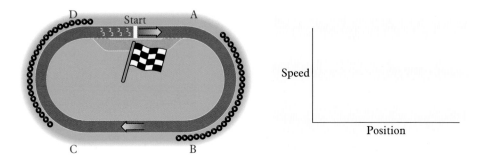

a What will happen to the speed of the kart between Start and A?
b What will happen to its speed as it goes around the corner from A to B?
c Where will the kart reach its highest speed?
d Copy the axes.
e Sketch a graph to show the speed of the kart as it goes once around the track.

2 Here is another go-kart track. The kart starts at S.
   a Describe the speed of the kart once it has reached its full speed.
   b Sketch a graph of the speed of the kart. Use the same axes as in question **1**.

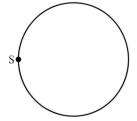

● **3** Look at this go-kart track.
   Sketch a graph to show the speed of the kart as it goes around the track.

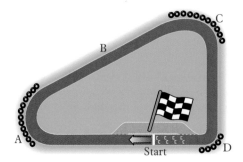

Exercise 13:10 – Designing a water tank

A water company are looking at new designs for water storage tanks.
The tanks need to hold 10 000 litres of water.
Here are some of the designs that have been suggested.

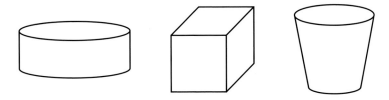

1 For each of the designs sketch a graph of the **height** of the water as they are filled up using a hose. Think about the **rate** at which the height would change.

2 Which of your graphs are straight lines and which are curves? Explain your answers.

● **3** Here is a graph for a fourth water tank.
Draw a sketch of the tank by looking at the graph.

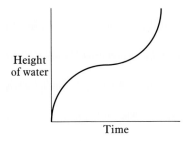

4 Design some water tanks of your own and sketch the graphs that go with them.

1 How long is it between these times?
   a 7.20 a.m. and 8.52 p.m.   **c** 14:35 and 23:42
   b 10.36 a.m. and 3.17 p.m.   **d** 21:46 and 17:18 the next day.

2 Geoff is a long distance lorrydriver. He travels from London to Scotland.
   a On the way there he drives 560 km in 8 h. Work out his average speed.
   b On the way back he drives 665.6 km in 12 h 48 min. Work out his average
      speed.

3 Adam enjoys cycle rides. He cycles around the Norfolk Broads.
   He travels a distance of 72 km.
   He rides at an average speed of 12 km/h. How long does it take him?

4 Gordon is a train driver. He drives for $2\frac{1}{7}$ h at an average speed of 74 km/h. How
   far does the train go?

5 An air pump fills a dinghy with 448 litres of air in 1 minute 52 seconds.
   Give this as a rate in:
   a litres per second   **b** litres per minute   **c** litres per hour

6 This graph shows the journeys of two farm lorries from Rainham to
   Sandwich and back. Jon sets off at 10.00 a.m. and Andy sets off at 10.10 a.m.

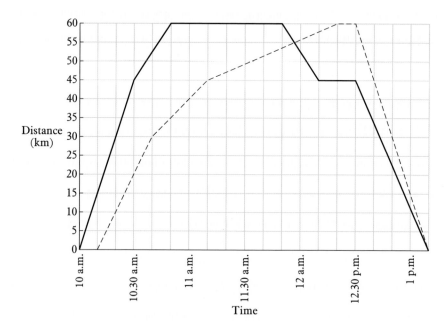

   a How far had Jon's lorry travelled before Andy set off?
   b Calculate Andy's slowest speed on the way to Sandwich. Give your
      answer in km/h.
   c Andy passed Jon driving in the other direction. What time did this happen?

7 This table shows the costs of recorded delivery letters.

Weight up to ...	60 g	100 g	150 g	200 g	250 g
Cost	90 p	104 p	120 p	135 p	147 p

Draw a graph to show these costs.

8 Last year Netty went to Belgium for a sightseeing trip.
She converted her £ into Belgian Francs.
The rate was £1 = 50 Francs.
  a Draw axes from £0 to £100 and 0 Francs to 5000 Francs.
  b Draw a conversion graph.
  c Netty took £60. How many Francs did she get?
  d This year, the rate is £1 = 55 Francs.
     Put a new line on your graph to show this year's rate.

9 Ned is doing a parachute jump for charity.
As he jumps out of the plane, his speed increases rapidly.
He slows down suddenly as his parachute opens and then floats to the
ground at a steady speed.

  a Which of these three graphs shows Ned's jump?
    Explain your answer.

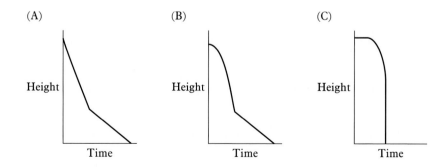

  b Explain why the other two graphs are wrong.
  c Sketch a graph of Ned's speed as he falls to the ground.

1 A spaceship sets off for Mars. It travels at 28 450 miles/h.
   The route it takes is approximately 200 million miles.
   How long does it take to get there:
   a in hours   **b** in days

2 A roller coaster goes along this track.

   a Sketch a graph of the height of the roller coaster above the ground as
        it moves along the track. What do you notice?
   b Sketch a graph of the **speed** of the roller coaster as it moves along the
        track.
   c Explain the connection between your two graphs.

3 During the summer of 1995 the south west of England had swarms of
   ladybirds. This was because there were lots of greenfly around.
   Ladybirds live on greenfly!
   This graph shows the number of greenfly during the summer.

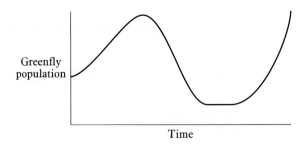

   a Make a copy of this sketch graph. It does not have to be exact.
   b Sketch the number of ladybirds on the same graph.
        Think carefully about how long it will take for the ladybird
        population to increase.

1 This is an extract from a TV programme guide.

BBC1	pm
4:35	Eastenders
6:00	News
6:25	Songs of Praise
7:00	Wildlife on One
7:30	Fawlty Towers
8:00	Ground Force
8:40	Sun Holiday
9:20	As Time Goes By

   a How long does Eastenders last?

   b Kevin records Songs of Praise and Sun Holiday. What is the total length of these two programmes?

   c Kevin uses a 3 hour tape. How long will be left on the tape when he has recorded the two programmes?

2 A Japanese train travels with a speed of 200 km per hour.
How far does it travel in

   a 4 hours   **b** $\frac{1}{2}$ hour   **c** 12 minutes

3 **a** A bus travels 130 km in 2.5 hours.
   Find the average speed of the bus.

   b Martin travels 43 miles in 40 minutes.
   Find his average speed in miles per hour.

4 Hattie can make 210 chocolates in half an hour.

   a Give this as a rate in chocolates per hour.

   b Give this as a rate in chocolates per minute.

   c How long does Hattie take to make one chocolate?
   Give your answer in seconds to 1 dp.

5 Mrs Rogers makes model animals.
The table shows the number of animals she made in one week.

Day	Mon	Tues	Wed	Thurs	Fri	Sat	Sun
Number of animals	8	12	19	9	4	7	14

Draw a vertical line graph to show this data.

6 Marty is going to pick up a new bike.
He walks to the shop then cycles back home.
The graph shows the journey.

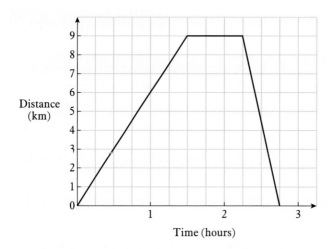

Time (hours)

a How far is it from Marty's home to the shop?
b How long was he in the shop?
c How long did Marty take to cycle home?
d At what speed did Marty cycle home?
e What was Marty's average speed for the whole journey?
Give your answer to 1 dp.

7 The graph shows the delivery
charge for a carpet warehouse.
The charge depends on the
mileage.
a Jan lives 18 miles away.
How much does it cost her
to have a carpet delivered?
b Peter's delivery charge was
£6.
Copy this sentence. Fill in
the missing numbers.
Peter lives between ... and
... miles from the
warehouse.

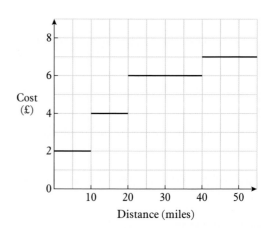

14 Trigonometry

CORE

1 Introduction
Measuring sides in right angled triangles
Working out ratios of pairs of sides
Defining sin, cos and tan

2 Finding an angle
Using trigonometry to find angles
Solving real-life problems

3 Finding a side
Using trigonometry to find lengths
Working in isosceles triangles
Solving real-life problems

QUESTIONS

EXTENSION

TEST YOURSELF

1 Introduction

Trigonometry is all about finding lengths and angles in triangles. It is used a lot in building and surveying.

Exercise 14:1

1 Look at this right angled triangle.
It has a 30° angle at the base.

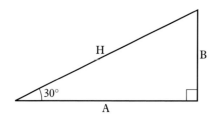

a Draw a right-angled triangle like this.
The angles must be the same as this.
It does not matter how long the sides are.
b Measure all three sides of the triangle to the nearest millimetre.
Be as accurate as you can.
Mark the lengths on your triangle.
c Draw two more triangles that have the same angles as before.
Make the lengths of the sides different.
Mark the lengths on each side. Number your triangles.
d Record your results in a table like this.
Leave the last three columns blank.

Diagram number	length A	length B	length H			

2 **a** For each of the triangles, calculate length **B** ÷ length **A**.
Fill in the answers in the fifth column of your table.
Round your answers to 3 dp where necessary.

Diagram number	length A	length B	length H	**B ÷ A**	**A ÷ H**	**B ÷ H**

b What do you notice about these numbers?
Now make sure that your calculator is working in degrees.

c Key in: tan **3** **0**

You should get *0.577350269*
Write down the answer.
Compare it with your answers to B ÷ A in your table.

3 **a** For each triangle, calculate length **A** ÷ length **H**.
Fill in the answers in your table.
b Fill in the answers to length **B** ÷ length **H** in your table.

c Key in: cos **3** **0**

Write down your answer.

d Key in: sin **3** **0**

Write down your answer.
e Compare the calculator answers with your table.
Which answer goes with which column?

---

tangent The value of tan **3** **0**

is called the **tangent of 30°**.
It is normally written tan 30° and said 'tan thirty'.

sine The value of sin **3** **0**

is called the **sine of 30°**.
It is normally written sin 30° and said 'sine thirty'.

cosine The value of cos **3** **0**

is called the **cosine of 30°**.
It is normally written cos 30° and said 'cos thirty'.

---

4 **a** Draw a right-angled triangle like this with a 50° angle.

b Measure the sides and record your results.

c Work out B ÷ A, A ÷ H and B ÷ H.

d Compare your answers to part **c** with tan 50°, cos 50° and sin 50°. Write down what you notice.

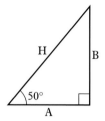

This sort of trigonometry only works in right-angled triangles.
The values stored in the calculator are very accurate and are much easier than taking measurements.

Sin, cos and tan always have the same value for right angled triangles with the same angle. The size of the triangle does not matter. It is the angles in the triangle that are important.

 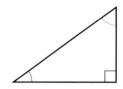 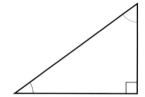

The sides of the triangle are given special names so that it is easy to write the formulas down.

Hypotenuse   The **hypotenuse** is always the longest side. It never touches the right angle.

Opposite   The **opposite** is the side *opposite* the angle you are working with. It is one of the two shorter sides.

Adjacent   The **adjacent** is the side *next* to the angle you are working with. It touches that angle.

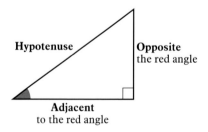

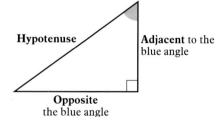

Exercise 14:2

1 Copy this table. Leave space for 10 triangles.

Triangle	Hypotenuse	Opposite the marked angle	Adjacent to the marked angle
a **b**	C	D	E

2 For each of these triangles, decide which sides are the **H**ypotenuse, the **O**pposite and the **A**djacent for the marked angle. Fill in the table. The first one is done for you.

a

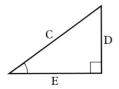

f

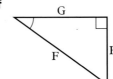

b

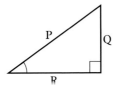

g

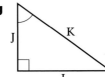

c

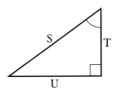

h

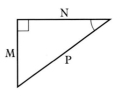

d

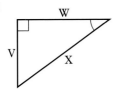

i

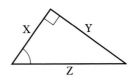

e

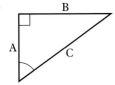

j

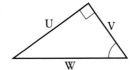

You can now write down formulas for sin, cos and tan using the names of the sides of the triangle.

Look at this triangle.
The sides are labelled for angle *a*

$$\sin a = \frac{\textbf{Opposite}}{\textbf{Hypotenuse}}$$

$$\cos a = \frac{\textbf{Adjacent}}{\textbf{Hypotenuse}}$$

$$\tan a = \frac{\textbf{Opposite}}{\textbf{Adjacent}}$$

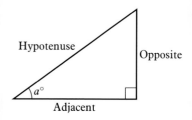

Some people remember SOHCAHTOA which comes from the first letters of **S**in equals **O**pposite divided by **H**ypotenuse, **C**os equals **A**djacent ...

These are often shortened to

$$\sin a = \frac{\text{Opp}}{\text{Hyp}} \qquad \cos a = \frac{\text{Adj}}{\text{Hyp}} \qquad \tan a = \frac{\text{Opp}}{\text{Adj}}$$

A useful rhyme to remember these is:

The	**Cat**	**Sat**
On	**An**	**Orange**
And	**Howled**	**Horribly**

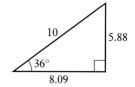

Example   Look at this triangle.
Work out sin 36°, cos 36° and tan 36°.

$$\sin 36° = \frac{\text{Opp}}{\text{Hyp}} = \frac{5.88}{10}$$

$$= \textbf{0.588} \text{ to 3 dp}$$

$$\cos 36° = \frac{\text{Adj}}{\text{Hyp}} = \frac{8.09}{10}$$

$$= \textbf{0.809} \text{ to 3 dp}$$

$$\tan 36° = \frac{\text{Opp}}{\text{Adj}} = \frac{5.88}{8.09}$$

$$= \textbf{0.727} \text{ to 3 dp}$$

Exercise 14:3

Give all your answers to 3 dp.

1 Work out sin a, cos a and tan a.

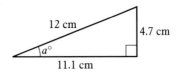

2 Work out sin b, cos b and tan b.

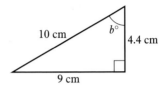

3 Work out sin c, cos c and tan c.

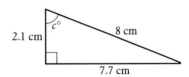

4 Work out sin d, cos d and tan d.

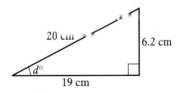

5 **a** Work out sin e, cos e and tan e.
   b Work out sin f, cos f and tan f.

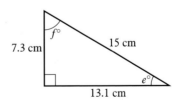

6 Here are the sizes of the angles used in questions **1–5**.

$a = 23°$ $b = 64°$ $c = 75°$ $d = 18°$ $e = 29°$ $f = 61°$

Use your calculator to check your answers for questions **1–5**.

2 Finding an angle

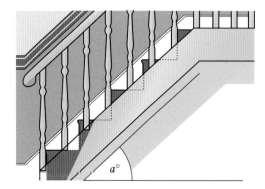

There is a legal limit on the value of angle a in houses. The maximum value is 42°.

Stairs cannot be steeper than this.

To find the angle marked a in this triangle:

Which lengths do you know?

The 2 m side is opposite to a
The 4 m side is adjacent to a

Which formula do you need?

$$\sin a = \frac{\text{Opp}}{\text{Hyp}} \qquad \cos a = \frac{\text{Adj}}{\text{Hyp}} \qquad \tan a = \frac{\text{Opp}}{\text{Adj}}$$

Only the tan formula has opposite **and** adjacent in it.

Fill in the formula

$$\tan a = \frac{2}{4}$$

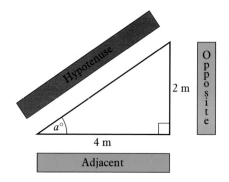

Make sure that your calculator is working in degrees.

Key in:

to get $a = 26.6°$ (1 dp).

You can use the other two formulas in the same way.

Exercise 14:4

For each question:
a Copy the triangle. Label the sides Hyp, Opp, Adj.
b Find the angle marked with a letter. Round your answer to 1 dp.
Check that your answers seem reasonable.

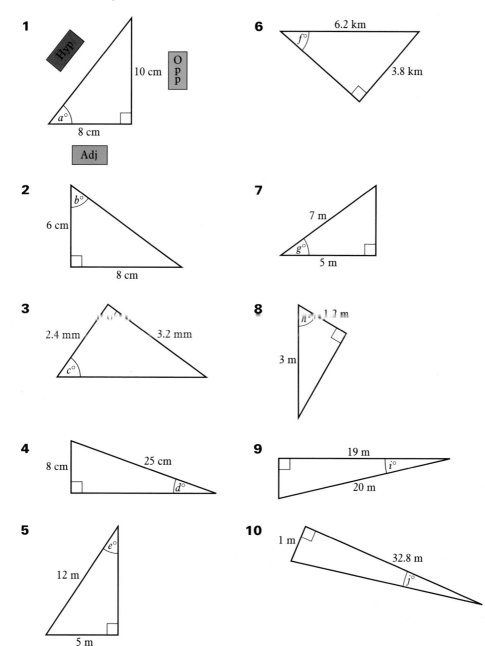

1

Hyp

10 cm

Opp

$a°$

8 cm

Adj

2

$b°$

6 cm

8 cm

3

2.4 mm

3.2 mm

$c°$

4

8 cm

25 cm

$d°$

5

$e°$

12 m

5 m

6

6.2 km

$f°$

3.8 km

7

7 m

$g°$

5 m

8

$h°$ 1.2 m

3 m

9

19 m

$i°$

20 m

10

1 m

32.8 m

$j°$

349

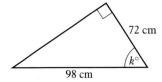

11

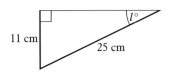

12

In some questions you have to find more than one angle.

You draw a separate triangle for each angle that you need to find.
In this diagram you need to find angles $m°$ and $n°$.

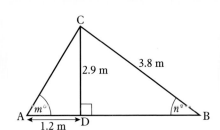

To find $m°$ draw triangle ADC separately.
Then you work out $m°$ in the usual way.

Which formula do you need?
Only the tan formula has opposite **and** adjacent in it.

Fill in the formula $\tan m = \dfrac{2.9}{1.2}$

Key in:

 2nd F **tan** **(** **2** **.** **9** **÷** **1** **.** **2** **)** **=**

 SHIFT **tan** **(** **2** **.** **9** **÷** **1** **.** **2** **)** **=**

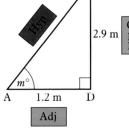

to get $m = 67.5°$ (1 dp).

You then work out $n°$ by drawing triangle BCD separately. This gives $n° = 49.7°$ (1 dp).

13

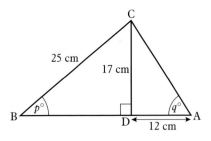

● **14**   ABCD is a rectangle.

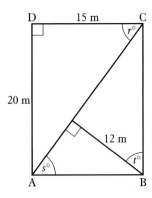

Exercise 14:5

In this exercise, round all your answers to 1 dp.

1 A flight of stairs rises 2.6 m. The
horizontal distance under the
stairs is 2.85 m.
  a What is the angle that the
    stairs make with the ground?
  The biggest angle allowed by law
  is 42°.
  b Is this angle legal?
  • **c** How could it appear to be legal
    in a report?

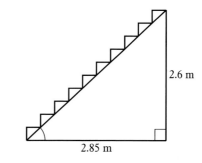
2.6 m
2.85 m

2 Evel Knievel is a world famous
motorcycle stuntman.
What is his angle of take off if he
uses this ramp?

20 m
6.2 m

3 Claire Batin 'the human fly' is
about to climb this overhang in
the Pyrenees.
What angle does she need to climb
out from the vertical?

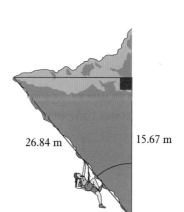
26.84 m
15.67 m

4 This is the descent slope of one of
the world's tallest roller coasters.
What is the angle made with the
ground?

50 m
28.4 m

3   Finding a side

How could you find the width of the Grand Canyon without crossing it?

To find the side marked a in this triangle:

Which length do you know?
The length marked 2 m is the hypotenuse.

Which length do you need to find?
The length marked a is opposite the 40° angle.

Which formula do you need?

$$\sin a = \frac{\text{Opp}}{\text{Hyp}} \quad \cos a = \frac{\text{Adj}}{\text{Hyp}} \quad \tan a = \frac{\text{Opp}}{\text{Adj}}$$

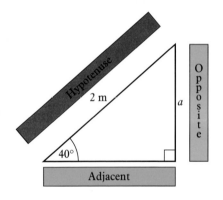

Only the sin formula has opposite **and** hypotenuse in it.

Fill in the formula $\sin 40° = \dfrac{a}{2}$

Multiply both sides of the equation by 2 $2 \times \sin 40° = a$

Make sure that your calculator is working in degrees.

Key in: [2] [sin] [4] [0] [=]

to get $a = 1.29$ m (3 sf).

You can use the other two formulas in the same way.

Exercise 14:6

For each question:
a Copy the triangle. Label the sides Hyp, Opp, Adj.
b Find the length of the side marked with a letter.
Round your answer to 3 sf.
Check that your answers seem reasonable.

1

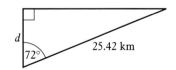

2

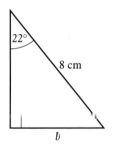

3

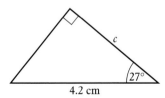

4

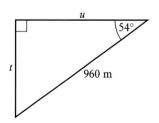

5

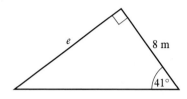

6

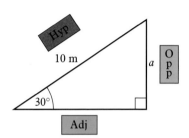

7

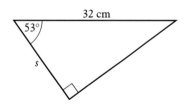

8

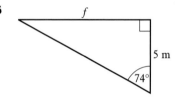

In some questions you have to work out more than one length. You draw a separate triangle for each length you need to find. In this diagram you need to find length *a* before you can find length *b*.

To find *a* draw triangle ADC separately. Then you work out *a* in the usual way.

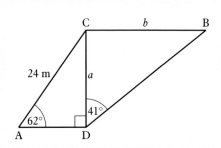

Which formula do you need?

Only the sin formula has opposite **and** hypotenuse in it.

Fill in the formula $\sin 62° = \dfrac{a}{24}$

Multiply both sides of the equation by 24 $\quad 24 \times \sin 62° = a$

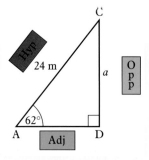

Key in: 2 4 sin 6 2 =

to get $a = 21.2$ m (3 sf).

You will need this in the next part but you must not use this rounded answer. Keep the **calculator** value of *a* on your calculator display. Now work out *b* by drawing triangle BCD.

Which formula do you need?

Only the tan formula has opposite **and** adjacent in it.

Fill in the formula $\quad \tan 41° = \dfrac{b}{21.19...}$

Multiply both sides of the equation by 21.19... $\quad 21.19... \times \tan 41° = b$

a is still on your calculator display.

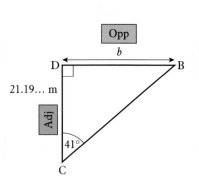

Key in:  × tan 4 1 =

to get $b = 18.4$ m (3 sf).

9

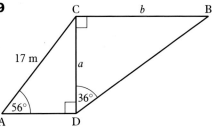

10

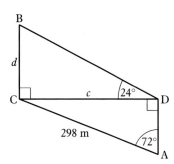

Working in isosceles triangles

You can split an isosceles triangle into 2 right-angled triangles.

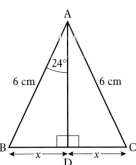

To find the base in this triangle split the triangle down the middle.
The angle in each half is $48 \div 2 = 24°$.

Now you have two right angled triangles.
These triangles are exactly the same.
They are congruent.
Call the base of each triangle x.

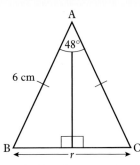

Look at triangle ABD $\sin 24° = \dfrac{x}{6}$

Multiply both
sides by 6 $6 \times \sin 24° = x$

$r = 2x$ so multiply
both sides by 2 to get $12 \times \sin 24° = r$

This gives $r = 4.88$ cm (3 sf).

11

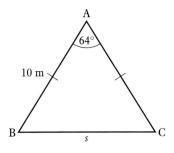

12

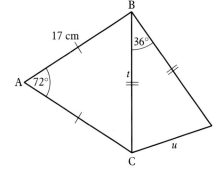

Exercise 14:7

In this exercise, round all your answers to 3 sf.

1 Billy is 27 metres from the base of a
tree.
He measures the angle shown to the top
of the tree. It is 42°. Find the height of
the tree.

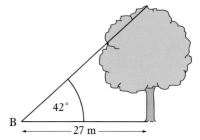

2 Sharon has climbed up the
Impossible Pinnacle in the Cuillin
hills. She sees her companion
Jacqui further along on the ridge.
Another friend takes this picture
and measures the angle shown.
Jacqui is 120 m from the base of
the pinnacle. Find the height of
the pinnacle.

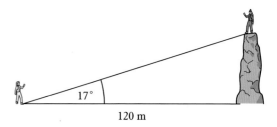

3 Rachel is running down the cliff path
marked in red.
  a How far has she descended
vertically?
  b How far to the left or right of point
A is she when she reaches B?

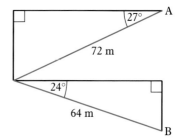

4 This is a section of the Grand Canyon.

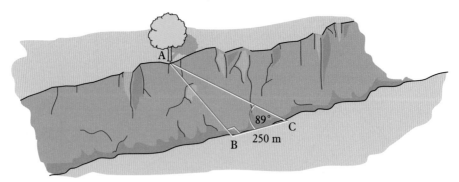

Sally stands at B. This is the point directly opposite the tree at A.
She then walks 250 m to C. Sally measures the angle BCA to be 89°.
Use Sally's measurements to find the distance AB across the Grand Canyon.

Exercise 14:8

In this exercise you will need to find angles and sides.
Find the angles and sides marked with letters.

1

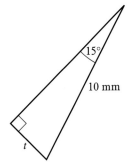

5

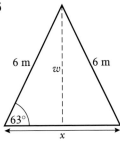

2

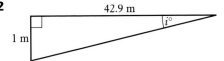

6

3

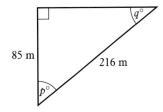

7 ABCD is a rectangle.

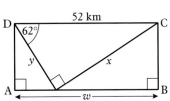

4

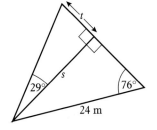

1 Asif has drawn a right-angled triangle RST.
   a Write down the value of cos t for Asif's triangle.
   b Write down the value of sin r.
   c Write down what you notice about your answers to parts **a** and **b**.

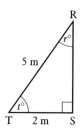

2 Round your answers to 1 dp in this question.
   a Find the angle BAC.   **b** Find the angle YXZ.

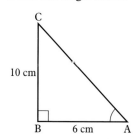

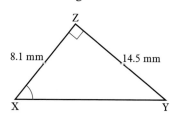

3 Round your answers to 3 sf in this question.
   a Find the length JK.   **b** Find the length RS.

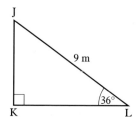

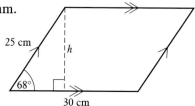

4 Susan wants to find the area of this parallelogram. She starts by working out the height.
   a Find the height h.
   b What is the area of the parallelogram? Round your answers to 3 sf.

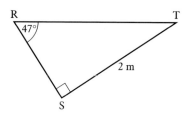

5 A UFO is 20 km from a mountain top. Its angle of descent is 22°. How high is it above the mountain?

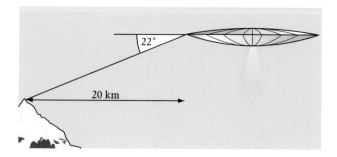

6 In each part of this question give the angles to a sensible degree of accuracy.

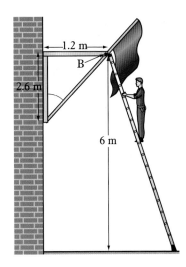

  a Henry is making a support for a flagpole on the town hall.
  He uses two planks. One is 2.6 m and the other is 1.2 m long.
  Find the angle between the pole and the wall.

  b Ten years later Neil comes to check the bolt at B with a ladder. B is 6 m above the pavement. The ladder is 8 m long. Calculate the angle that the ladder makes with the pavement.

7 A stuntwoman makes a motorcycle jump from the top of one skyscraper to another. One building is 10 m higher than the other. The angle across from the roof of one building to the other is 72°. Calculate the horizontal distance that she must jump.

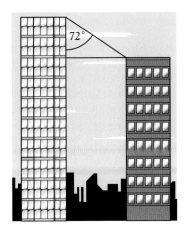

8 Ryan is crossing a mountain crevasse. He has to do it in two stages.
He abseils down from A to D and then pushes off from D to the pinnacle at B.
He then throws the same rope to Terry at C.
If the rope is 7 m long and the angle ABC is 106°, find the distance AC.

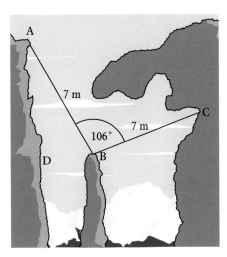

1 Find the angles marked with a letter.
Give your answers to a sensible
degree of accuracy.

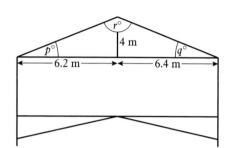

2 Madison bridge has a roof.
The roof is not symmetrical.
Some special ironwork is needed
over the ridge.
  a Find angles p and q.
  b Use these to work out angle r.

3 Steve has to drive his dumper up the
track in a quarry. The track is a
collection of slopes shown in red on
the diagram. After a lot of excavation
Steve's boss asked him to work out
the depth of the quarry. This is
Steve's diagram. He measured the
angles shown with a clinometer.
  a What is the depth of the quarry?
  b What is the width of the quarry
    used for the tracks?

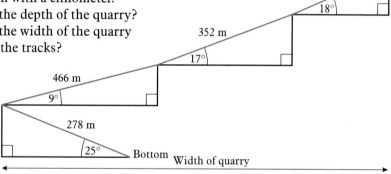

4 The picture shows the jib of a crane.
Using the information given, work
out the angle between the arms of the
jib.

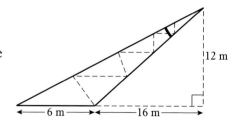

1 Find the angles marked with letters.
Give your answers to 1 dp.

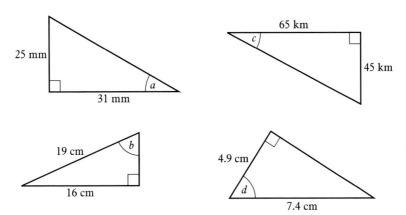

25 mm

31 mm

a

65 km

c

45 km

19 cm

16 cm

b

4.9 cm

7.4 cm

d

2 A railway climbs a cliff.
The track climbs steadily for 680 m.
The cliff is 147 m high.
Find the angle x.
Give your answer to 1 dp.

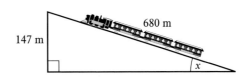

680 m

147 m

x

3 Find the sides marked with letters.
Give your answers to 3 sf.

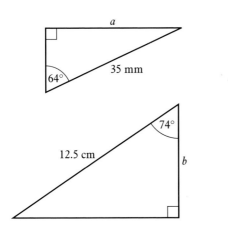

a

35 mm

64°

156 m

25°

c

74°

12.5 cm

b

35°

45 cm

d

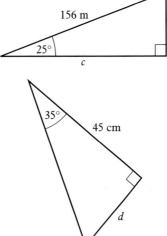

4 Find the angle x in this rectangle.
Give your answer to 1 dp.

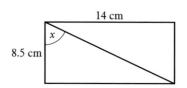

14 cm

x

8.5 cm

5 A boat leaves port and sails 21 nautical miles north and then 15 nautical miles east.
Find the bearing of its new position from the port.

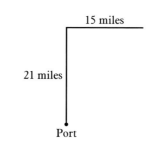

15 miles

21 miles

Port

6 Find the length x in this equilateral triangle.
Give your answer to 3 sf.

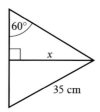

60°

x

35 cm

7 Matthew is using a ski-lift.
The lift travels 532 m at an angle of 43°.
How high does the lift climb?
Give your answer to 3 sf.

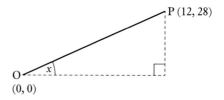

532 m

43°

8 a The point P has co-ordinates (12, 28).
O is the origin (0, 0).
Find the angle x, to 1 dp.

b The co-ordinates of G and H are (2, 3) and (14, 9) respectively.
Find the angle y, to 1 dp.

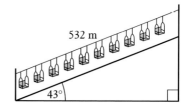

P (12, 28)

O
(0, 0)

x

H (14, 9)

y

G
(2, 3)

15 Algebra: changing form

CORE

1 Brackets
Collecting like terms
Multiplying out brackets
Multiplying out two brackets

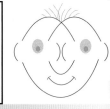

2 Factorising
Looking for common factors
Factorising quadratics

QUESTIONS

EXTENSION

TEST YOURSELF

1 Brackets

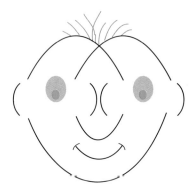

Let's face it, its about time you learnt how to multiply out brackets!

First, here is a recap of some of the skills you learnt in Chapter 6.

Collecting terms

Collecting terms means adding or subtracting terms in an equation or formula to make it simpler.
To collect terms together they must have exactly the same letters in them.

Example

Simplify these by collecting terms where possible.

a $t + t + t + t + t$ **c** $3ab^2 + 5ab^2 - 2ab^2$
b $3a + 6bc + 2a - 4bc$ **d** $3a^2b + 5ab^2$

  a Adding 5 ts together gives 5 lots of t.
     $t + t + t + t + t = 5 \times t = 5t$

  b The terms involving a can be collected together.
    So can the terms with bc in them.
    You can't collect the as and the bcs together.
     $3a + 6bc + 2a - 4bc = 5a + 2bc$

  c The terms all involve ab^2 so these can be collected.
     $3ab^2 + 5ab^2 - 2ab^2 = 6ab^2$

  d Both terms involve a and b and 'squared' but the power 2 is on a different letter in each term.
    These terms **cannot** be collected.

Exercise 15:1

1 Simplify these by collecting terms.
- **a** $g + g + g + h + h$
- **b** $k + k + k - s - s - s$
- **c** $t + t - t + h - h + h$
- **d** $k + k + k + r - r + r - r$
- **e** $y + y + t - y + t + t$
- **f** $a + a + a - a - a + b$

2 Simplify these by collecting terms.
- **a** $3g + 3g + 7g + 2g$
- **b** $5m + 7m - 5m + 3k + 5k$
- **c** $3t + 7t + 5s - 6s + 9s$
- **d** $3r - 6y + 5w - 9w$
- **e** $7y - 6y + 2h - 4h + y$
- **f** $5a - 12a + 3b - 5b + 8c$

3 Simplify these by collecting terms.
- **a** $3ab + 9ab$
- **b** $7mn - 5mn + 4mn$
- **c** $6ts - 2st$
- **d** $13pr - 8pr + 6kw - 10kw$
- **e** $9xy - 11xy + 3xz - 4xz$
- **f** $5ad - 9da + 6bc - 6cb$

Horace loves collecting things!

4 Simplify these by collecting terms where possible.
When it is not possible to collect terms, give a reason.
- **a** $3x^2 + 7x^2$
- **b** $7x^2 - 8x^2$
- **c** $5t^2 + 2t^3 + 2t^3$
- **d** $9r^2s - 6rs^2$
- **e** $5y^2 - 6y^2 - y^3$
- **f** $5a^2 - 3a^2 + 6a^3$

5 Simplify these by collecting terms where possible.
When it is not possible to collect terms, give a reason.
- **a** $7x^2 + 4x^2 + 8y^2 - 3y^2$
- **b** $11x^2 - 15x^2 - 7z^2 - 2z^2$
- **c** $5t^2y - 3h + 6ty^2 + 8h^2$
- **d** $8a^2b - 3a^2b - 3a^2b$
- **e** $3xy^2 + 9xy - 12x^2y$
- **f** $3x^2yz + 3yx^2z - zyx^2$

You also learnt how to multiply out brackets.

Example

Multiply out these brackets.
a $4(x + 7)$ **b** $-6(x^2 - 4)$ **c** $7(x^2 + 3x - 4)$

a To work out $4(x + 7)$ multiply the 4 and the x by the 7.
$$4(x + 7) = 4 \times x + 4 \times 7$$
$$= 4x + 28$$

b Notice that there is a minus sign outside the bracket.
$$-6(x^2 - 4) = -6 \times x^2 + (-6) \times (-4)$$
$$= -6x^2 + 24$$

c It doesn't matter how many terms there are in the bracket.
$$7(x^2 + 3x - 4) = 7 \times x^2 + 7 \times 3x + 7 \times (-4)$$
$$= 7x^2 + 21x - 28$$

Exercise 15:2

Multiply out these brackets.

1 $6(x + 3)$

2 $2(y - 5)$

3 $7(3x + 5)$

4 $5(7x - 3)$

5 $-3(x + 7)$

6 $4(2x - 1)$

7 $-6(5x + 5)$

8 $-5(y^2 - 3)$

9 $6(2y^2 - 4y)$

10 $5(x^2 - 3x - 7)$

11 $-4(x^2 + 5y - y^2)$

12 $-5(2xy - x^2z)$

You can also have letters outside the brackets.

Example

Multiply out these brackets.
a $c(d + 4)$ **b** $f(5f - 7)$ **c** $y^2(2y - x)$

a To work out $c(d + 4)$, multiply the d and the 4 by c.
$$c(d + 4) = c \times d + c \times 4$$
$$= cd + 4c$$

b In this part, notice that $f \times f$ gives you f^2.
$$f(5f - 7) = f \times 5f - f \times 7$$
$$= 5f^2 - 7f$$

c Always make sure that letters are written in alphabetical order.
$$y^2(2y - x) = y^2 \times 2y - y^2 \times x$$
$$= 2y^3 - xy^2$$

Exercise 15:3

Multiply out these brackets.

1 $x(x + 3)$ **4** $x(3x - 7)$ **7** $y(y^3 - 5y^2)$

2 $a(b - 7)$ **5** $x^2(2x + 4)$ **8** $4g(g^2 + 5g - 2)$

3 $c(c + 9)$ **6** $y(x^2 - 8)$ • **9** $xy^2(xy - xy^3)$

Multiplying out two brackets

Multiplying one bracket by another is just slightly more complicated. You have to remember to multiply *all* of the terms in the second bracket by *all* of the terms in the first bracket.

Here is a simple way of remembering how to do this.

Example   Multiply out $(x + 4)(x - 2)$.

(1) Multiply the two **F**irst terms together: $(x + 4)(x - 2)$ x^2

(2) Multiply the two **O**utside terms together: $(x + 4)(x - 2)$ $-2x$

(3) Multiply the two **I**nside terms together: $(x + 4)(x - 2)$ $4x$

(4) Multiply the two **L**ast terms together: $(x + 4)(x - 2)$ -8

(5) Collect all the terms together: $x^2 - 2x + 4x - 8$
$= x^2 + 2x - 8$

You can remember this using the word **FOIL**.
If you draw lines between the terms as you multiply them, you get a face! This may also help you to remember to multiply all the terms.

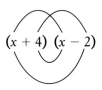

Exercise 15:4

1 Copy this diagram.
Use it to help you multiply out $(x + 3)(x + 2)$.

$(x + 3)(x + 2)$

2 Copy this diagram.
Use it to help you multiply out $(x + 5)(x + 8)$.

$(x + 5)(x + 8)$

3 Multiply out each of these pairs of brackets.

   a $(x + 3)(x + 7)$

   b $(x + 4)(x - 7)$

   c $(x + 3)(x - 9)$

   d $(x - 4)(x + 5)$

   e $(x + 5)(x - 3)$

   f $(x - 4)(x + 2)$

   g $(x - 10)(x - 5)$

   h $(x - 4)(x - 8)$

4 Multiply out each of these pairs of brackets.

   a $(2x + 3)(x + 2)$

   b $(3x + 4)(x - 3)$

   c $(4x + 3)(x - 1)$

   d $(3x - 4)(x + 9)$

   e $(2x + 5)(x - 6)$

   f $(7x - 1)(2x + 2)$

   g $(2x - 10)(3x + 6)$

   h $(5x - 4)(5x - 6)$

2 Factorising

Terry and Louise are doing an investigation.

They have found different formulas for the same problem.

They want to know if they are the same.

Factorising is the opposite of multiplying out brackets.
When you factorise you put brackets in!

The first thing to look for is a common factor in the numbers.

Example

Factorise $6x + 10y$

The numbers 6 and 10 both have a factor of 2.
2 is the biggest number that divides exactly into 6 and 10.
You take the 2 outside a bracket as a factor.
$6x + 10y = 2(\qquad)$

Next, you work out what goes inside the bracket.
$2 \times 3x = 6x$ and $2 \times 5y = 10y$
So inside the bracket you are left with $3x + 5y$.

This means that $6x + 10y = 2(3x + 5y)$.

You can check that 2 is the largest factor you could have taken out by looking at what is left inside the bracket.
3 and 5 have no common factors so the 2 is correct.

Exercise 15:5

1 Factorise each of these.
Use the hints to help you in parts **a** to **g**.

a $6x + 14 = 2($ $)$ **h** $9x - 15$

b $3x - 9 = 3($ $)$ **i** $10x - 15$

c $8y - 12 = 4($ $)$ **j** $18y - 12$

d $5t + 15 = 5($ $)$ **k** $27t - 18$

e $14x - 7 = 7($ $)$ **l** $15x - 10y + 20z$

f $16x - 12 = 4($ $)$ **m** $6y - 6x - 6z$

g $24y - 36 = 12($ $)$ **n** $12e + 4f - 24g$

You can also take letters outside brackets as common factors.

The expression $xy + xz$ has a common factor of x.
$xy + xz$ has an x in both terms.
So $xy + xz = x(y + z)$

The expression $y^2 + y$ has a common factor of y.
$y^2 + y$ has a y in both terms.
So $y^2 + y = y(y + 1)$

Notice the 1 at the end of the bracket. It is very important.
If you multiply the bracket out you must get back to where you started.
$$y(y + 1) = y \times y + y \times 1$$
$$= y^2 + y$$

If you missed the 1 out, you would not get the y term at the end.

---

2 Factorise each of these.
Use the hints to help you in parts **a** to **g**.

a $tx + ty = t($ $)$ **h** $pq - p^2$

b $ab + ac = a($ $)$ **i** $t^3 + t$

c $3x - xy = x($ $)$ **j** $x^3 + x^2 + x$

d $5x - 2xz = x($ $)$ **k** $8xz - 3ax$

e $y^2 + 5y = y($ $)$ **l** $g^4 + g^2$

f $3x^2 + 5x = x($ $)$ **m** $7x + 13x^3$

g $2j + 4jk = 2j($ $)$ **n** $5y^2 + 3y + 4yz$

Sometimes you can take out numbers *and* letters as factors.

Example

Factorise completely $15x^2 - 10x$.

15 and 10 have a common factor of 5.
So $15x^2 - 10x = 5(3x^2 - 2x)$

$3x^2$ and $2x$ have a common factor of x.
So $15x^2 - 10x = 5x(3x - 2)$

You could do this all at once by seeing that the common factor is $5x$.

Exercise 15:6

1 Factorise each of these.
Use the hints to help you.
  a $6x^2 + 3x = 3x($)
  b $15y^2 - 5y = 5y($)
  c $4st + 8sr = 4s($)
  d $9t^2 - 3st = 3t($)

2 Factorise each of these.
  a $10x^2 + 5x$
  b $12y^2 + 6y$
  c $18st - 27sr$
  d $40t^2 + 30st$

3 Factorise each of these.
  a $6x^2 + 3xy - 12xz$
  b $5t^2 - 5tr - 5ts$
  c $4ab^2 + 8ab - 12a^2b$
  d $36h^3 - 12h^2 + 18h$

4 Kelly factorises $24y^3 - 18y^2 + 30yz$.
She writes the answer as $3(8y^3 - 6y^2 + 10yz)$.
  a Explain how you can tell that Kelly has not *fully* factorised the expression.
  b Factorise the expression fully.

371

Factorising quadratics

Exercise 15:7

1 Multiply out each of these pairs of brackets:

   a $(x + 3)(x + 7)$ e $(x + 5)(x - 3)$

   b $(x + 4)(x - 7)$ f $(3x - 4)(2x + 2)$

   c $(x + 3)(x - 9)$ g $(6x - 4)(2x - 5)$

   d $(x - 4)(x + 5)$ h $(7x - 4)(2x - 8)$

2 Copy this table. Use your answers to question **1** parts **a** to **e** to fill it in. The first one is done for you.

	number at end of 1st bracket	number at end of 2nd bracket	coefficient of x	constant term
a	3	7	10	21
b	4	-7		
c	3	-9		
d	-4	5		
e	5	-3		

In question **2** you should have noticed that when you multiply out two brackets that both start with x:

The **coefficient of x** is found by *adding* the two numbers at the end of the brackets together.

The **constant term** is found by *multiplying* the two numbers at the end of the brackets together.

Example $(x + 4)(x - 7) = x^2 \quad -3x \quad -28$

$+4 + -7 = -3$ $+4 \times -7 = -28$

Once you know these facts, you can use them to reverse the process. This means taking a quadratic expression and splitting it back into two brackets.

This process is known as **factorising a quadratic**.

Example

Factorise $x^2 + 5x + 6$.

The brackets will be $(x + ?)(x + ?)$.

The two numbers at the end of the brackets
add together to give 5 and
multiply together to give 6.

The two numbers that do this are 2 and 3.
So $x^2 + 5x + 6 = (x + 2)(x + 3)$

3 Factorise these quadratic expressions.

a $x^2 + 7x + 10$

b $x^2 + 10x + 16$

c $x^2 + 12x + 27$

d $x^2 + 14x$

e $x^2 + 15x + 36$

f $x^2 - 3x - 18$

g $x^2 - 7x - 30$

h $x^2 + 4x - 32$

i $x^2 + 6x - 40$

j $x^2 - x$

You will also find it helpful to look at the signs in the equation you are factorising.

$x^2 + 5x + 6$ The number at the end is $+6$.
$= (x + ?)(x + ?)$ The numbers must be the same sign so that they
multiply to give a $+$.
They must both be $+$ because they add to give $+5$.

$x^2 - 7x + 10$ The number at the end is $+10$.
$= (x - ?)(x - ?)$ The numbers must be the same sign so that they
multiply to give a $+$.
They must both be $-$ because they add to give -7.

$x^2 + 3x - 10$ The number at the end is -10.
$= (x + ?)(x - ?)$ The numbers must have different signs so that they
multiply to give a $-$.
The $+$ number must be bigger because they add to
give a $+$ total.

4 Factorise these quadratic expressions.

a $x^2 + 5x - 14$ f $x^2 - x - 12$

b $x^2 - 4x - 5$ g $x^2 + x - 12$

c $x^2 - 12x + 32$ h $x^2 - 7x - 44$

d $x^2 + 17x + 60$ ● i $x^2 + x + 0.25$

e $x^2 + 8x - 20$ ● j $x^2 - 9$

Difference of two squares	A quadratic expression which is in the form $x^2 - a^2$ is known as the **difference of two squares**. Difference means subtract. The same rules still work when you are factorising it.

Example

Factorise $x^2 - 16$.
There is no x term so the numbers in the two brackets add to give 0 and multiply to give -16.
They are $+4$ and -4.
$x^2 - 16 = (x - 4)(x + 4)$

The general rule is $x^2 - a^2 = (x - a)(x + a)$

Exercise 15:8

1 Factorise these quadratic expressions.

a $x^2 - 25$ e $x^2 - 49$

b $x^2 - 36$ ● f $x^2 - b^2$

c $x^2 - 100$ ● g $x^2 - 0.25$

d $x^2 - 1$ h $x^2 - 289$

2 You can use this method to speed up some calculations.

a Copy this and fill in the gaps.
$$36^2 - 34^2 = (36 + ...)(36 - ...)$$
$$= \quad ... \times ...$$
$$=$$

b Use the same method to work out $49^2 - 48^2$.

c Work out $1001^2 - 999^2$.

d Work out $1\,000\,001^2 - 999\,999^2$.

Exercise 15:9

Sharon is still struggling with her algebra.
She is still trying to cope without
Key Maths!

Here is her factorising homework.

Decide which questions are correct and
which are wrong.
For the questions you think are wrong,
write out correct answers.

1 $3x + 6 = 3(x + 6)$

2 $xy + xz = x(y + z)$

3 $4y^2 + 5y = y^2(4 + 5)$

4 $sp^2 - sp = s(p^2 - p)$

5 $6ax + 4ay + 3az = 2a(3x + 2y + 1\frac{1}{2}z)$

6 $15x^2y + 5xy^2 = 5xy(3xy + y)$

7 $x^2 + 3x + 2 = (x + 3)(x + 1)$

8 $x^2 + 5x - 6 = (x - 2)(x - 3)$

9 $x^2 + 7x + 12 = (x + 3)(x + 4)$

10 $x^2 - 16 = (x - 4)(x - 4)$

11 $x^2 - 121 = (x - 11)(x + 11)$

12 $18^2 - 16^2 = (18 - 16)(18 + 16)$
$$= 2 + 34$$
$$= 36$$

1   Simplify these by collecting terms.

a $5f + 2f + 7f + 2f$ **g** $5w - 4x + 2y - 3w$

b $4n + 3n - 2n + 3j + 4j$ **h** $7d - 5d + 3e - e + 4f$

c $2v + 5v + 4h - 5h + 9h$ **i** $6b - 12b + 3c - 4c + 6d$

d $6ab + 5ab$ **j** $11gh - 7gh + 8jk - 11jk$

e $4mn - 3mn + 5mn$ **k** $6ab - 4ab + 7ac - 5ac$

f $5ba - 2ab$ **l** $3ac - 7ca + 9bc - 3cb$

2   Simplify these by collecting terms where possible.
When it is not possible to collect terms, give a reason.

a $5x^2 + 8x^2$ **g** $12x^2y - 6xy^2$

b $6y^2 - 7y^2$ **h** $7y^3 - 6y^3 - y^3$

c $4p^2 + 4t^3 + 4t^3$ **i** $4a^2 - 3a^2 + a^3$

d $9p^2 + p^2 + 4q^2 - 3q^2$ **j** $7a^2b - 4a^2b - 2a^2b$

e $12a^2 - 14a^2 - 8c^2 - 2c^2$ **k** $7cd^2 + 10cd - 11c^2d$

f $6a^2b - 3c + 8ab^2 + 8c^2$ **l** $2p^2qr + 4qp^2r - rqp^2$

3   Find the perimeter of each of these.
Simplify your answers.

a

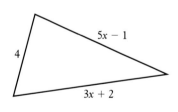

c

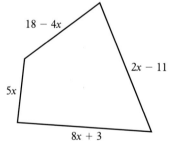

b

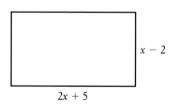

d

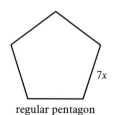

regular pentagon

4 Multiply out these brackets.

a $4(x + 2)$

b $3(y - 3)$

c $6(2x + 3)$

d $5(5x - 1)$

e $x(x + 2)$

f $a(b - 8)$

g $c(c + 1)$

h $-2(x + 3)$

i $3(3x - 4)$

j $-3(4x + 1)$

k $-4(y^2 - 4)$

l $x(4x - 5)$

m $x^2(x + 2)$

n $b(a^2 - 3)$

o $4(3y^2 - 7y)$

p $6(5x^2 - 2x - 6)$

q $-5(2x^2 + 3y - y^2)$

r $-2(4xy - 3x^2z)$

s $y(3y^2 - 3x^2)$

t $2k(k^2 + 3k - 2)$

u $xy(x^2y - xy^2)$

5 Multiply out each of these pairs of brackets.

a $(x + 2)(x + 4)$

b $(x + 4)(x - 5)$

c $(x + 5)(x - 8)$

d $(x - 3)(x + 4)$

e $(2x + 2)(x - 2)$

f $(4x + 1)(x - 6)$

g $(3x - 5)(x + 7)$

h $(2x + 5)(2x - 4)$

i $(4x - 3)(3x + 1)$

j $(3x - 8)(4x - 4)$

k $(3x - 10)(3x - 5)$

l $(7x - 4)(2x + 2)$

m $(2x - 10)(3x + 2)$

n $(5x - 3)(5x - 5)$

6 Find the area of each of these rectangles.
Multiply out any brackets and simplify your answers.

a

7

$x + 5$

c

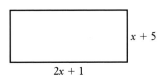

$x + 5$

$2x + 1$

b

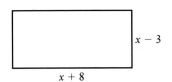

$x - 3$

$x + 8$

d

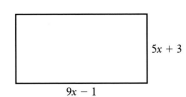

$5x + 3$

$9x - 1$

7 Factorise each of these.
Use the hints to help you in parts **a** to **g**.

a $6x + 12 = 6($ $)$ **h** $4x - 8$

b $4x - 12 = 4($ $)$ **i** $8x - 12$

c $9y - 15 = 3($ $)$ **j** $24y - 12$

d $6t + 18 = 6($ $)$ **k** $24t - 16$

e $16x - 8 = 8($ $)$ **l** $20x - 15y + 20z$

f $12x - 8 = 4($ $)$ **m** $3y - 3x - 3z$

g $20y - 30 = 10($ $)$ **n** $12e + 4f - 24g$

8 Factorise each of these.
Use the hints to help you in parts **a** to **d**.

a $ta + tb = t($ $)$ **e** $pr - p^2$

b $ax + ay = a($ $)$ **f** $k^3 + k$

c $6x - xy = x($ $)$ **g** $r^3 + r^2 + r$

d $4x - 3xy = x($ $)$ **h** $6xy - 3ax$

9 Factorise each of these.
Use the hints to help you in parts **a** to **c**.

a $8y^2 + 4y = 4y($ $)$ **d** $12q^2 - 3pq$

b $20t^2 - 5t = 5t($ $)$ **e** $12w^2 + 6w$

c $4r^2 + 8rs = 4r($ $)$ **f** $30f^2 + 20fg$

10 Factorise these quadratic expressions.

a $x^2 + 5x + 4$ **f** $x^2 - 2x - 24$

b $x^2 + 9x + 14$ **g** $x^2 - 8x - 20$

c $x^2 + 14x + 40$ **h** $x^2 + 2x - 35$

d $x^2 + 16x$ **i** $x^2 + 7x - 30$

e $x^2 + 13x + 36$ **j** $x^2 - 3x$

11 Factorise these quadratic expressions.

a $x^2 - 16$ **e** $x^2 - 64$

b $x^2 - 49$ **f** $x^2 - 0.64$

c $x^2 - 121$ **g** $x^2 - y^2$

d $x^2 - 4$ **h** $x^2 - 256$

1 A rectangle has a length of $(x + 5)$ cm and a width of $(x - 2)$ cm.

    a If the perimeter of the rectangle is 24 cm find the value of x.

    b If the area of the rectangle is 60 cm^2 show that $x^2 + 3x - 70 = 0$

2 When you square an expression you need to multiply it by itself.
If the expression is in a bracket this means that you must multiply the bracket by itself.

So $(x + 2)^2$ means $(x + 2)(x + 2)$

Work these out.

    a $(x + 2)^2$ **c** $(x - 3)^2$ **e** $(2x + 3)^2$ **g** $(2x - 3)^2$

    b $(x + 4)^2$ **d** $(x - 5)^2$ **f** $(3x + 8)^2$ **h** $(3x - 4)^2$

3 Not all quadratic expressions start with just x^2.
Many start with $2x^2$ or $3x^2$ etc.
If you want to factorise $2x^2 + 7x + 3$ you need to start by deciding what goes at the beginning of each bracket.
One of the brackets must begin with a $2x$.
This is the only way to get $2x^2$ as the first term.
So $2x^2 + 7x + 3 = (2x + ?)(x + ?)$
The two numbers at the end of the brackets must still multiply together to give the constant term.
So you need to try different pairs of values at the end of the brackets until you get the right answer.

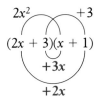

$2x^2$ $+3$

$(2x + 3)(x + 1)$

   $+3x$

   $+2x$

$2x^2$ $+3$

$(2x + 1)(x + 3)$

   $+x$

   $+6x$

This is wrong because the $+3x$ and the $+2x$ give you $+5x$ and you need $+7x$.

This is right. The $+x$ and the $+6x$ give you $+7x$.

Factorise these quadratics.

    a $2x^2 + 7x + 3$ **c** $2x^2 + 12x + 10$ **e** $5x^2 + 2x - 3$

    b $3x^2 + 13x + 4$ **d** $7x^2 + 22x + 3$ **f** $2x^2 + 3x - 9$

1 Simplify these by collecting like terms.

  a $5k - 2k + k + 7k - 4k$

  b $10x - 3y + 2y - x + 4x$

  c $2d + d^2 - 4 + 5d^2 - 8 + 3d$

  d $6ab^2 + 3a^2b - 8ab^2$

2 Multiply out these brackets and simplify where possible.

  a $4(y - 5)$ **c** $2s(6s - 1)$ **e** $(x + 8)(2x - 1)$

  b $3(x^2 + 2x)$ **d** $b^2(8b + 1)$ **f** $(5x - 9)(4x - 1)$

3 **a**   Find the perimeter of this quadrilateral. Simplify your answer.

    b   The perimeter is 38 cm. Write down an equation in x. Solve your equation.

    c   Use your answer to part **b** to find the lengths of the four sides.

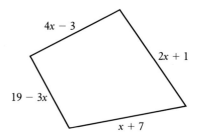

4 Write down the area of this rectangle.
Multiply out the brackets and simplify the answer.

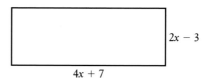

5 Factorise each of these.

  a $6t - 4$ **c** $24ab^2 + 10ab$

  b $12y^2 + 4y$ **d** $12x^2 - 6xy + 9xy^2$

6 Factorise these quadratic expressions.

  a $x^2 + x - 12$ **c** $y^2 - 10y + 16$

  b $a^2 + 8a + 7$ **d** $x^2 - 81$

16 Statistics: about average

1 Averages

During most races cars will make at least one pit stop to change the tyres. Mechanics have been known to change all four tyres in less than 5 seconds.

Average	An **average** is a value that you use to represent a set of data. It is a single value that tells you about the size of the data.

Exercise 16:1

1 **a** Choose a single value to represent this data.
You don't have to do any calculations.

   6   7   7   7   6   7   7   5   9

   b Explain how you chose the value.

 ● **c** Write down *two* things about the data that make it easy to choose a value.

2 **a** Try to use the same method to find a single value to represent this set of data.
Explain why the method does not work this time.

   1   2   3   1   2   3   1   2   3

 ● **b** Try to use the same method to find a value for this set of data.
Explain why the method doesn't give you a good value to use.

   36   1   35   32   1   33   39   1   37

3 This is the data from question **2** again. The data is now in order of size.
Use a new method to choose a value to represent each set of data.
You still don't have to do any calculations.
Explain your new method.

   a 1   1   1   2   2   2   3   3   3
   b 1   1   1   32   33   35   36   37   39

4 **a** Use your new method to find a value to represent each of these sets of data.
  (1) 7 9 10 11 13
  (2) 7 9 10 15 19
  (3) 7 9 10 28 36
b Explain a possible weakness of your new method.

5 **a** Try to use your new method to find a value to represent this set of data.

     16 20 17 25 22 24

Explain why the method does not work as well this time.
b You can find a value to represent the data in part **a** if you change the method slightly. Explain what to do.

6 **a** This is the data from question **4** again.
Use a new method to choose a value to represent each set of data.
You *do* need to do some calculations now.
  (1) 7 9 10 11 13
  (2) 7 9 10 15 19
  (3) 7 9 10 28 36
b Explain your new method.
c Use your new method to find a value to represent this data.

     110 114 149 138 162

Explain a possible weakness of your new method.

7 **a** Use your new method to find a value to represent this data.
     15 18 14 16 19 17 20 607
  b Explain why the method doesn't give you a good value to use.
● **c** Which method would you use to find a value to represent this data?

● **8** Explain why you need more than one type of average.
Write down the strengths and weaknesses of each method.

You have just used three types of average.
The first type that you used is called the **mode**. This is the easiest average to find if it exists.
The second type is called the **median**.
This works well if you have some extreme values that could distort your average.
The last type is called the **mean**.
This is the average that people usually think is the best.
It uses every value. But it can be distorted by extreme values.

Mean	To find the **mean** of a set of data: (1) find the total of all the data values (2) divide the total by the number of data values.

Example	These are the times that a team of mechanics took to change the tyres during 5 pit stops. Find the mean time.

Times (seconds)   7.3   8.2   7.9   9.6   7.5

The total time is

$$7.3 + 8.2 + 7.9 + 9.6 + 7.5 = 40.5 \text{ seconds}$$

The mean time is

$$40.5 \div 5 = 8.1 \text{ seconds}$$

Exercise 16:2

1 These are the pit stop times, in seconds, for three teams of mechanics.
Find the mean time for each team.

  a Williams   7.6   8.3   7.9   9.2   7.8   8.6   8.0
  b McLaren   6.1   7.9   7.0   6.3   8.2
  c Lotus   8.3   9.0   8.1   7.8
  d Use your means to write down the team that, on average, is:
    (1) the fastest   (2) the slowest

2 These are the number of wins per make of car between 1980 and 1990.

Ferrari	McLaren	Lotus	Williams	Brabham	Tyrrell
104	104	79	78	35	23

  a Find the mean number of wins for these makes.
  b Write down the make of car whose number of wins is closest to the mean.
  c Write down the make of car whose number of wins is furthest from the mean.

3 Each car manufacturer wants to set the fastest time for a lap.
These are the numbers of fastest laps set by each of the main
manufacturers between 1980 and 1990.

Ferrari	McLaren	Lotus	Williams	Brabham	Tyrrell
119	69	71	83	40	20

Find the mean number of fastest laps for these makes of car.

4 These are the times that a team of mechanics took to change the tyres
during 3 pit stops.

   Time (seconds)   8.1   7.9   9.2

a Find the mean time.
b After the next pit stop the new mean time was 8.3 seconds.
How long did this pit stop last?

5 Chris is testing a new type of car. These are his lap times, in seconds, for
his first six test laps.

   79   81   84   84   88   82

a Find the mean of these lap times.
b Chris drives another lap and his new mean time is 82 seconds.
How long did he take for his seventh lap?
c Chris drives one more lap.
He wants the overall mean time to be 81 seconds.
How fast must he drive the last lap?

Mode

The **mode** is the most common or most popular data value.
It is sometimes called the **modal value**.
The mode is most useful when one value appears much more
often than any other value. If the data values are too varied then
you should not use the mode.

Example

These are the numbers of wins for drivers in a season.

Andretti	Mansell	Hunt	Sena	Ascari	Prost	Schumacher
6	9	6	7	6	7	8

What is the modal number of wins?

6 is the number of wins that appears the most.
The modal number of wins is 6.

Exercise 16:3

1 These are the numbers of wins for drivers in another season.

Mansell	Senna	Lauda	Fangio	Prost	Hill	Brabham
9	8	5	6	7	5	5

What is the modal number of wins?

2 These are the numbers of most consecutive wins for some drivers.

Mansell	Senna	Lauda	Moss	Fangio	Prost	Hill	Brabham
5	4	3	3	4	4	3	4

What is the modal number of consecutive wins?

3 The bar chart shows the ages of Jason's favourite racing drivers. What is the modal age?

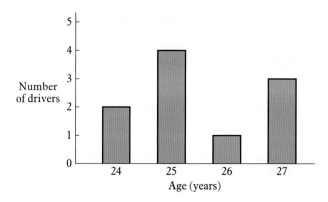

4 The table shows the number of wins per driver in Formula 1 races during the 1997 season.

Driver	Coulthard	Villeneuve	Frentzen	Schumacher	Berger	Hakkinen
Number of wins	2	7	1	5	1	1

  a What is the modal number of wins for these drivers?
  b Is the mode a good average to use here? Explain your answer.
  c If you included *all* the drivers who took part in the 1997 season, what do you think the modal number of wins would be?

Median	To find the median you put all the data values in order of size. The **median** is then the **middle** value.

Example These are the numbers of Grands Prix entered by some drivers.

Lauda	Bonnier	Fittipaldi	Mansell	Brabham	Surtees	Berger
171	102	144	185	126	111	163

Find the median number of Grands Prix entered.

Write the numbers in order. Start with the smallest.

102   111   126 (144) 163   171   185

Find the middle number. It is 144.
The median number is 144.

Sometimes there are two numbers in the middle.
When this happens: add the two middle numbers together
divide the answer by 2

Example These are the pulse rates of 8 drivers when they are resting.

32   41   43 (46   50) 57   63   67

Find the median.
There are two numbers in the middle: 46 and 50

46 + 50 = 96   96 ÷ 2 = 48

The median is 48.

---

5 These are the pit stop times, in seconds, for three different teams of mechanics.
Find the median time for each team.
 a Williams   7.6   8.3   7.9   9.2   7.8   8.6   8.0
 b McLaren   6.1   7.9   7.0   6.3   8.2
 c Lotus   8.3   9.0   8.1   7.8

6 These are the lengths, in miles, of some Grands Prix circuits.

Spa	Monza	Silverstone	Monaco	Imola	Montreal	Hockenheim
4.350	3.604	3.142	2.068	3.042	2.765	4.234

Find the median length of these circuits.

7 **a** Find the median number of wins for the drivers in question **1**.
 b Find the median number of consecutive wins for the drivers in question **2**.

You can find averages from frequency tables.

This table shows the number of pit stops taken by Formula 1 drivers in one race.

Number of stops	Frequency
1	2
2	11
3	10
4	1
Total = 24	

this row shows that 10 cars stopped 3 times → (points to row 3)

The **modal number** of stops is the number with the highest frequency.
The mode is 2.
There are a lot of 3s that get ignored if you use the mode.

The **median** is the middle value.
There are 24 data values. They are

1, 1, 2, 2, 2, 2, 2, 2, 2, 2, 2, (2, 2,) 3, 3, 3, 3, 3, 3, 3, 3, 3, 3, 4

The two middle values are both equal to 2.
So the median is 2.
The median gives the same result as the mode. Both methods ignore the high number of 3s.

The **mean** is $\dfrac{\text{Total number of stops}}{\text{Total frequency}}$

You need to find the total number of stops.
To do this you need to add another column to the table.
You work out the number of stops on each row.

Number of stops	Frequency	Stops × frequency
1	2	$1 \times 2 = 2$
2	11	$2 \times 11 = 22$
3	10	$3 \times 10 = 30$
4	1	$4 \times 1 = 4$
	Total = 24	Total = 58

10 cars stopped 3 times.
This gives 30 stops

The mean number of stops is $\frac{58}{24} = 2.41... = 2.4$ to 1 dp.

Even though it is impossible to have 2.4 stops, the mean gives a value that represents the data. It is more than 2 and allows for the high number of 3s.

Exercise 16:4

1 The times that teams take to change tyres have been rounded to the nearest second.
The table shows the number of teams for each time.

Time (seconds)	Frequency	Time × frequency
8	2	8 × 2 = 16
9	4	
10	7	
11	3	
	Total =	Total =

a Copy the table.
Fill in the last column and the totals.
b Find the mean time.
Give your answer to 1 dp.
c Write down the modal time.
d Find the median time.

2 The table shows the number of mechanics that teams have.

Number of mechanics	Frequency	Mechanics × frequency
5	3	
6	7	
7	10	
8	6	
	Total =	Total =

a Copy the table.
Fill in the last column and the totals.
b Find the mean number of mechanics.
Give your answer to 1 dp.
c Write down the modal number of mechanics.
d Find the median number of mechanics.

3 The times that some Formula 1 teams took to change a set of tyres have been rounded to the nearest second. One of the teams struggled with a faulty wheel nut.
The table shows the number of teams for each time.

Time (seconds)	Frequency	Time × frequency
5	2	
6	3	
7	7	
8	1	
87	1	
	Total =	Total =

a Copy the table.
Fill in the last column and
the totals.
b Find the mean time.
Give your answer to 1 dp.
c Write down the modal time.
d Find the median time.
e Which average does not represent
the data well in this question?

4 The average number of children per family in the UK is often quoted as 2.4 even though it is impossible to have 2.4 children.
a Which average has been used to give this figure?

A recent newspaper article claims that the figure for Scotland has fallen to 1.5 children per family. The article goes on to say that the Scottish race will disappear within 20 generations unless the trend is reversed.

b Round 2.4 and 1.5 to the nearest
whole number.
c Explain why the mean number of
children per family should be given
to at least one decimal place.
d What advantage does the mean have
over the mode and median to
represent the number of children
per family?

There is a quicker way to find the median.
Here is the data about the numbers of Grands Prix entered by 7 drivers.
The middle value is the 4th in the list.

102   111   126   (144)   163   171   185

You can find the term number that you need by:

adding 1 to the number of terms $7 + 1 = 8$
and then dividing by 2 $8 \div 2 = 4$

This still works for an even number of values.
Here is the data from the last example about the number of pit stops
during a race.

Number of stops	Frequency
1	2
2	11
3	10
4	1
Total = 24	

There are 24 data values. $(24 + 1) \div 2 = 12\frac{1}{2}$
So you want to find the $12\frac{1}{2}$th value.
You want the value that is halfway between the 12th and the 13th terms.

You can write all the terms out to find the 12th and the 13th terms as before.
But this could take a long time if there were 100 terms!
There is a quick way of deciding what the 12th and 13th terms are.
Look at the totals as you go down the table.

Number of stops	Frequency	Running total
1	2	2
2	11	$2 + 11 = 13$
3	10	
4	1	
Total = 24		

By the time you've listed
the 2s you have 13 terms.
So the 12th and 13th
terms must both be 2

So the median is 2.

Exercise 16:5

1 Find the position of the middle term if the total frequency is:
  a 19   **b** 35   **c** 20   **d** 38   **e** 60

2 The table shows how many races some drivers have entered.

Number of races	Frequency
8	9
9	5
10	7
11	10

  a Find the total number of drivers.
  b Find the mean number of races that they have entered.
     Give your answer to 1 dp.
  c Write down the modal number of races entered.
  d Find the median number of races entered.

3 The table shows the ages in years of Formula 1 racing cars that are still in use.

Age (years)	Frequency
1	15
2	18
3	10
4	4
5	1

  a Find the total number of cars.
  b Find the mean age of the cars.
     Give your answer to 1 dp.
  c Write down the modal age of the cars.
  d Find the median age of the cars.

2 Get it together

The picture shows all the people who work in a car factory.
The senior management get paid much more than the cleaners.
The management say that the average salary for all the people who work in the factory is £17 000.
Do you think that this is a fair claim?
Which measure of average do you think they are using?

When you are dealing with a lot of data you can put the data into groups.
This makes the data easier to deal with but you can only *estimate* averages.

Here are the boys' results in a Year 10 maths test.
They have been grouped in tens.

Mark	31 to 40	41 to 50	51 to 60	61 to 70	71 to 80	81 to 90	91 to 100
Number of boys	5	14	28	35	24	16	9

Look at the first column.
You know that 5 boys scored between 31 and 40 but you do not know *exactly* what each of them scored.

To work out an estimate for the mean, you have to assume that all 5 of them scored the mark in the middle of the group.

This middle value is $\dfrac{31 + 40}{2} = 35.5$

In the same way you have to assume that the 14 people in the second column all scored the middle of that group.

This middle value is $\dfrac{41 + 50}{2} = 45.5$

Work out the mid-points and draw a new table which looks like this.

Mark (mid-point)	35.5	45.5	55.5	65.5	75.5	85.5	95.5
Number of boys	5	14	28	35	24	16	9

Now you can work out the mean as if these were the scores that everybody got.

$$\text{Mean} = \frac{35.5 \times 5 + 45.5 \times 14 + 55.5 \times 28 + 65.5 \times 35 + 75.5 \times 24 + 85.5 \times 16 + 95.5 \times 9}{130}$$

$$= \frac{8700.5}{130}$$

$$= 66.9 \, (1 \, \text{dp})$$

This is only an *estimate* for the mean.
You have assumed that all the people in each group have scored the middle mark in each group.
This may not be true, so your mean may well be wrong!

When data is grouped you cannot tell which data value is the most common.
So you cannot find the mode.
You can only say which group has the most values in it.
This group is called the **modal group**.
For the boys' test marks the modal group is 61 to 70 marks.

You cannot say what the median is either! You cannot write out the values in order to find the middle one. You can estimate the median value and you will see how to do this in Chapter 25 of Intermediate II.

You can only estimate the range too!
An **estimate for the range** is the *biggest possible* value take away the *smallest possible* value.

For the boys' marks the biggest possible value is 100 and the smallest is 31.
An estimate for the range is 69 marks.

Exercise 16:6

1 Here are the girls' scores in the same maths test.

Mark	31 to 40	41 to 50	51 to 60	61 to 70	71 to 80	81 to 90	91 to 100
Number of girls	2	19	21	26	21	19	12

a Copy this table. Fill in the mid-points for each group of marks.

Mark (mid-point)	35.5						
Number of girls	2	19	21	26	21	19	12

b Work out an estimate for the mean. Give your answer to 1 dp.
c Write down the modal group for the girls' marks.
d Write down an estimate for the range of the marks.

2 Norman asks his form how long it takes them to get to school.
He asks for the time to the nearest minute.

Time (min)	1 to 5	6 to 10	11 to 15	16 to 20	21 to 25	26 to 30	31 to 35
Number of pupils	2	7	10	5	3	2	1

a Copy this table. Fill in the mid-points for each group of times.

Time (mid-point)	3						
Number of pupils	2	7	10	5	3	2	1

b Work out an estimate for the mean. Give your answer to 1 dp.
c Write down the modal group for the times.
d Write down an estimate for the range of the times.

3 Here are the wages of the people who work at the car factory.

Wages (£)	1–10 000	10 001–20 000	20 001–30 000	30 001–100 000
Number of people	25	39	10	6

a Copy this table. Fill in the mid-points for each group.

Wages (mid-point)				
Number of people	25	39	10	6

b Work out an estimate for the mean.
   Give your answer to the nearest £.
c Write down the modal group for the wages.
d Write down an estimate for the range of the wages.
e Do you think that your answer to part **b** is a fair average?
   Explain your answer.

Exercise 16:7 – Back at the races

1 The table shows the time, to the nearest second, that people spent queuing at the turnstiles.

Time (secs)	1–20	21–30	31–40	41–60
Number of people	3	17	32	28

a Work out an estimate for the mean time spent queuing.
b Write down the modal group for the time spent queuing.
c Work out an estimate for the range of time spent queuing.

2 The table shows the amount of money spent at a race meeting.

Money spent (£)	0.01–10	10.01–20	20.01–30	30.01–40	40.01–50
Number of people	6	14	28	19	13

a Write down the modal class.
b Work out an estimate of the mean amount of money spent by each person.

Sometimes the groups that you have to use are written using algebra.
This usually happens when you have continuous data.
These are some of the ways that groups can be written.

$10 < x \leqslant 20$ This means that the values in the group are between 10 and 20.
20 is included in the group. 10 is not.
You use 10 and 20 to find the middle of the group.
15 is the middle of the group.

$10 \leqslant x < 20$ This means that the values in the group are between 10 and 20.
This time 10 is included in the group. 20 is not.
You still use 10 and 20 to find the middle of the group.
15 is the middle of the group.

$10- \quad 20- \quad 30-$ This means that the first group is values of 10 and more.
20 is in the second group.
So another way of writing the first group is $10 \leqslant x < 20$
The middle of this group is 15 as before.

$-10 \quad -20 \quad -30$ This means that the first group is values up to and including 10.
20 is in the second group. 10 is not.
So another way of writing the second group is $10 < x \leqslant 20$
The middle of this group is 15 as before.

3   The table shows the time spent by people travelling to a race meeting.

Time (min)	$10 \leqslant x < 60$	$60 \leqslant x < 120$	$120 \leqslant x < 180$	$180 \leqslant x < 240$
Number of people	29	145	204	31

   a   Write down an estimate for the range of the times.
   b   Work out an estimate for the mean time spent travelling.

4   The table shows the engine sizes in litres of the cars in the car park at the meeting.

Engine size (litres)	-1	-2	-3	-4
Number of cars	32	181	112	45

   a   Write down the modal group of the engine sizes.
   b   Work out an estimate for the mean engine size.

Averages can be used to show trends in data.
Look at this graph.
It shows Rob's weekly scores in cricket.
The lines drawn on the graph are trend lines.
The blue line shows that Rob is improving.
The red line shows that Rob is getting worse.
But which line is correct?

To answer this question we can use a moving average.

Here are Rob's scores for the first 10 weeks of the season:

15   25   10   15   13   20   12   18   15   17

The average of the first 4 weeks' scores is $(15 + 25 + 10 + 15) \div 4 = 16.25$

Now remove the first week and add in the fifth week.
The average of these scores is $(25 + 10 + 15 + 13) \div 4 = 15.75$

Now remove the second week and add in the sixth week.
The average of these scores is $(10 + 15 + 13 + 20) \div 4 = 14.5$

This is called a 4-point moving average.
It is called a moving average because the data values you are using move along one each time.
It is called 4-point because it always includes 4 data values.

These are the values you get if you calculate all the moving averages.

16.25   15.75   14.5   15   15.75   16.25   15.5

These moving averages show that the trend is actually that Rob's scores are staying steady.

The moving average can be plotted on the graph to show the trend.
You do not have to use a 4-point moving average.
You can use 3-point, 5-point or any other number.

Moving averages are used by businesses to show trends in their sales. They are useful when sales are affected by seasonal trends. Sales of ice-cream or wellys are examples that are affected by the season!

Exercise 16:8

1 These are the numbers of people travelling on a train each day for 10 days.

     45   31   50   36   48   38   46   39   49   56

    a Work out the average of the first 4 values.
    b Remove the first value and add in the fifth value.
        Work out the average of these values.
    c Remove the second value and add in the sixth value.
        Work out the average of these values.
    d Continue to work out the 4-point moving average for the rest of the
        data. Show your working and write down each value.

2 Alan records his golf scores over a period of 8 weeks.
These are his scores:

     84   87   81   92   86   95   79   83

Work out a 3-point moving average for Alan's scores.
Show your working and write down each value.

You can plot the moving average on a graph to produce a trend line.

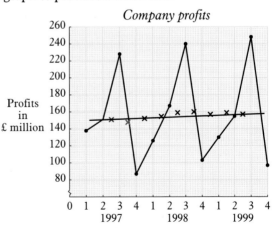

Company profits

This graph shows a company's
profits in each quarter of the year
over a period of 3 years.
A 4-point moving average has been
calculated for this data.
The **first average** is from
quarters 1, 2, 3 and 4.
On the graph the average is plotted
in the middle of these values.
The first value is plotted between
quarters 2 and 3.

The second average value covers
quarters 2, 3, 4 and 1.
It is plotted between quarters 3
and 4.

Once all the points are plotted, a line of best fit is drawn through them.
This is the trend line.

---

3 This table shows the number of computers a shop sold in each quarter of the year over a period of 3 years.

	1998	1999	2000
1st quarter	315	340	351
2nd quarter	571	590	592
3rd quarter	446	470	491
4th quarter	963	989	

a Copy these axes onto graph paper and draw a graph to show this data.

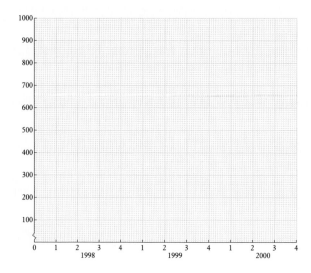

b Calculate a 4-point moving average from the data in the table.
c Plot the moving average as a set of points onto your graph. Use a different colour if you can.
d Draw a line of best fit through your points to produce a trend line.
e Why is it difficult to use your trend line to predict the sale for the last quarter of 2000?

4 A school wants to publish data on its GCSE exam results.
The Headteacher uses the data on the percentage of pupils gaining 5 or more A*–C grades.
This is the data for the last 8 years.

Year	1993	1994	1995	1996	1997	1998	1999	2000
% 5 A*–C	46	49	50	45	40	48	45	50

a Plot this data on a graph.
b Work out a 3-point moving average for this data.
c Plot the averages on your graph.
The first point should be plotted at 1994.
d Draw a line of best fit to show the trend of the data.

1   These are Penny's marks for tests in five subjects.

Maths (%)	65	53	57	71	60	72
English (%)	82	64	51	74	64	49
History (%)	64	50	58	63	59	66
Art (%)	58	64	78	56	71	66
French (%)	57	46	62	49	56	63

   a   Find the mean mark for each subject.
   b   Use the means to decide which are Penny's best and worst subjects.
   c   Find the median mark for each subject.

2   Find the median of each set of data.
   a   7, 5, 7, 3, 9, 2, 1, 6, 3   **c**   35, 38, 28, 31, 42, 30
   b   13, 18, 25, 20   **d**   3.4, 2.6, 4.8, 3.8, 1.9, 2.0, 1.5

3   Write down the mode of each set of data.
   a   2, 3, 5, 3, 2, 6, 3, 1, 8   **c**   23, 27, 24, 28, 26, 25, 24, 21
   b   18, 17, 12, 16, 17, 18, 17   **d**   2, 4, 7, 4, 3, 2, 6, 7, 2, 4, 7, 4

4   George has scored a mean of 12 runs in the last four cricket matches.
   a   What is his total number of runs in all four matches?
   b   His mean score must be 15 or more for him to be picked for the
      school team. How many runs must he make in the next match if he is
      to be picked for the school team?

5   The noon-day temperature was measured at Silverstone on 30
   consecutive days. The results are shown in the frequency table.

Temperature (°C)	12	13	14	15	16	17	18
Number of days	1	7	4	3	6	2	7

   a   Find the mean temperature to 1 dp.
   b   Write down the modal temperatures.
   c   Find the median temperature.

6 Trish asked all the people in her class how much money they spend each month. Here are her results:

Amount (£)	0–9.99	10–14.99	15–19.99	20–24.99	25–50
Number of people	3	7	9	7	4

a Copy this table. Fill in the mid-points for each group.

Amount (£) (mid-point)					
Number of people	3	7	9	7	4

b Work out an estimate for the mean.
Give your answer to the nearest penny.
c Write down the modal group for the amount of money spent.
d Write down an estimate for the range of the amount of money spent.

7 A factory has two machines that make bottle caps.
The table shows the number of rejects per day for the two machines over a period of time. Neither machine had more than 30 rejects on any one day.

Number of rejects	1–	6–	11–	16–	21–	26–
Machine A	4	13	16	12	8	7
Machine B	2	24	3	9	12	10

a Draw a separate table for Machine A showing the mid-points for each group.
b Work out an estimate for the mean.
Give your answer to 1 dp.
c Draw a separate table for Machine B and use it to work out an estimate for the mean.
d Use the two means to compare the two machines.
e Write down the modal class for each machine.
f Use the modes to compare the two machines.

8 These are the numbers of people who used the mobile library each week for the last 9 weeks.

237   308   296   167   372   255   271   310   362

a Work out the average of the first 3 values.

b Remove the first value and add in the fourth value. Work out the average of these values.

c Remove the second value and add in the fifth value. Work out the average of these values.

d Continue to work out the 3-point moving average for the rest of the data.

9 Jane makes wedding cakes.
These are the numbers of cakes she made each month for 2000.

January	12	July	39
February	16	August	32
March	24	September	29
April	20	October	18
May	27	November	5
June	26	December	12

Work out a 4-point moving average for the number of cakes that Jane made.

10 Chris is a driving instructor.
These are the number of his pupils who passed their driving test first time each quarter.

	1998	1999	2000
1st quarter	15	18	17
2nd quarter	24	20	18
3rd quarter	20	23	19
4th quarter	14	19	24

Work out a 4-point moving average for the data.

1   Anna is testing a new route to work. These are her times, in minutes, for the first five journeys:

     23   17   22   19   21

   a   Find the mean of these times.
   b   After her sixth journey her new mean time is 20 minutes.
      How long did she take for this journey?
   c   Anna drives to work another four times.
      She works out the overall mean to be 22.5 minutes.
      Find the mean for these last four journeys.

2   Steve is doing a survey of how much people earn in a week.
He has drawn these bar-charts to show his results for 100 women and 100 men.

For parts **a** to **c** work out the answers for (1) women and (2) men.
   a   Work out an estimate for the mean weekly wage.
   b   Write down the modal class.
   c   Write down an estimate of the range of the weekly wages.
   d   Steve wants to tell people that women are as well paid as men.
      Can he use his data to back up this idea?
   e   Use the data to show Steve that he is wrong.

1 Mia recorded the time that each of 20 patients had to wait at a
   dental practice.
   This is her data. The times are in minutes.

   5   9   11   2   4   6   9   12   13   7
   3   5   10   14   12 8   7   10   5   4

   Find **a** the mode   **b** the median   **c** the mean

2 These are the number of goals that Tom's football team scored in each
   match last season.

Number of goals	0	1	2	3	4
Number of matches	7	11	7	2	3

   a How many matches did Tom's team play last season?
   b Find the mean number of goals scored per match.
   c Write down the modal number of goals.

3 These are the attendances at a safari park for 5 days.

   256   328   156   208   297

   a Find the mean attendance.
   b After the 6th day the mean attendance was 259.
   How many attended on the 6th day?

4 Six girls and six boys took part in a contest.
   They had to solve a page of logic problems and were scored out of 50.
   These were the scores of the girls:

   38   29   47   39   46   45

   a What was their mean score?
   b What was the range of the girls' scores?

   The mean of the boys' scores was 41 and the range was 26.
   c Compare the girls' scores with the boys' scores.

5 The table shows the amount of money, in £s, that families spent on transport in one week.

Amount, A (£)	Number of families
$0 < A \leqslant 10$	6
$10 < A \leqslant 20$	14
$20 < A \leqslant 30$	22
$30 < A \leqslant 40$	17
$40 < A \leqslant 50$	8

a Copy the table.
Add a column to your table showing the mid-points of the amounts of money.

b Work out an estimate for the mean amount spent on transport.

c Explain why the mean you calculated in part **b** is only an estimate for the actual mean.

d Write down the modal group.

6 The table shows the number of pupils in a village primary school for a period of 8 years.

Year	1993	1994	1995	1996	1997	1998	1999	2000
Pupils	40	32	41	39	37	40	45	39

a Copy the axes onto graph paper and draw a graph to show this data.

b Work out a 4-point moving average for the data.

c Plot the moving average as a set of points on your graph.

d Draw a line of best fit through your points to produce a trend line.

e Why is it difficult to use your trend line to predict the number of pupils for year 2001?

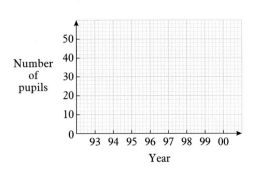

17 Round and round

QUESTIONS

EXTENSION

TEST YOURSELF

1 Circumference and perimeter

The Earth moves in an orbit around the Sun. It takes the Earth 365 days, 5 hours, 48 minutes and 46 seconds to complete one orbit.

The Earth moves so that it is always between 91.4 and 94.6 million miles from the Sun.

If you take the orbit to be a circle of radius 93 million miles that takes 365 days to complete, then we are hurtling through space at more than 66 700 miles per hour!

Diameter	The distance across a circle is called the **diameter**. A diameter must pass through the centre of the circle.

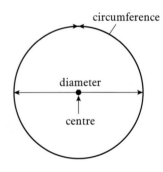

Circumference	The **circumference** of a circle is the distance around the edge of the circle. The circumference depends on the diameter of the circle.

π	If you divide the circumference of any circle by its diameter you always get the same answer. This answer is a special number called pi. You say this as 'pie' and you write π.

For all circles
Circumference = $\pi \times$ diameter
This rule is often written $C = \pi d$

Key in $\boxed{\pi}$ on your calculator.

You should get 3.1415927

You might get more digits than this.
It depends which calculator you have.

Example   Find the circumference of this circle.

$$C = \pi d$$
$$= \pi \times 8$$

Key in: | π | $\times$ | 8 | $=$ |

25.132741

= 25.1 cm to 1 dp

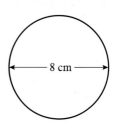
8 cm

Exercise 17:1

1 Find the circumference of these circles. Give your answers to 1 dp.

a
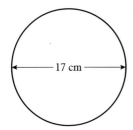
17 cm

d
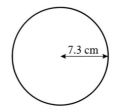
7.3 cm

b

17.1 cm

e
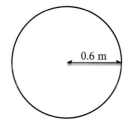
0.6 m

c
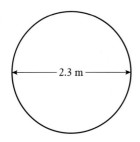
2.3 m

f
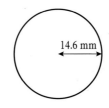
14.6 mm

2 This is a photo of a motorway roundabout.
The diameter of the roundabout is 62 m.
Find the circumference of the roundabout.
Give your answer to the nearest metre.

3 Henry lives in a circular windmill.
He is a bit eccentric.
Every day he walks around the
outside of his house 100 times.
The windmill has a radius of 3.2 m.
  a How far does Henry walk each
    time he goes round his house?
  b How far does Henry walk each
    day? Give your answer to the
    nearest metre.

4 David is stencilling around the
circumference of a circular table. The
diameter of the table is 130 cm.
  a Find the circumference of the
    table.
David is using a stencil that is 20 cm
long.
  b How many times can David repeat
    the pattern around the table?
 • **c** The pattern must be evenly
    spaced. How much space should
    David leave between each pattern?

• **5 a** Write down the formula for the circumference, C, of a circle with
    diameter d.

  b Rearrange the formula to show that $d = \dfrac{C}{\pi}$.

    This is the formula that you need to use to find the diameter if you
    are given the circumference.

  c Find the diameter of a circle that has a circumference of 20 cm.

Radius

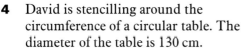

The **radius** of a circle is the distance from the centre to the
circumference. The radius is half the diameter.

Example

The circumference of a circle is 38 cm.
Find   **a** the diameter   **b** the radius

  a Use the formula $d = \dfrac{C}{\pi}$

$$d = \frac{38}{\pi}$$

Key in:

$d = 12.1$ cm to 1 dp   to get *12.095776*

b The radius is half the diameter.
Don't use the rounded value for the diameter.

Keep the exact value from part **a** in
your calculator display and halve that.
Then round your answer.

12.095776

Key in: ÷ 2 =

to get 6.0478878

$r = 6.0$ cm to 1 dp

Exercise 17:2

1 Find
(1) the diameter
(2) the radius
of a circle with a circumference of:
a 80 cm **b** 25 cm **c** 120 cm **d** 47.3 cm
Give all your answers to 1 dp.

2 The circumference of a circle is 4 m.
Find **a** the diameter **b** the radius
Give your answers to 2 dp.

3 Find the radius of a circle that has a circumference of 124 cm.
Give your answer to 1 dp.

4 The world's largest Big Wheel is the
Cosmoclock 21 at Yokohama City in
Japan. It has a circumference of
1031 feet. Find the radius of the
wheel. Give your answer to the
nearest foot.

| Perimeter | The **perimeter** of a shape is the distance around the edge of the shape. |

To find the perimeter add up
the lengths of all the sides.
The perimeter of this shape is
    $4 + 6 + 10 + 14$
    $= 34$ cm

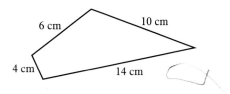

6 cm   10 cm

4 cm   14 cm

Exercise 17:3

1 Find the perimeter of each of these shapes.

a
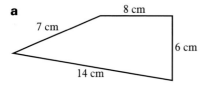
8 cm
7 cm
6 cm
14 cm

b
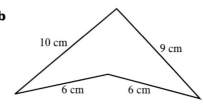
10 cm
9 cm
6 cm   6 cm

2 Find the perimeter of each of these shapes.
There is enough information to be able to do these questions!

a
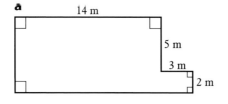
14 m
5 m
3 m
2 m

b
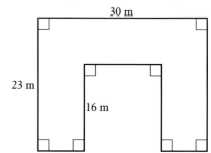
30 m
23 m
16 m

3 Find the perimeter of an equilateral triangle with sides of length 3.5 cm.

4 The Pentagon is the building that holds
the offices of the US defence department.
It is the largest office building in the
world.
It is a regular pentagon.
Each outside wall is 281 m long.
Find the perimeter of the building.

For a circle the perimeter is the circumference.

Example Find the perimeter of this shape.

The shape is a rectangle and a semi-circle.

Add up the lengths around the edge of the
rectangle first.

Red perimeter = 12 + 18 + 12
= 42 cm

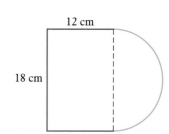
12 cm
18 cm

Now work out the blue part of the perimeter.
This is half of the circumference of a circle with diameter 18 cm.

$$\text{Blue perimeter} = \tfrac{1}{2} \times \pi \times d$$
$$= \tfrac{1}{2} \times \pi \times 18$$
$$= 28.3 \text{ cm to 1 dp}$$

Key in:

Now add up the two parts of your answer.

$$\text{Total perimeter} = 42 + 28.3$$
$$= 70.3 \text{ cm}$$

Exercise 17:4

Work out the perimeter of each of these shapes. Give all of your answers to 1 dp.

1

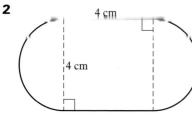
16 cm
20 cm

2

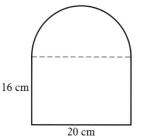
4 cm
4 cm

3

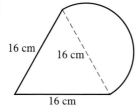
16 cm
16 cm
16 cm

4

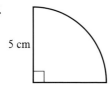
5 cm

5

8 cm
16 cm

6

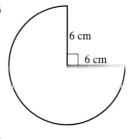
6 cm
6 cm

● 7

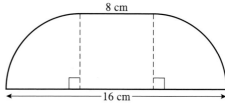
3 cm
4 cm · 4 cm
4 cm · 4 cm

● 8

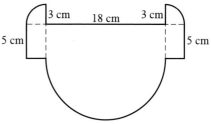
3 cm · 18 cm · 3 cm
5 cm · 5 cm

413

Sometimes a question will ask you to give an *exact* answer.

You have been working out circumferences using $\pi = 3.141592654$ on your calculator. Although this gives you 9 decimal places and is very accurate, it is not exact. This is because π is a decimal which goes on forever. You could never write the exact answer down as a decimal, however many digits your calculator had.

The only way to give an exact answer is to leave π in your answer.

Example   Find the circumference of a circle with radius 12 cm.
Leave your answer in terms of π.

$$\text{Circumference} = \pi \times \text{diameter}$$
$$C = \pi \times 24$$
$$= 24\pi$$

This is the exact answer.
Leave answers like this if you are asked for an exact answer or asked to leave your answer in terms of π.

Exercise 17:5

1   Find the circumference of each of these circles.
Leave your answers in terms of π.

a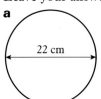
22 cm

b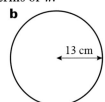
13 cm

c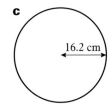
16.2 cm

2   Find the exact perimeter of this shape.

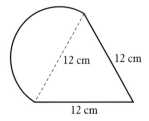
12 cm   12 cm

12 cm

Using dimensions

You can use the dimension of a formula to help you decide what the formula is for. You will see more of this in *Intermediate II*.

Dimension

The **dimension** of a formula is the number of lengths that are multiplied together.

Length has **one** dimension.

$C = 2d$ is a length formula.

Any formula for length can only involve constants and **one** length.

2 is a constant.
d is a length.

Constant

A **constant** has no dimension. It is just a number.
2, 3, 1.7, and π are all constants.

Area has **two** dimensions.

$A = \pi r^2$ is an area formula.

Any formula for area can only involve constants and **two** lengths that are multiplied together.

π is a constant.
$r^2 = r \times r$
which is length $\times$ length.

Volume has **three** dimensions.

$V = \frac{4}{3}\pi r^2 h$ is a volume formula.

Any formula for volume can only involve constants and **three** lengths that are multiplied together.

$\frac{4}{3}$ and π are constants.
$r^2 h = r \times r \times h$ which is
length $\times$ length $\times$ length

Exercise 17:6

1 In this question p, q and r are lengths.
Write down the dimension of each of these expressions.

a p	**c** $2rq$	**e** pqr	**g** $3pq$
b $3p$	**d** $4pq$	**f** $5kr$	**h** $5p$

2 In this question l, b, h and r are lengths.
Which of these formulas could be for length?

a $3l$	**b** $2\pi l$	**c** $r(r + h)$	**d** $2\pi(r + b)$

3 In this question p, q, r, s and t are lengths.
Write down what each formula could represent.

a $p + s$	**c** $2rq + 4st$	**e** $5p + r$	**g** p^3
b $3q + 5t$	**d** $4pq + 2rp$	**f** $5\pi p + 3r$	**h** p^2q

2 Units of length

At the start of the 19th century French scientists invented a new unit of length. They worked out the distance from the North Pole to the Equator and divided it by 10 million. They called this distance 1 metre. The metric system of weights and measures is named after the metre.

Metric units of length

The **metric units of length** are millimetres (mm), centimetres (cm), metres (m) and kilometres (km).

$$1 \text{ cm} = 10 \text{ mm}$$
$$1 \text{ m} = 100 \text{ cm}$$
$$1 \text{ km} = 1000 \text{ m}$$

Example

Change each of these to the units given.

a 16 cm to mm   **c** 0.98 km to m
b 3.7 m to cm   **d** 2.3 m to mm

a There are 10 mm in every cm.
So   16 cm = 16 × 10 mm
         = 160 mm

b There are 100 cm in every m.
So   3.7 m = 3.7 × 100 cm
        = 370 cm

c There are 1000 m in every km.
So 0.98 km = 0.98 × 1000 m
         = 980 m

d Do this question in two stages.
There are 100 cm in every m.
So   2.3 m = 2.3 × 100 cm
        = 230 cm
There are 10 mm in every cm.
So   230 cm = 230 × 10 mm
         = 2300 mm

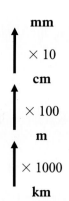

mm
× 10
cm
× 100
m
× 1000
km

Exercise 17:7

1 Change each of these lengths into mm.

a	7 cm	**d**	163 cm	**g**	0.6 cm	● **j**	2 m
b	32 cm	**e**	19.8 cm	**h**	23.5 cm	● **k**	5.2 m
c	125 cm	**f**	0.7 cm	**i**	10.4 cm	● **l**	67 m

2 Change each of these lengths into cm.

a	3 m	**d**	243 m	**g**	0.7 m	● **j**	3 km
b	24 m	**e**	24.1 m	**h**	12.6 m	● **k**	3.2 km
c	212 m	**f**	0.45 m	**i**	120.1 m	● **l**	56 km

3 Change each of these lengths into m.

a	4 km	**d**	159 km	**g**	0.74 km	**j**	0.342 km
b	82 km	**e**	32.8 km	**h**	23.51 km	**k**	5.122 km
c	121 km	**f**	0.5 km	**i**	10.42 km	**l**	67.341 km

4 Change each of these lengths into mm.

a	6 cm	**d**	113 m	**g**	0.8 m	**j**	4 cm
b	42 m	**e**	15.6 cm	**h**	23.1 cm	**k**	7.2 m
c	1.1 km	**f**	0.6 km	**i**	20.4 m	**l**	0.17 km

Example Change each of these to the units given.

a 230 mm to cm   **c** 9780 m to km

b 135 cm to m   **d** 1340 mm to m

a Every 10 mm make a cm.
Find how many lots of 10 mm are in 230 mm.
230 ÷ 10 = 23 so 230 mm = 23 cm

b Every 100 cm make a m.
Find how many lots of 100 cm there are in 135 cm.
135 ÷ 100 = 1.35 so 135 cm = 1.35 m

c Every 1000 m make a km.
Find how many lots of 1000 m there are in 9780 m.
9780 ÷ 1000 = 9.78 so 9780 m = 9.78 km

d Do this question in two stages.
Every 10 mm make a cm. So 1340 mm = 1340 ÷ 10 = 134 cm
Every 100 cm make a m. So 134 cm = 134 ÷ 100 = 1.34 m

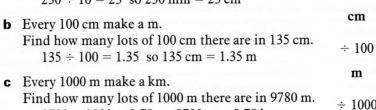

mm
÷ 10
cm
÷ 100
m
÷ 1000
km

Exercise 17:8

1 Change each of these lengths into cm.

a	70 mm	**d**	1630 mm	**g**	6 mm	**j**	9.3 mm
b	320 mm	**e**	198 mm	**h**	13.5 mm	**k**	5.2 mm
c	1250 mm	**f**	7 mm	**i**	10.4 mm	**l**	6.71 mm

2 Change each of these lengths into m.

a	400 cm	**d**	2430 cm	**g**	70 cm	**j**	3000 mm
b	2500 cm	**e**	241 cm	● **h**	6 cm	**k**	320 mm
c	2120 cm	**f**	45 cm	● **i**	8.1 cm	● **l**	56 mm

3 Change each of these lengths into km.

a	40 000 m	**d**	2100 m	**g**	7480 m	● **j**	3422 cm
b	8000 m	**e**	3200 m	**h**	2315 m	**k**	5 122 000 mm
c	3000 m	**f**	5210 m	**i**	104 200 cm	● **l**	67 341 mm

● **4** Change each of these lengths into km.

a	6000 m	**d**	1 213 000 mm	**g**	2800 cm	**j**	4 m
b	420 m	**e**	156 000 mm	**h**	1.2 m	**k**	720 cm
c	13 410 cm	**f**	232.6 m	**i**	70 000 mm	**l**	51 cm

5 Dave swims 40 lengths of the swimming pool each day.
The pool is 50 m long.
How many km does Dave swim each day?

6 The measurements of kitchen units are always given in mm.
Chris needs a unit to fit in a space that measures 150 cm × 58 cm × 87 cm.

He can buy units in three sizes.

Unit A   1600 mm × 500 mm × 870 mm
Unit B   1470 mm × 550 mm × 870 mm
Unit C   1500 mm × 600 mm × 870 mm

Which unit should he buy?
Explain your answer.

Imperial units of length

The **imperial units of length** are inches (in), feet (ft), yards (yd) and miles (m).

This system is mainly used in the UK and the USA.

Because m is used for metres as well as miles you have to be careful! In this section we will not use these abbreviations for the imperial units.

$$1 \text{ foot } = 12 \text{ inches}$$
$$1 \text{ yard } = 3 \text{ feet}$$
$$1 \text{ mile } = 1760 \text{ yards}$$

Example

Change each of these to the units given.

a 3 feet to inches   **c** 6 feet 3 inches to inches

b 4 yards to feet   **d** $2\frac{1}{2}$ miles to yards

a There are 12 inches in every foot.

So   3 feet $= 3 \times 12$ inches

          $= 36$ inches

inches

↑ $\times 12$

b There are 3 feet in every yard.

So   4 yards $= 4 \times 3$ feet

          $= 12$ feet

feet

↑ $\times 3$

c   6 feet $= 6 \times 12$ inches

            $= 72$ inches

So 6 feet 3 inches $= 72 + 3$ inches $= 75$ inches

yards

↑ $\times 1760$

d There are 1760 yards in every mile.

So $2\frac{1}{2}$ miles $= 2\frac{1}{2} \times 1760$ yards

           $= 4400$ yards

miles

Exercise 17:9

1 Change each of these lengths into inches.

a 7 feet	**d** 30 feet	**g** 6 feet 3 inches	**j** 9 feet 9 inches
b 10 feet	**e** $2\frac{1}{2}$ feet	**h** 15 feet 4 inches	**k** 5 feet 7 inches
c 12 feet	**f** $5\frac{1}{2}$ feet	**i** 10 feet 7 inches	**l** $7\frac{3}{4}$ feet

2 Change each of these lengths into feet.

a 4 yards	**d** 24 yards	**g** 1250 yards	**j** 300 yards 2 feet
b 2 yards	**e** 40 yards	**h** 6 yards 2 feet	**k** $3\frac{1}{2}$ yards
c 12 yards	**f** 155 yards	**i** 8 yards 1 foot	**l** $5\frac{1}{3}$ yards

3 Change each of these lengths into yards.

a 3 miles	**d** 21 miles	**g** 7 miles 123 yards	**j** $3\frac{1}{2}$ miles
b 8 miles	**e** 30 miles	**h** 20 miles 345 yards	**k** $5\frac{1}{2}$ miles
c 12 miles	**f** 50 miles	**i** 15 miles 129 yards	**l** $6\frac{1}{4}$ miles

---

Example Change each of these to the units given.

    a 108 inches to feet   **c** 9680 yards to miles

    b 12 feet to yards   **d** 15 840 feet to miles

a Every 12 inches makes a foot.

    Find how many lots of 12 inches are in 108 inches.

        $108 \div 12 = 9$ so 108 inches = 9 feet

inches

$\downarrow \div 12$

b Every 3 feet make a yard.

    Find how many lots of 3 feet are in 12 feet.

        $12 \div 3 = 4$ so 12 feet = 4 yards

feet

$\downarrow \div 3$

c Every 1760 yards make a mile.

    Find how many lots of 1760 yards are in 9680 yards.

        $9680 \div 1760 = 5.5$ so 9680 yards make 5.5 miles.

        5.5 miles is the same as $5\frac{1}{2}$ miles.

yards

$\downarrow \div 1760$

miles

d Do this question in two stages.

    Every 3 feet make a yard.   So 15 840 feet = $15\,840 \div 3$ = 5280 yards

    Every 1760 yards make a mile. So 5280 yards = $5280 \div 1760 = 3$ miles

---

Exercise 17:10

1 Change each of these lengths into feet.

    a 24 inches   **b** 60 inches   **c** 120 inches   **d** 144 inches

2 Change each of these lengths into yards.

    a 15 feet   **b** 24 feet   **c** 120 feet   **d** 3540 feet

3 Change each of these lengths into miles.

    a 3520 yards   **b** 21 120 yards   **c** 11 440 yards   **d** 18 480 yards

4 Change each of these lengths into miles.

a 31 680 feet	**c** 32 736 feet	**e** 27 456 yards	**g** 126 720 inches
b 18 480 feet	**d** 11 264 yards	**f** 35 376 feet	**h** 221 760 inches

---

Example   Change 6336 yards into miles and yards.

Every 1760 yards make a mile.
Find how many lots of 1760 yards are in 6336 yards
       6336 yards = 6336 ÷ 1760 = 3.6 miles
     3.6 miles is the same as 3 miles and 0.6 of a mile left over.
       0.6 mile   = 0.6 × 1760 = 1056 yards.
     So 3.6 miles = 3 miles 1056 yards

---

5   Change each of these lengths into miles and yards.
     a   5104 yards   **c**   25 344 yards   **e**   36 696 yards   • **g**   29 568 feet
     b   18 480 yards   **d**   24 024 yards   • **f**   11 088 feet   • **h**   95 040 inches

6   Change each of these lengths into yards and feet.
     a   13 feet   **c**   122 feet   **e**   12 233 feet   • **g**   396 inches
     b   47 feet   **d**   3421 feet   • **f**   96 inches   • **h**   420 inches

7   Change each of these lengths into feet and inches.
     a   78 inches   **b**   183 inches   **c**   561 inches   • **d**   380 inches

Converting between imperial and metric units

                                   Conversion number
1 inch is about 2.5 cm   **2.5**
1 foot is about 30 cm   **30**
1 yard is about 90 cm   **90**
1 yard is about 0.9 m   **0.9**
1 mile is about 1.6 km   **1.6**

If you want to convert from imperial to metric units you have to know these.
It might help you to remember the conversion numbers.

To change from imperial to metric
you **multiply** by the conversion number.
To change from metric to imperial
you **divide** by the conversion number.

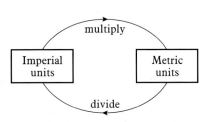

Example

    a Convert 4 yards to cm.
    b Convert 56 km to miles.

    a Every yard is about 90 cm.
       Multiply by the conversion number.
       4 yards = 4 × 90 = 360 cm

    b There are about 1.6 km in every mile.
       Divide by the conversion number.
       56 km = 56 ÷ 1.6 = 35 miles

Exercise 17:11

Give your answers to 1 dp when you need to round.

1 Change each of these lengths into cm.
a 2 inches	**d** 120 inches	**g** 21 feet	**j** 12 yards
b 14 inches	**e** 3 feet	**h** 40 feet	**k** 25 yards
c 22 inches	**f** 5 feet	**i** 5 yards	**l** $6\frac{1}{2}$ yards

2 Change each of these lengths into m.
a 5 yards	**c** 50 yards	**e** 200 yards	● **g** 36 fcct
b 20 yards	**d** 125 yards	**f** 500 yards	● **h** 354 feet

3 Change each of these lengths into km.
a 35 miles	**b** 110 miles	**c** 240 miles	**d** 500 miles

4 Change each of these lengths into inches.
a 25 cm	**c** 120 cm	**e** 21 cm	**g** 121 cm
b 40 cm	**d** 150 cm	**f** 47 cm	**h** 253 cm

5 Change each of these lengths into feet.
a 60 cm	**c** 45 cm	**e** 255 cm	● **g** 9 m
b 180 cm	**d** 135 cm	● **f** 50 cm	● **h** 180 m

6 Change each of these lengths into yards.
a 45 m	**c** 2 m	**e** 34 m	**g** 120 m
b 22.5 m	**d** 14 m	**f** 40 m	**h** 250 m

7 Change each of these lengths into miles.
a 8 km	**c** 120 km	**e** 15 000 km	**g** 100 km
b 40 km	**d** 5000 km	**f** 30 km	**h** 21 km

Exercise 17:12

1 Dave is 6 feet tall.
What is his height in cm?

2 Helen lives 3 km out of town.
How far from town does Helen live in miles?

3 A ruler is 12 inches long.
How many cm is this?

4 The distance from Sheffield to Leeds is about 60 km.
How far is this in miles?

5 A holiday brochure says that a hotel is 300 yards from the beach.
Convert this distance into
   a   metres   **b**   centimetres

● **6** Alice is going to a meeting in Paris.
She is travelling at 60 miles per hour.
She has just passed a road sign telling
her that Paris is 140 km away.
She has to be there in $1\frac{1}{2}$ hours.
Will she get there in time if she
travels at this speed?

You also need to be able to estimate lengths.
To do this you need to think about things that you know well.
Here are a few examples but you may think of others that help you more.

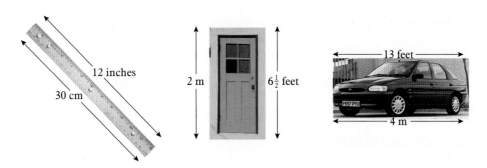

30 cm   12 inches   2 m $6\frac{1}{2}$ feet   13 feet   4 m

Exercise 17:13

Estimate the length of each of these.
Give your answers in both of the units shown.

1

a cm
b inches

2

a cm
b inches

3

a m
b feet

4

a cm
b inches

5

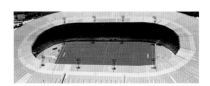

a m
b yards

6

a m
b feet

7

a m
b yards

8

a m
b yards

1 Find the circumference of these circles. Give your answers to 1 dp.

a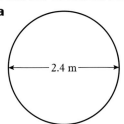
2.4 m

b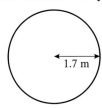
1.7 m

c
7.8 cm

2 Find
(1) the diameter (2) the radius
of a circle with a circumference of:
a 70 cm **b** 45 cm **c** 320 cm **d** 47.1 cm
Give all your answers to 1 dp.

3 The circumference of a circle is 7 m.
Find **a** the diameter **b** the radius
Give your answers to 2 dp.

4 Find the perimeter of each of these shapes.

a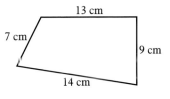
13 cm
7 cm
9 cm
14 cm

b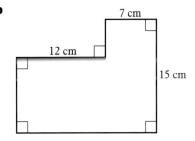
7 cm
12 cm
15 cm

5 Find the perimeter of a regular pentagon with sides of length 4.5 cm.

6 Find the perimeter of this racetrack.
Both ends are semi-circles.
Leave your answer in terms of π.

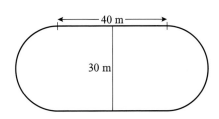
40 m
30 m

7 In this question r, s and t are lengths.
Write down the dimension of each of these expressions.
a s **c** $3rs$ **e** rst **g** $145s$
b $2t$ **d** $56st$ **f** $4t$ **h** $472rt$

8 **a** Change each of these lengths into mm.
    (1) 6 cm   (2) 143 cm   (3) 0.7 cm   (4) 3 m
  b Change each of these lengths into cm.
    (1) 4 m   (2) 233 m   (3) 0.8 m   (4) 5 km
  c Change each of these lengths into m.
    (1) 7 km   (2) 129 km   (3) 0.74 km   (4) 0.142 km

9 **a** Change each of these lengths into cm.
    (1) 56 mm   (2) 163 mm   (3) 9 mm   (4) 8 mm
  b Change each of these lengths into m.
    (1) 900 cm   (2) 56 cm   (3) 3000 mm   (4) 600 mm
  c Change each of these lengths into km.
    (1) 4000 m   (2) 6100 m   (3) 8910 cm   (4) 7593 mm

10 **a** Change each of these lengths into inches.
    (1) 5 feet   (2) 20 feet   (3) 2 feet 3 inches   (4) 7 feet 3 inches
  b Change each of these lengths into feet.
    (1) 5 yards   (2) 14 yards   (3) 125 yards   (4) 20 yards 2 feet
  c Change each of these lengths into yards.
    (1) 4 miles   (2) 25 miles   (3) 3 miles 523 yards (4) $7\frac{1}{2}$ miles

11 **a** Change each of these lengths into feet.
    (1) 48 inches   (2) 72 inches   (3) 240 inches   (4) 144 inches
  b Change each of these lengths into yards.
    (1) 18 feet   (2) 27 feet   (3) 126 feet   (4) 6510 feet
  c Change each of these lengths into miles.
    (1) 3520 yards   (2) 21 120 yards   (3) 11 440 yards   (4) 18 480 yards
  d Change each of these lengths into miles.
    (1) 31 680 feet   (2) 32 736 feet   (3) 27 456 yards   (4) 126 720 inches

12 Copy these. Fill them in.
  a 1 metre is just over … feet.
  b 1 yard is about … metre.
  c 1 inch is about … cm.
  d 1 foot is about … cm.
  e 1 mile is about … km.
  f 1 yard is about … cm.

13 **a** Change 20 inches into cm.
  b Change 48 miles into km.
  c Change 200 cm into inches.
  d Change 16 km into miles.

1 Assume that the Earth travels in a circle of radius 93 million miles around the sun in 365 days.
How far does it travel in 1 day?

2 Each wheel of Andrea's bicycle has a radius of 35 cm.
How many complete turns of each wheel are needed for the bicycle to travel 50 metres?

3 A triangle has sides of length p cm, $(p + 4)$ cm and $(p - 5)$ cm.
  a Write down and simplify an expression for the perimeter of the triangle.
The perimeter is 41 cm.
  b Use your answer to part **a** to write down an equation for the perimeter.
  c Solve the equation in part **b** and find the length of each side of the triangle.

4 Each side of the square is $2p$ cm long.
Each side of the equilateral triangle is $(3p - 1)$ cm long.

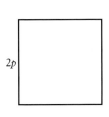 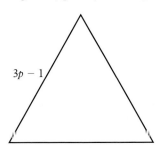

  a Write down and simplify an expression for
    (1) the perimeter of the square
    (2) the perimeter of the triangle.
The two shapes have the same perimeter.
  b Write down an equation that tells you that the two perimeters are equal.
  c Solve the equation in part **b**.
  d Work out the length of the side of
    (1) the square   (2) the triangle

5 The distance from Liverpool to Manchester is about 40 miles.
5 miles are about the same as 8 km.
Use this information to find the distance from Liverpool to Manchester in km.

1   The wheel of Mary's bicycle has a radius of 16 cm.
- **a**   Find the circumference of the wheel.
- **b**   Mary cycles 4 km.
  How many complete revolutions does the wheel make?

2   Work out the perimeter of this shape.

8 cm

3   Find the exact perimeter of this shape.

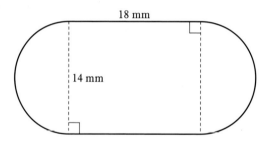

18 mm

14 mm

4   Change
- **a**   47 mm to cm   **d**   4 yards to feet
- **b**   7.2 m to cm   **e**   7 miles to yards
- **c**   36 in to feet   **f**   6.5 yards to inches

5   There are 2.54 cm in 1 inch.
Change
- **a**   1 foot into cm   **c**   20 yards into metres
- **b**   2 yards into cm   **d**   3 metres into inches

18 Pythagoras' theorem

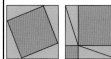

QUESTIONS

EXTENSION

TEST YOURSELF

1 **Finding areas**

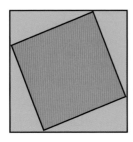 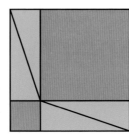

This picture shows you one of the many proofs of Pythagoras' theorem.

Can you see how it works?

| **Pythagoras' theorem** | **Pythagoras' theorem** says that in any right-angled triangle, the area of the square on the hypotenuse is equal to the sum of the areas of the squares on the other two sides. |

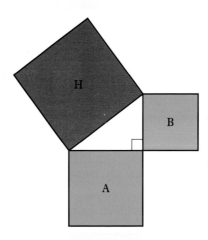

In this right-angled triangle, Pythagoras' theorem tells you that
area **H** = area **A** + area **B**

Example   Find the red area in this diagram.

The red area is the sum of the blue areas.
   Red area = 15 + 20
         = 35 cm²

When you are finding the area on the hypotenuse you add the areas of the other squares.

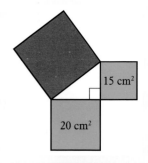

Exercise 18:1

1 Find the red area in each of these.

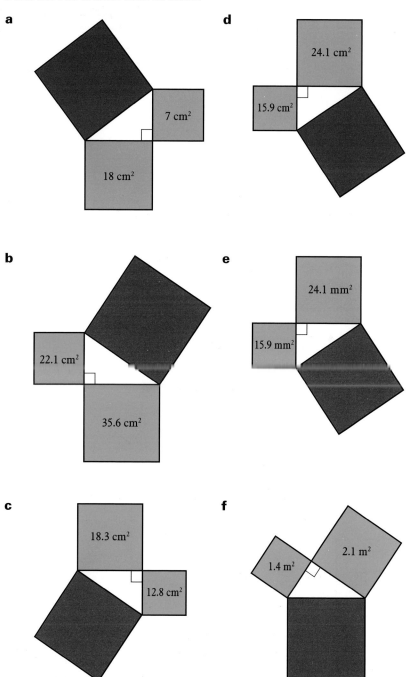

a

7 cm²

18 cm²

d

24.1 cm²

15.9 cm²

b

22.1 cm²

35.6 cm²

e

24.1 mm²

15.9 mm²

c

18.3 cm²

12.8 cm²

f

2.1 m²

1.4 m²

Example Find the missing blue area in this diagram.

The red area is the sum of the blue areas.

$$40 = 18 + \text{blue area}$$

So blue area $= 40 - 18$

$$= 22 \text{ cm}^2$$

When you are finding an area that is not on the hypotenuse you take the areas of the other two squares away.

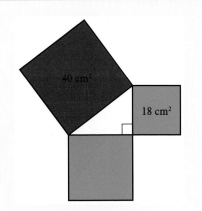

40 cm²

18 cm²

---

2 Find the blue area in each of these.

a

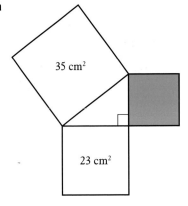

35 cm²

23 cm²

c

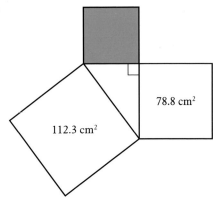

78.8 cm²

112.3 cm²

b

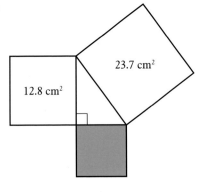

23.7 cm²

12.8 cm²

d

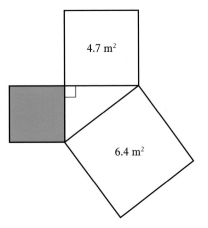

4.7 m²

6.4 m²

e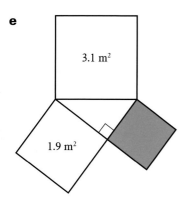

f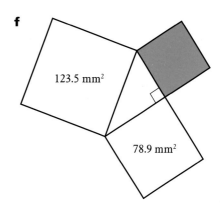

3 Helen is working out the area of the red square in this diagram.
She says that the area is 56 cm². Explain how you know that she is wrong.

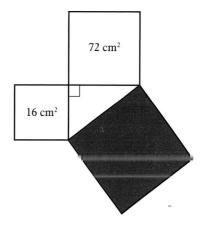

4 Jamie is working out the area of the blue square in this diagram.
He says that the area is 54 cm².
  a Explain how you know that he is wrong.
  b Explain how he got his answer.

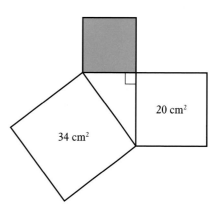

Pythagoras' theorem is usually written using the lengths of the sides of the triangle.

You need to remember that the area of a square with side a is a^2.

In this right-angled triangle, Pythagoras' theorem tells you that

$$h^2 = a^2 + b^2$$

The square of the hypotenuse is equal to the sum of the squares of the other two sides.

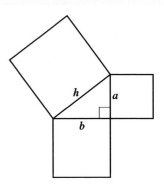

Example Find the area of each of the coloured squares.

The area of the red square is $10 \times 10 = 100 \text{ cm}^2$
The area of the blue square is $7 \times 7 = 49 \text{ cm}^2$

By Pythagoras' theorem the area of the green square is
$$100 - 49 = 51 \text{ cm}^2$$

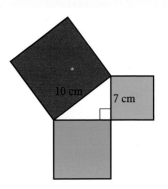

Exercise 18:2

1 Find the area of each of the coloured squares.

a

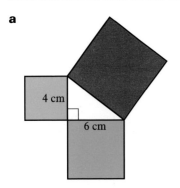

b

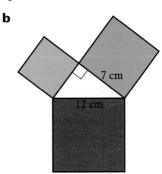

c

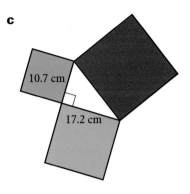

10.7 cm

17.2 cm

d

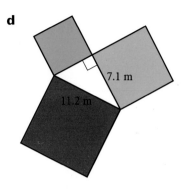

7.1 m

11.2 m

2 Find the area of the green square in each of these.

a

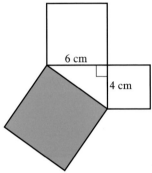

6 cm

4 cm

c

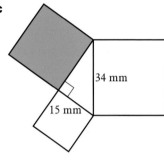

34 mm

15 mm

b

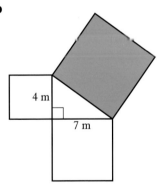

4 m

7 m

d

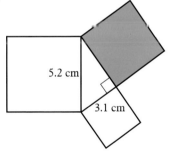

5.2 cm

3.1 cm

3 Eddie is trying to find the area of the green square.
He says that the area is 125 cm².
How do you know that he has to be wrong?

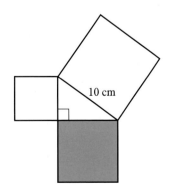

10 cm

2 Finding lengths

Working in right-angled triangles has been important since the beginning of time. The oldest surviving Pyramid is the Djoser Step Pyramid at Saqqâra in Egypt, which was built around 2630 BC. Pythagoras 'discovered' his theorem in about 500 BC, over 2000 years after the ancient Egyptians had seen the importance of right angles!

Although Pythagoras' theorem talks about areas, it is usually used to find the length of a side in a right-angled triangle.
You can also use trigonometry to find the length of a side in a right-angled triangle. When you want to use trigonometry you need to know an angle.
It is quicker to use Pythagoras' theorem when you don't know or want the angles. You need to know two of the sides.
Then you can find the missing side.

Example   Find the length of the hypotenuse of this triangle.

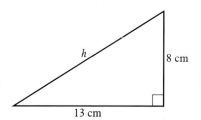

When you write out your answer to a question where you use Pythagoras' theorem, you must show your working.

Start by saying that you are using Pythagoras' theorem.	Using Pythagoras' theorem
Put the lengths into the formula.	$h^2 = 8^2 + 13^2$
Work out the squares.	$= 64 + 169$
Simplify your answer.	$= 233$
Now square root.	$h = \sqrt{233}$
Give your answer to a sensible accuracy.	$h = 15.3$ cm to 1 dp

Always check that the hypotenuse is the longest side in the triangle.
If the answer that you get for the hypotenuse is smaller than one of the other sides then you must have done something wrong!

Exercise 18:3

1 Find the length of the hypotenuse in each of these triangles.
Give your answers to 1 dp.

a

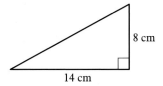

8 cm

14 cm

d

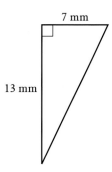

7 mm

13 mm

b

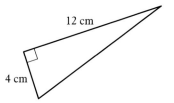

12 cm

4 cm

e

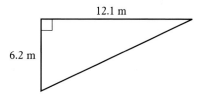

12.1 m

6.2 m

c

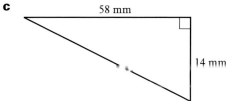

58 mm

14 mm

f

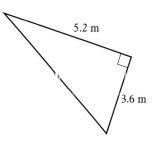

5.2 m

3.6 m

2 a Find the hypotenuse in each of these triangles.

(1)

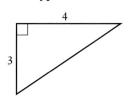

4

3

(3)

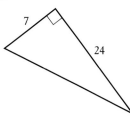

7

24

(2)

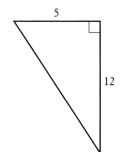

5

12

(4)

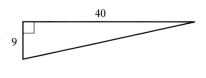

40

9

b Copy this table. Fill in the last column using your results from part **a**.

Triangle	Lengths of sides	
(1)	3	4
(2)	5	12
(3)	7	24
(4)	9	40

The sides in the triangles in question **2** are all whole numbers.

Pythagorean triple

When three whole numbers work in Pythagoras' theorem, the set of three numbers is called a **Pythagorean triple**.

3 4 5 is a Pythagorean triple because $3^2 + 4^2 = 5^2$

3 **a** Find the hypotenuse in each of these triangles.

(1)

(3)
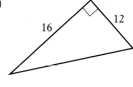

(2)
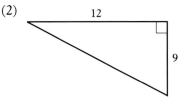

(4)
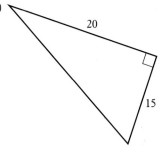

b All of the Pythagorean triples in part **a** are based on one Pythagorean triple. Explain how.
c Start with the Pythagorean triple 5 12 13.
Write down four more Pythagorean triples that are based on this one.
d Can you find a new Pythagorean triple that is not based on any you have seen so far. Try 8 for the smallest side.

4 Jill takes a short cut across this rectangular field to get home.
She walks along the diagonal of the field.
  a How far does she walk?
 • **b** Jill walks at 4 km per hour.
    How much time does she save by taking this short cut?
    Give your answer in seconds.

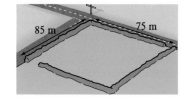

5 Farmer John is very proud of his square fields.
Every day he walks from his house along the diagonal of each field to get to his barn.
How far does he walk to get to his barn?

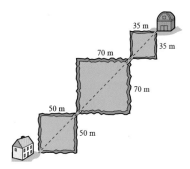

6 This transmitter is supported by 4 cables. Each cable is attached to a point on the mast that is 30 m above the ground. Each cable is attached to the ground 20 m from the base.
  a How long is each cable?
  b How much cable is used altogether?

7 Ben is making a roof support.
He has joined two pieces of timber at right angles like this.
What length of wood does he need to finish the structure?

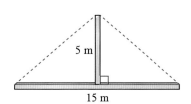

8 Diane is heading down a ski jump!
The height of the slope is 400 ft.
The horizontal distance across the bottom of the slope is 100 ft.
How far does Diane ski down the slope?

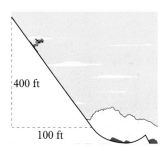

9 **a** Find the length of the sloping
edge of the roof of this house.

b Find the area of the roof.

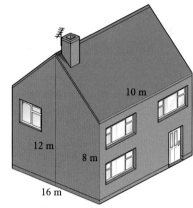

10 m

12 m

8 m

16 m

● **10** **a** Find the length of the
hypotenuse in this triangle.
Leave your answer as a
square root.

1

1

b Another triangle is added to the diagram like this.
How long is the hypotenuse of the second triangle.
Leave your answer as a square root.

c If you carried on adding triangles to your diagram, how
long would the hypotenuse of the 50th triangle be?

d How long would the hypotenuse of the nth triangle be?

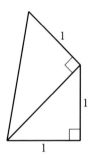

1

1

1

Finding one of the shorter sides

When you want to find one of the short sides, start by writing Pythagoras' theorem
in the usual order starting with hypotenuse^2 = ...

Then rearrange the equation to find the missing side.

Example Find the length of side a in this triangle.

Using Pythagoras' theorem:

$$23^2 = 18^2 + a^2$$
$$23^2 - 18^2 = a^2$$
$$529 - 324 = a^2$$

So $a^2 = 205$

Now square root:

$$a = \sqrt{205}$$
$$a = 14.3 \text{ cm to 1 dp}$$

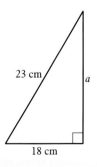

23 cm

a

18 cm

Check that the hypotenuse is the longest side. If the answer that you get for a short
side is bigger than the hypotenuse you must have done something wrong!

Exercise 18:4

1 Find the length of the missing side in each of these triangles.
Give your answers to 1 dp.

a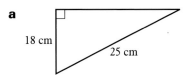

d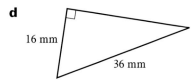

b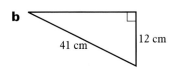

e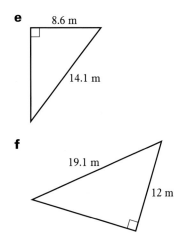

c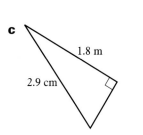

f

? A mast is held in position by
two wires.
Both wires are 20 m long.
The first is attached to the
ground 14 m from the base of the
mast.
The second is attached to the
ground 16 m from the base of the
mast.
How far is it between the two points
where the wires join the mast?

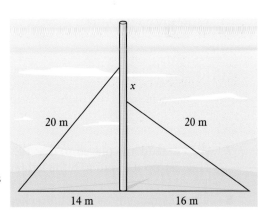

3 This is a cross section through the Great
Pyramid.
Each sloping side is about 180 m long.
The base of the pyramid is about 230 m.
How high is the pyramid?

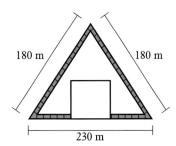

4 This is Katie's kite.
The wooden supports have cracked.
What length of wood does she
need to get to fix it?

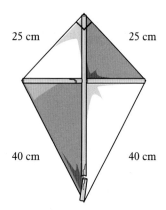

25 cm   25 cm

40 cm   40 cm

5 A stirring rod sticks out from the top of a beaker.
The beaker is 10 cm across the base.
The beaker is 15 cm tall.
The stirring rod is 25 cm long.
How much of the stirring rod is outside
the beaker?

6 This is a diagram showing a road
up a hill.
How far does the road rise
vertically up the hill?

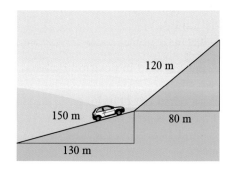

120 m

150 m   80 m

130 m

7 A 25 m ladder is placed so that the base is 12 m from a vertical wall.
How far up the wall will the ladder reach?

8 The diagram shows a shelf bracket.

The shelf must be horizontal and
must not overlap the bracket.
What is the greatest width of shelf
that this bracket can support?

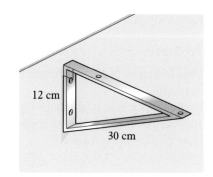

12 cm

30 cm

9 This is a picture of a child's slide.
What is the length of the ladder?

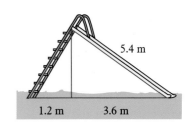

5.4 m

1.2 m   3.6 m

● **10** The diagram shows the positions of
two lighthouses.
A ship is due south of lighthouse A.
The ship is 50 km from lighthouse B.
How far is the ship from lighthouse A?

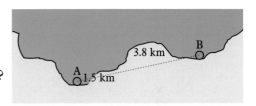

3.8 km

B

A
1.5 km

One or more of the lengths might be given as a square root of a number.
This is because it is more exact than a rounded decimal.

In fact this makes it very easy to square.
Remember that when you square the square root of a number you get back to the
original number!
This is because squaring and square rooting are inverses of each other.
So $\sqrt{8} \times \sqrt{8} = 8$.

Example   Find the length of the hypotenuse of this triangle.

$$x^2 = (\sqrt{8})^2 + (\sqrt{6})^2$$
$$= 8 + 6$$
$$= 14$$

So $x = \sqrt{14}$ cm

Leave your answer as a square root
if you are asked for an exact answer.

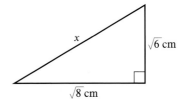

x

$\sqrt{6}$ cm

$\sqrt{8}$ cm

---

11 Find the lengths of the sides marked with letters.
Give exact answers.

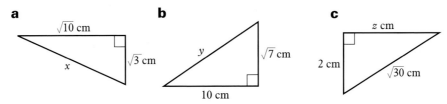

a

$\sqrt{10}$ cm

$\sqrt{3}$ cm

x

b

y

$\sqrt{7}$ cm

10 cm

c

z cm

2 cm

$\sqrt{30}$ cm

You can use Pythagoras' theorem to find the distance between two points.

Points A(1, 2) and B(6, 5) are marked on
this diagram.
B is 6 − 1 = 5 cm to the right of A.
B is 5 − 2 = 3 cm above A.

You can use Pythagoras' theorem to
find the distance AB.

$$(AB)^2 = 5^2 + 3^2$$
$$= 25 + 9$$
$$= 34$$
$$AB = \sqrt{34} = 5.83 \text{ cm (2 dp)}$$

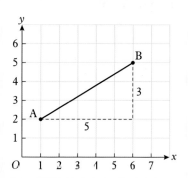

So the distance between A and B is $\sqrt{34}$ cm or 5.83 cm (2 dp).

Exercise 18:5

1 Find the distance between the following
pairs of points.
Give your answers to 2 dp.
a A and B
b C and D
c E and F
d A and F

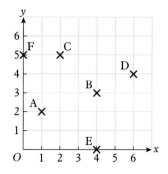

2 Find the distance between the points
A(2, 3) and B(6, 6).

3 A boat sails 4 nautical miles due east and then 7 km due south.
How far is the boat from its starting point?

4 Point B is 6 cm to the right of point A.
It is $\sqrt{61}$ cm in a straight line from A.

How far is point B above point A?

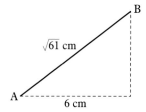

5 Three points are A(0, 1), B(3, 5) and C(6, 8).
a Find the distances AB and BC.
b Find the distance AC.

Exercise 18:6

1 **a** Draw a circle with radius 5 cm.
   b Draw a diameter AB in your circle.
   c Join A and B to any point on the circumference of the circle.
        Call this point P.
   d Measure the angle APB.
        This is called the angle in a semi-circle.

| **Angle in a semi-circle** | The **angle in a semi-circle** is the angle made by joining both ends of a diameter of a circle to a point on the circumference. The **angle in a semi-circle** is 90°. |

AB is a diameter of the circle centre O.

The angle APB is 90°.

This means that you can now use Pythagoras' theorem in semi-circles.

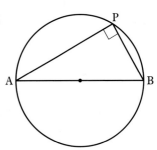

---

2 Find the length marked with a letter in each of these.

a

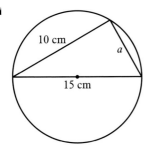

10 cm
a
15 cm

c

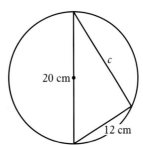

20 cm
c
12 cm

b

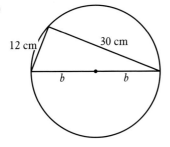

12 cm
30 cm
b   b

d

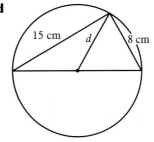

15 cm
d
8 cm

1 Find the red area in each of these.

a

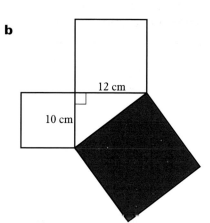

13 cm²

24 cm²

b

12 cm

10 cm

2 Find the blue area in each of these.

a

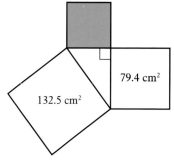

79.4 cm²

132.5 cm²

b

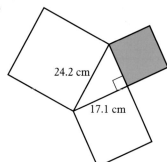

24.2 cm

17.1 cm

3 Find the length of the hypotenuse in each of these triangles.
Give your answers to 1 dp.

a

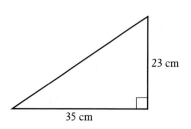

23 cm

35 cm

b

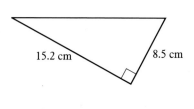

15.2 cm

8.5 cm

4 Find the length of the missing side in each of these triangles.
Give your answers to 1 dp.

a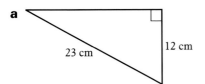

b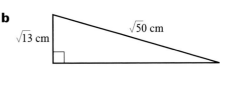

5 This diagram shows the position of
three ports.
Two of the ports are on one side of the
river and the other port is on the opposite
side.
The distance from A to B is 75 km.
The distance from B to C is 65 km.
Find the distance between ports A and C.

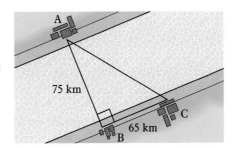

6 Here is a table for showing some Pythagorean triples.

a	b	h
3	4	
	12	13
7		
		41

a Copy the table. Fill it in.
b Add an extra 5 rows to your table.
There is a pattern in each column.
Fill in the next 5 entries in each column.
c Check that your five extra rows are all Pythagorean triples.
d There are other Pythagorean triples that are not part of this pattern.
Write down one of them. Use 8 as the smallest number.
Can you find any more? You cannot use any multiples of the ones in
the pattern or of your answer to this part!

7 The diagram shows a chord of a circle.

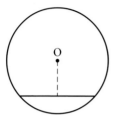

The circle has radius 8 cm.
The chord is 13 cm long.
Find the distance from the centre of the circle, O, to the chord.

8 Gerald is taking a stroll around the grounds of Holkom Hall.
He walks along the red route.
The paths are shown in blue.
  a How far has Gerald walked altogether?
  b How far north has Gerald moved?
  c How far west has Gerald moved?
  d How far is Gerald from his starting point?
  e Gerald returns home along the paths.
     He walks at 1 m/s. How much quicker is his return journey?

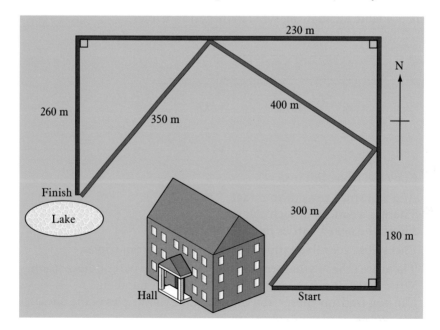

1 The diagram shows an equilateral triangle of side 12 cm.

   a Copy the diagram. Split the triangle into two right-angled triangles.

   b Use Pythagoras' theorem to find the height of the triangle.

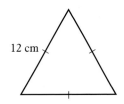

12 cm

2 **a** Write down an expression for the square of the hypotenuse in this triangle. Simplify your answer.

   b Write down the square of each of the other two sides.

   c Write down Pythagoras' theorem for the triangle.

   d Solve the equation to find the value of x.

x

5

$x + 1$

3 Show that the distance between the two points (x_1, y_1) and (x_2, y_2) is
$$\sqrt{(x_2 - x_1)^2 + (y_2 - y_1)^2}$$

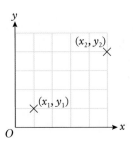

4 Find the lengths labelled with letters in this diagram.

You will need to use trigonometry as well as Pythagoras' theorem.

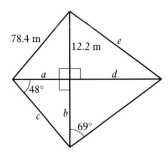

78.4 m

12.2 m

e

a

d

48°

c

b

69°

5 Forester Fred patrols four rectangular woods. Every day he walks along the red route from home, through the woods to Old Harry Oak and back home. How far does he walk each time he walks this route?

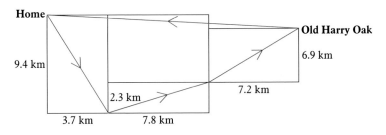

Home

Old Harry Oak

9.4 km

6.9 km

2.3 km

7.2 km

3.7 km

7.8 km

449

1 Find the coloured area in each of these:

a

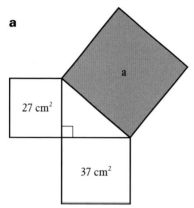

b

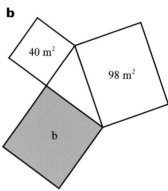

2 Find the lengths marked with letters.

a

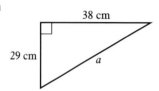

c

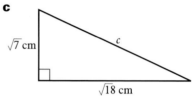

b

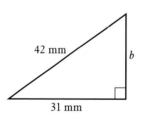

d

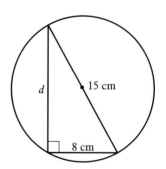

3 Write down the missing number in each of these Pythagorean triples.

a 3 4 ...   **c** ... 12 13

b 7 ... 25   **d** 8 ... 17

4 Find the length OR.

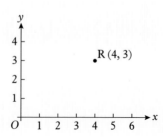

5   Find the distance between P and Q where
P is the point (2, 5) and Q is the point (7, 15).

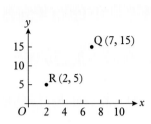

6   Find the missing length in this trapezium.

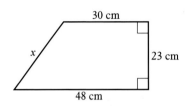

7   A ship sails from a port to an oil rig.
The oil rig is 47 nautical miles north
and 62 nautical miles east of the port.
Find the distance between the port
and the oil rig.

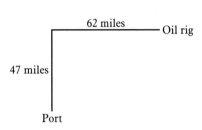

8   An aircraft travels 2800 m while rising 1500 m and then 5000 m while
rising 1000 m. How much horizontal distance has it covered in this time?

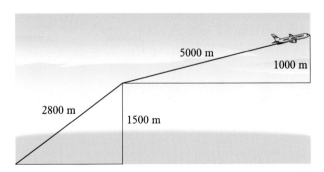

CHAPTER 1

1   **a**   A(-2, 1), B(4, 0), C(3, -4), D(0, -3)

    b   P: $y = 3$ Q: $x = 2$ R: $y = -2$ S: $x = -4$

    c   (1) $y = 0$ (2) $x = 0$

2   **a**   5 squares to the left and 3 squares

      down or $\begin{pmatrix} -5 \\ -3 \end{pmatrix}$ **b**

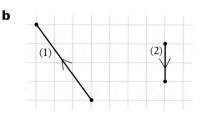

3

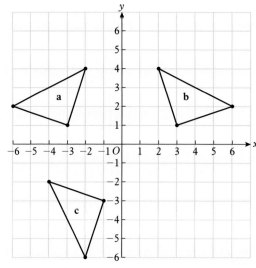

4   **a**   a translation 3 squares down and 2 squares to the right

    b   a translation of $\begin{pmatrix} -3 \\ 4 \end{pmatrix}$

    c   a rotation of $270°$ anticlockwise about the point (2, -3)

5

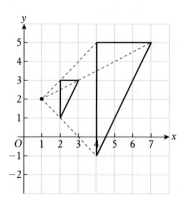

6 a, b, c

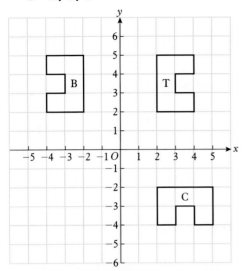

d Reflection in the line $y = x$

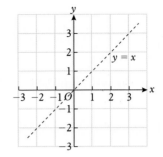

CHAPTER 2

1 a 700 (seven hundred)   **b** 70 000 (seventy thousand)

2 a (1) 140 709   (2) 141 000
  b (1) Ninety five thousand and eighty two   (2) 95 100

3 a

Car	Price in £	Price to nearest £100
Ford Ka	9595	9 600
Nissan Micra	9550	9 600
Peugeot 106	9070	9 100
Rover Mini Cooper	9630	9 600
Vauxhall Corsa	9295	9 300
Fiat Punto	9995	10 000

  b Peugeot 106, Vauxhall Corsa, Nissan Micra, Ford Ka, Rover Mini Cooper, Fiat Punto

4 2.07, 2.3, 2.54, 2.65, 2.91, 2.98, 3.07, 3.1

5 a $2978 > 2798$ **c** $2.17 < 2.71$
  b $-7 > -9$ **d** $0 > -10$

6 a 4567   **b** 7645

7 a 80   **c** 67 000   **e** 0.84
  b 4000   **d** 400   **f** 56.1

8 £39.07 = 3907p; $3907 \div 80.9 = 48.29419 \ldots = 48l$ to nearest litre

9 **a** $\dfrac{100 - 60}{20} = \dfrac{40}{20} = 2$ **b** $\sqrt{78} \approx \sqrt{81} = 9$

   c $\sqrt{\dfrac{6 \times 7}{3}} = \sqrt{\dfrac{42}{3}} = \sqrt{14} \approx \sqrt{16} = 4$ or $\sqrt{\dfrac{6 \times 7}{3}} = \sqrt{2 \times 7} = \sqrt{14} \approx \sqrt{16} = 4$

10 **a** $\frac{4}{10} = \frac{2}{5}$ **b** $\frac{22}{100} = \frac{11}{50}$ **c** $\frac{375}{1000} = \frac{15}{40} = \frac{3}{8}$

11 $\frac{7}{8} = 7 \div 8 = 0.875$, $\frac{4}{5} = 0.8$, $\frac{91}{100} = 0.91$

So the decimals are: 0.875, 0.83, 0.8, 0.91

In order this gives: 0.8, 0.83, 0.875, 0.91

So the answer is: $\frac{4}{5}, 0.83, \frac{7}{8}, \frac{91}{100}$

CHAPTER 3

1 Total number of cans $= 27 + 11 + 22 = 60$

Angle for 1 can $= 360° \div 60 = 6°$

Drinks sold from drinks machine

Drink	Number sold	Working	Angle
Cola	27	27 × 6°	162°
Orange	11	11 × 6°	66°
Water	22	22 × 6°	132°
Total	60		360°

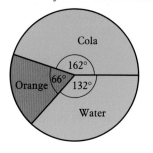

2 **a, c**

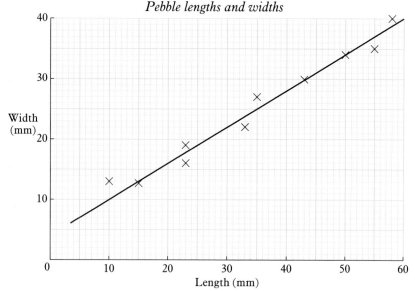

Pebble lengths and widths

Width (mm)

Length (mm)

b (strong) positive correlation

c 29 mm (approximately)

3 a, b

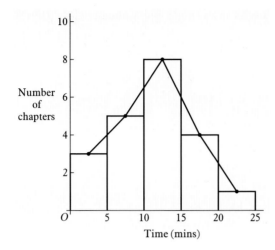

4 Number of people using cars and taxis has increased a lot.
Number of people using trains is about the same.
Number of people using buses and coaches has gone down slightly.
Number of people using pedal cycles has gone down slightly and is very close to zero.

5

Stem	Leaf
2	7 8 9
3	0 1 2 5 6 8 9
4	0 1 2 4

Key: 3|2 means 32 seconds

6 a 174 cm   **b** 165 cm

CHAPTER 4

1 a 1, 3, 13, 21   **c** 1, 3, 10, 21   **e** 2, 3, 13
b 1, 16   **d** 8, 16   **f** 1, 2, 3, 8

2

3   6   9   12 (15) 18   21   24   27 (30) 33   15 is the LCM.

5   10 (15) 20   25 (30) 35   The lights flash together every 15 seconds.

3 a

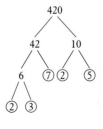

$420 = 2 \times 2 \times 3 \times 5 \times 7$

b

220

22   10

(2)   (11)(2)   (5)

$220 = 2 \times 2 \times 5 \times 11$
$420 = 2 \times 2 \times 3 \times 5 \times 7$
Highest common factor $= 2 \times 2 \times 5 = 20$

4 $24 = 2 \times 2 \times 2 \times 3$. The 3 shows that $\frac{1}{24}$ gives a recurring decimal.

5   **a** 7, 3   **b** 162, 486   **c** 0.18, 0.21

6   second term $= 4 \times 10 - 20 \ = 40 - 20 \ = 20$
third term $\ = 20 \times 10 - 20 = 200 - 20 = 180$

7 $11 \times 1 = 11$ The first 5 terms are 11, 22, 33, 44, 55
$11 \times 2 = 22$
$11 \times 3 = 33$
$11 \times 4 = 44$
$11 \times 5 = 55$

8   **a** $6n$ **b** $9n$

9   The sequence for $5n$ is 5, 10, 15, 20, 25
   a You need to add 1 to each term of the sequence $5n$.
      The formula is $5n + 1$.
   b You need to subtract 3 from each term of the sequence $5n$.
      The formula is $5n - 3$.

10   **a**

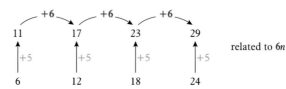

related to $6n$

   b The formula is $6n + 5$.

11   **a**

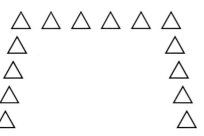

b 5, 8, 11, 14

   c

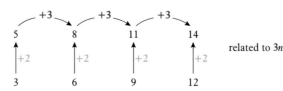

related to $3n$

   The formula is $3n + 2$.

12   **a** $n = 1$ $6 \times 1 - 5 = 1$ **c** $6n - 5 = 55$
      $n = 2$ $6 \times 2 - 5 = 7$ $6n = 60$
      $n = 3$ $6 \times 3 - 5 = 13$ $n = 10$
      The first 3 terms are 1, 7, 13.   i.e. the 10th term is 55.
   b $n = 20$ $6 \times 20 - 5 = 115$

CHAPTER 5

1   **a**   2   **b** -5 **c** -8 **d** -15

2   **a** -40 **b** $+20$

3   **a** -9 **b** $+3$ **c** -1

4   **a** $-11, -16$ **b** $-40, -20$

5   **a** $3 > -2$ **b** $-6 > -9$ **c** $-1 < 0$

6   **a**   Brian -8; Norma -2; Julia -10
     b   Julia -10; Brian -8; Norma -2

7   **a** -12 **b** -58 **c** -35 **d**   18

8   **a**   16   **b** -27 **c** -125

9   **a** -7 **b**   3   **c** -3

10   **a** $5 \times -8 = -40$ **e** $-100 \div 25 = -4$
     b $-6 + 16 = -10$ **f** $-30 \times -4 = 120$
     c $7 - 5 = 2$ **g** $2.05 \times -1000 = -2050$
     d $\dfrac{-12}{-2} = 6$ **h** $\dfrac{-7}{-7} = 1$

11   **a** $w = 4 \times -5 - 12 = -20 - 12 = -32$
     b $v = -15 + (-8 \times 9) = -15 - 72 = -87$

CHAPTER 6

1   **a** $8f - 7f = 1f = f$
     b $4x - x = 3x$; $3x^2 + 5x^2 = 8x^2$ so $4x + 3x^2 - x + 5x^2 = 3x + 8x^2$
     c $4t \times 2t = 4 \times 2 \times t \times t = 8t^2$
     d $3q \times 16q = 18q^2$

2   **a** $20x - 5$ **c** $7a^2 - 14a + 63$ **e** $m^3 + 4m^2$
     b $-24 + 15x^2$ **d** $4y^2 - 3y$ **f** $21x - 15x^2$

3   **a** $4g - 3 = 21$ **d** $3a + 13 = 5a$ **g** $6d + 8 = 29 - d$
           $4g = 24$ $13 = 2a$ $7d + 8 = 29$
            $g = 6$ $6.5 = a$ $7d = 21$
                                    $a = 6.5$ $d = 3$
     b $\dfrac{x}{5} + 6 = 10$ **e** $14s - 5 = 9s + 20$ **h** $7(3x - 12) = 42$
           $\dfrac{x}{5} = 4$ $5s - 5 = 20$ $21x - 84 = 42$
            $x = 20$ $5s = 25$ $21x = 126$
                                     $s = 5$ $x = 6$
     c $8x = 5x - 12$ **f** $\dfrac{24}{x} = 8$
           $3x = -12$ $24 = 8x$
             $x = -4$ $3 = x$
                                   $x = 3$

4

Value of x	Value of $x^2 - 30$	
20	370	too small
50	2470	too small
60	3570	too big
55	2995	too small
56	3106	too small
57	3219	too big
56.5	3162.25	too big
56.4	3150.96	too small
56.45	3156.6025	too big
-20	370	too small
-50	2470	too small
-55	2995	too small
-56.5	3162.25	too big
-56.4	3150.96	too small
-56.45	3156.6025	too big

$x = 56.4$ to 1 dp.

$x = 56.4$ to 1 dp.

5 **a** $14 + 2x + 4x - 10 = 6x + 4$ **b** $6x + 4 = 34$
   c $6x = 30$
      $x = 5$
   d 14 cm, $2x = 2 \times 5 = 10$ cm, $4x - 10 = 4 \times 5 - 10 = 20 - 10 = 10$ cm
   e isosceles

CHAPTER 7

1 $4 : 11$

2 **a** $3 : 2$ **b** $2 : 3$ **c** $10 : 15 = 2 : 3$

3 **a** 1.5 m $= 150$ cm $150 : 75 = 2 : 1$
   b £2.40 $= 240$ p $240 : 60 = 4 : 1$
   c $3 l = 3000$ ml $250 : 3000 = 1 : 12$
   d 2 h $= 120$ min $120 : 15 = 8 : 1$
   e 2.4 km $= 2400$ m $2400 : 80 = 240 : 8 = 30 : 1$
   f 2 tonnes $= 2000$ kg $2000 : 750 = 8 : 3$

4 **a** (1) $1 : \frac{18}{6} = 1 : 3$ (2) $17 : 23 = 1 : \frac{23}{17} = 1 : 1.35$ to 2 dp.
   b (1) $\frac{14}{3} : 1 = 4.67 : 1$ to 2 dp   (2) $\frac{125}{280} : 1 = 0.45 : 1$ to 2 dp.

5 $8 \times 25 = 200$ cm^2

6 **a** Total parts $= 5 + 3 = 8$ **b** $\frac{5}{8}$
      Value of 1 part $= £40 \div 8 = £5$
      $3 \times £5 = £15$

7 Total parts $= 2 + 3 + 5 = 10$
   Value of 1 part $= 180° \div 10 = 18°$
   $2 \times 18° = 36°$ $3 \times 18° = 54°$ $5 \times 18° = 90°$
   so the angles are 36°, 54° and 90°.

8 **a** 5×250 ml $= 1250$ ml
   b $1350 = 3 \times 450$ so $3 \times 300 = 900$ ml orange juice
   c $150 = 300 \div 2$ so $450 \div 2 = 225$ ml lemonade

9 **a** $\frac{3}{7}$ **b** $\frac{4}{7}$

10 **a** $\frac{3}{10}$ **b** $\frac{1}{10}$ **c** $\frac{6}{10} = \frac{3}{5}$

11 Small Cost of 10 ml = $135 \div 15 = 9\,$p
Medium Cost of 10 ml = $215 \div 25 = 8.6\,$p
Large Cost of 10 ml = $350 \div 40 = 8.75\,$p
The Medium size is the best value for money as 10 ml costs only 8.6p.

12 **a, b**

Number of labels ordered	50	90	180	340
Cost	£1.25	£2.25	£4.50	£8.50

CHAPTER 8

1 **a** gradient $= \dfrac{\text{vertical change}}{\text{horizontal change}}$
$= \dfrac{2}{2} = 1$

b gradient $= -\dfrac{4}{2} = -2$

2 **a** $\dfrac{11-3}{4-2} = \dfrac{8}{2} = 4$ **b** $\dfrac{3-9}{2-0} = -\dfrac{6}{2} = -3$

3 **a** $y = 5x - 3$ **b** $y = -2x$

4 **a** 3 **b** 1 **c** −6

5 **a** −7 **b** 1 **c** 0

6 Any line where the number multiplying x is 7 e.g. $y = 7x + 4$, $y = 7x$, $y = 7x - 10$ etc.

7 **a** $y = 3x + 1$ **b** $y = -x + 3$

8 **a** $a = £10$ **b** $b =$ gradient $= \dfrac{60 - 10}{25 - 0} = \dfrac{50}{25} = £2$

9 $5x - 2y = 10$

when $y = 0$, $5x = 10$
$x = 2$

when $x = 0$, $-2y = 10$
$y = -5$

∴ Plot points $(2, 0)$ and $(0, -5)$
and join them to give the line.

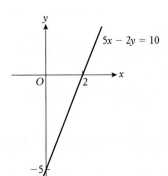

10 **a** not linear (x^2 term) **b** linear **c** not linear $\left(\dfrac{4}{x}\ \text{term}\right)$

CHAPTER 9

1 **a** $\frac{2}{12} = \frac{1}{6}$

b $\frac{1}{4} + \frac{3}{8} = \frac{2}{8} + \frac{3}{8} = \frac{5}{8}$

c $\frac{1}{2} - \frac{1}{6} = \frac{3}{6} - \frac{1}{6} = \frac{2}{6} = \frac{1}{3}$

d $3 + 4 = 7; \frac{1}{4} + \frac{5}{8} = \frac{2}{8} + \frac{5}{8} = \frac{7}{8}; 7\frac{7}{8}$

e $\frac{23}{4} - \frac{5}{2} = \frac{23}{4} - \frac{10}{4} = \frac{13}{4} = 3\frac{1}{4}$

f $\frac{3 \times 1}{5 \times 4} = \frac{3}{20}$

g $\frac{13}{6} \times \frac{7}{2} = \frac{91}{12} = 7\frac{7}{12}$

h $\frac{3}{8} \div \frac{1}{4} = \frac{3}{8} \times \frac{4}{1} = \frac{12}{8} = \frac{3}{2} = 1\frac{1}{2}$

i $1\frac{3}{4} \div 2\frac{1}{3} = \frac{7}{4} \div \frac{7}{3} = \frac{7}{4} \times \frac{3}{7} = \frac{21}{28} = \frac{3}{4}$

2 $\frac{3}{4} = \frac{6}{8}$ so $\frac{5}{8}, \frac{3}{4}$

3 $\frac{5}{6} \times 72; 72 \div 6 = 12; 5 \times 12 = 60$ oz

4 **a** $\frac{3}{x} = \frac{12}{4x}$ ($\times 4$)

c $\frac{30}{10x} = \frac{3}{x}$ ($\div 10$)

b $\frac{5}{x} = \frac{15}{3x}$ ($\times 3$)

d $\frac{18}{6x} = \frac{3}{x}$ ($\div 6$)

5 $w = A \div l = 3\frac{3}{4} \div \frac{5}{8} = \frac{15}{4} \div \frac{5}{8} = \frac{15}{4} \times \frac{8}{5} = \frac{120}{20} = 6$

6 **a** 33%

b 12 out of 25 = 4 × 12 out of 4 × 25 = 48 out of 100 = 48%

c 35%

d 0.81

e $\frac{5}{8} = 5 \div 8 = 0.625 = 62.5\%$

f $\frac{49}{100}$

7 $16 + 9 = 25; \dfrac{16}{25} = \dfrac{16 \times 4}{25 \times 4} = \dfrac{64}{100} = 64\%$

8 **a** 25% of 360 = 360 ÷ 4 = 90

b 10% of £375 = £37.50

40% of £375 = £37.50 × 4 = £150

9 3% of 864 = 0.03 × 864 = 25.92 ≈ 26

10 **a** 17.5% = 0.175 so 0.175 × £380 = £66.50

b £380 + £66.50 = £446.50

11 **a** 10% of 560 = 56 so 20% of 560 = 112

560 + 112 = 672

b 10% of £250 = £25 so 30% = £75

£250 − £75 = £175

12 **a** $\dfrac{703}{950}$ **b** $\dfrac{703}{950} \times 100 = 74\%$

13 Profit $= £1920 - £1500 = £420$

Percentage profit $= \dfrac{420}{1500} \times 100 = 28\%$

14 **a** Davies Electricals   **b** Davies Electricals
5% of £268 $= 0.05 \times £268 = £13.40$
£268 $-$ £13.40 $= $ **£254.60**
Buyrite
$\frac{1}{3}$ of £390 $= £390 \div 3 = £130$
£390 $-$ £130 $= $ **£260**
Discount TVs
25% of £350 $= £350 \div 4 = £87.50$
£350 $-$ £87.50 $= $ **£262.50**

CHAPTER 10

1 The multiples of 4 are 4, 8, 16, 24 and 40. So 5 out of the 8 numbers are multiples of 4 and so it is not fair.

2 $1 - 0.55 = 0.45$

3 $100\% - 67\% = 33\%$

4 **a** $\frac{7}{15}$ **b** $\frac{8}{15}$

5 $P(C') = 1 - 0.58 = 0.42$

6 They are not equally likely because there are more milk chocolates than plain chocolates.

7 $8 + 5 = 13$; P(Girl) $= \frac{8}{13}$

8 A probability can only lie between 0 and 1; -0.8 is not between 0 and 1.

9 **a** There is 1 odd number (3), probability $= \frac{1}{6}$
b There are 2 multiples of 6 (6, 18), probability $= \frac{2}{6} = \frac{1}{3}$
c There are 3 triangle numbers (3, 6, 10), probability $= \frac{3}{6} = \frac{1}{2}$
d There are 2 numbers less than 4, (2, 3) probability $= \frac{2}{6} = \frac{1}{3}$

10 **a** $7 + 11 + 12 + 13 + 8 + 9 = 60$ **d** $\frac{9}{60} = \frac{3}{20}$
b $\frac{7}{60}$ **e** $7 + 11 + 12 = 30, \frac{30}{60} \left(= \frac{1}{2}\right)$
c $12 + 9 = 21, \frac{21}{60}$

11 **a** $\frac{25}{80} \left(= \frac{5}{16}\right)$
b It should get closer to the true value of the probability of the colour blue. This probability is $\frac{1}{4}$ if the spinner is fair.

12 **a** Carry out an experiment.
b Look back at data for previous years.

CHAPTER 11

1

a

b

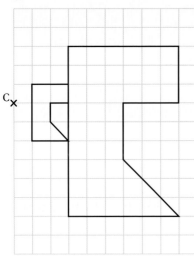

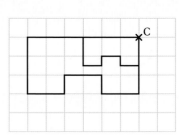

2 Scale factor $= 32 \div 8 = 4$
$a = 5 \times 4 = 20$ cm
$b = 9.5 \times 4 = 38$ cm
$c \times 4 = 48$ cm so $c = 48 \div 4 = 12$ cm

3 8.5 cm $\times 5 = 42.5$ cm

4 **a** 30 000 cm $= 300$ m $= 0.3$ km **b** $7 \times 0.3 = 2.1$ km

5 **a**

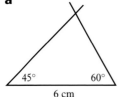

Diagrams are shown using a scale of 1 : 2

b

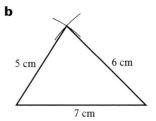

CHAPTER 12

1 **a** 7^5 **b** 4^3

2 **a** 1728 **b** 19 **c** 529 **d** 11 **e** 100 000 **f** 100

3 **a** $\frac{1}{8}$ **b** 5 **c** $\frac{3}{2}$

4 **a** 1 **b** $\frac{1}{4}$ **c** $\frac{4}{3}$

5 **a** $\frac{1}{5^4}$ **b** $\frac{1}{7}$ **c** $\frac{1}{a}$

6 **a** y^7 **c** $35t^5$ **e** $2x^6$ **g** h^2 **i** $3x^2y^{-3}$ **k** t^3
      b $6c^3$ **d** $s^1 = s$ **f** a^3b^{-3} **h** w^9 **j** a^{15} **l** 1

7 **a** 5 **b** 3 **c** 64 **d** 1

8 **a** 11 **b** 44.89 **c** 4 **d** 56

CHAPTER 13

1 **a**

25 min   1 hour

4.35   5   6   1 hour 25 min

   b 35 min + 40 min = 75 min = 1 hour 15 min
   c 3 hours − 1 hour = 2 hours, 2 hours − 15 min = 1 hour 45 min

2 **a** 200 × 4 = 800 km
   b 200 ÷ 2 = 100 km
   c 12 min = $\frac{12}{60}$ hour = $\frac{1}{5}$ hour; 200 ÷ 5 = 40 km

3 **a** Speed = $\dfrac{\text{Distance}}{\text{Time}} = \dfrac{130}{2.5}$ = 52 km/hour

   b 40 min = $\frac{2}{3}$ hour

   Speed = $\dfrac{\text{Distance}}{\text{Time}} = \dfrac{43}{\frac{2}{3}} = 43 \div \frac{2}{3} = 43 \times \frac{3}{2} = 64.5$ miles/hour

4 **a** 420 chocolates per hour
   b 7 chocolates per minute (420 ÷ 60)
   c 60 seconds ÷ 7 = 8.6 seconds (1 dp)

5

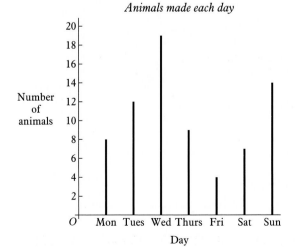

Animals made each day

6 **a** 9 km

   b 45 min (each square across is 15 min) .

   c $\frac{1}{2}$ hour (or 30 min)

   d Speed $= \dfrac{\text{Distance}}{\text{Time}} = \dfrac{9}{\frac{1}{2}} = 18$ km/hour

   e Average speed $= \dfrac{9+9}{2 \text{ hours } 45 \text{ min}} = \dfrac{18}{2.75} = 6.5$ km/hour (1 dp)

7 **a** £4   **b** Peter lives between 20 and 40 miles from the warehouse.

CHAPTER 14

1 $\tan a = \dfrac{\text{opp}}{\text{adj}} = \dfrac{25}{31}$

    $a = 38.9°$ (1 dp)

   $\sin b = \dfrac{\text{opp}}{\text{hyp}} = \dfrac{16}{19}$

    $b = 57.4°$ (1 dp)

   $\tan c = \dfrac{\text{opp}}{\text{adj}} = \dfrac{45}{65}$

    $c = 34.7°$ (1 dp)

   $\cos d = \dfrac{\text{adj}}{\text{hyp}} = \dfrac{4.9}{7.4}$

    $d = 48.5°$ (1 dp)

2 $\sin x = \dfrac{\text{opp}}{\text{hyp}} = \dfrac{147}{680}$

    $x = 12.5°$ (1 dp)

3 $\sin 64° = \dfrac{\text{opp}}{\text{hyp}} = \dfrac{a}{35}$

    $a = 35 \sin 64°$

      $= 31.5$ mm (3 sf)

   $\cos 74° = \dfrac{\text{adj}}{\text{hyp}} = \dfrac{b}{12.5}$

    $b = 12.5 \times \cos 74°$

      $= 3.45$ cm (3 sf)

   $\cos 25° = \dfrac{\text{adj}}{\text{hyp}} = \dfrac{c}{156}$

    $c = 156 \cos 25°$

      $= 141$ m (3 sf)

   $\tan 35° = \dfrac{\text{opp}}{\text{adj}} = \dfrac{d}{45}$

    $d = 45 \tan 35°$

      $= 31.5$ cm (3 sf)

4 $\tan x = \dfrac{\text{opp}}{\text{adj}} = \dfrac{14}{8.5}$

    $x = 58.7°$ (1 dp)

5 $\tan x = \dfrac{\text{opp}}{\text{adj}} = \dfrac{15}{21}$

    $x = 35.5376 \ldots$

      $= 36°$ to nearest degree.

Bearing is 036°.

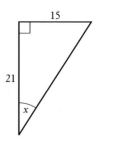

6 $\sin 60° = \dfrac{\text{opp}}{\text{hyp}} = \dfrac{x}{35}$

    $x = 35 \sin 60°$

      $= 30.3$ cm (3 sf)

7 $\sin 43° = \dfrac{\text{opp}}{\text{hyp}} = \dfrac{h}{532}$

$h = 532 \times \sin 43$

$\qquad = 363 \text{ m (3 sf)}$

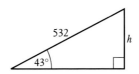

8 **a** $\tan x = \dfrac{\text{opp}}{\text{adj}} = \dfrac{28}{12}$

$\qquad x = 66.8° \text{ (1 dp)}$

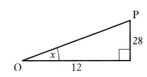

b $\tan y = \dfrac{\text{opp}}{\text{adj}} = \dfrac{12}{6}$

$\qquad y = 63.4° \text{ (1 dp)}$

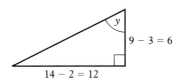

CHAPTER 15

1 **a** $7k$
    c $5d + 6d^2 - 12$

    b $13x - 1y = 13x - y$
    d $3a^2b - 2ab^2$

2 **a** $4y - 20$
  c $12s^2 - 2s$
  e $2x^2 + 15x - 8$

    b $3x^2 + 6x$
  d $8b^3 + b^2$
  f $20x^2 - 41x + 9$

3 **a** $4x - 3 + 2x + 1 + x + 7 + 19 - 3x = 4x + 24$

    b $4x + 24 = 38$

$\qquad\qquad 4x = 14$

$\qquad\qquad\; x = \frac{14}{4}$

$\qquad\qquad\quad = 3\frac{1}{2}$

    c $4x - 3 = 14 - 3 = 11;\; 19 - 3x = 19 - 10\frac{1}{2} = 8\frac{1}{2};$

$\qquad 2x + 1 = 7 + 1 = 8;\; x + 7 = 3\frac{1}{2} + 7 = 10\frac{1}{2}$

4 $(4x + 7)(2x - 3) = 8x^2 - 12x + 14x - 21 = 8x^2 + 2x - 21$

5 **a** $2(3t - 2)$
    c $2ab(12b + 5)$

    b $4y(3y + 1)$
    d $3x(4x - 2y + 3y^2)$

6 **a** $(x + 4)(x - 3)$
    c $(y - 2)(y - 8)$

    b $(a + 1)(a + 7)$
    d $(x - 9)(x + 9)$

CHAPTER 16

1 **a** 5 (it occurs most often)

    b 2, 3, 4, 4, 5, 5, 5, 6, 7, ⑦, ⑧, 9, 9, 10, 10, 11, 12, 12, 13, 14

$\qquad \text{Median} = \dfrac{7 + 8}{2} = 7.5$

    c Sum of all data $= 156$

$\qquad \text{Mean} = 156 \div 20 = 7.8$

2 **a** $7 + 11 + 7 + 2 + 3 = 30$

 b $0 \times 7 + 1 \times 11 + 2 \times 7 + 3 \times 2 + 4 \times 3 = 0 + 11 + 14 + 6 + 12 = 43$
 $43 \div 30 = 1.43$ (3 sf)

 c 1 goal

3 **a** $256 + 328 + 156 + 208 + 297 = 1245$; $1245 \div 5 = 249$

 b $6 \times 259 = 1554$; $1554 - 1245 = 309$

4 **a** $38 + 29 + 47 + 39 + 46 + 45 = 244$; $244 \div 6 = 40.7$ (3 sf)

 b range $= 47 - 29 = 18$

 c The boys' scores were higher on average but were less consistent as shown by their higher value for the range.

5 **a**

Amount, A (£)	Mid-point	Number of families	
$0 < A \le 10$	5	6	$5 \times 6 = 30$
$10 < A \le 20$	15	14	$15 \times 14 = 210$
$20 < A \le 30$	25	22	$25 \times 22 = 550$
$30 < A \le 40$	35	17	$35 \times 17 = 595$
$40 < A \le 50$	45	8	$45 \times 8 = 360$
Total		67	1745

 b $1745 \div 67 = £26.04$ to nearest penny.

 c Because the actual data is not used, and the mid-points have been used to represent the data.

 d $20 < A \le 30$

6 **a, c, d**

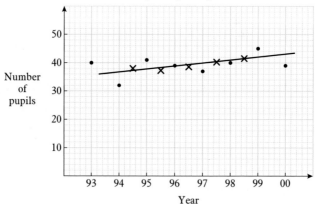

Pupils at primary school

 b $40 + 32 + 41 + 39 = 152$; $152 \div 4 = 38$ Plot this between 94 and 95.
 $32 + 41 + 39 + 37 = 149$; $149 \div 4 = 37.25$ Plot this between 95 and 96.
 $41 + 39 + 37 + 40 = 157$; $157 \div 4 = 39.25$ Plot this between 96 and 97.
 $39 + 37 + 40 + 45 = 161$; $161 \div 4 = 40.25$ Plot this between 97 and 98.
 $37 + 40 + 45 + 44 = 166$; $166 \div 4 = 41.5$ Plot this between 98 and 99.

 e The year 2001 is outside the range of the article. The numbers in the school could suddenly drop if a larger group of pupils than normal leave.

CHAPTER 17

1 **a** diameter = 2 × radius = 2 × 16 = 32 cm
circumference = π × diameter
$$= \pi \times 32 = 100.53 \dots \text{ cm}$$
$$= 101 \text{ cm (3 sf)}$$

b 4 km = 4000 m = 400 000 cm.
Number of revolutions = 400 000 ÷ 100.53 … = 3978.91 …
Number of **complete** revolutions = 3978

2 Circumference = π × 16 = 50.265 …
arc = circumference ÷ 4 = 50.265 … ÷ 4 = 12.566 … = 12.6 cm (3 sf)
Perimeter = 8 + 8 + 12.6
$$= 28.6 \text{ cm (3 sf)}$$

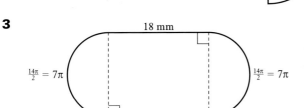

3

Circumference of circle = π × 14 = 14π
Circumference of half circle = 14π ÷ 2 = 7π
Perimeter = 7π + 18 + 7π + 18 = 14π + 36 mm

4 **a** 4.7 cm   **d** 4 × 3 = 12 feet
   b 720 cm   **e** 7 × 1760 = 12 320 yards
   c 36 ÷ 12 = 3 feet   **f** 6.5 × 3 = 19.5 feet = 19.5 × 12 = 234 inches

5 **a** 1 foot = 12 inches = 12 × 2.54 = 30.48 cm
   b 2 yards = 2 × 3 = 6 feet = 6 × 12 = 72 inches = 72 × 2.54 = 182.88 cm
   c 20 yards = 60 feet = 720 inches = 1828.8 cm = 18.288 m
   d 3 m = 300 cm = 300 ÷ 2.54 inches = 118 inches (3 sf)

CHAPTER 18

1 **a** 27 + 37 = 64 cm²   **b** 98 − 40 = 58 m²

2 **a** By Pythagoras' theorem
$$a^2 = 38^2 + 29^2$$
$$= 2285$$
$$a = 47.8 \text{ cm (3 sf)}$$

   b By Pythagoras' theorem
$$42^2 = b^2 + 31^2$$
$$b^2 = 42^2 - 31^2$$
$$= 803$$
$$b = 28.3 \text{ mm (3 sf)}$$

467

c By Pythagoras' theorem
$$c^2 = (\sqrt{7})^2 + (\sqrt{18})^2$$
$$= 7 + 18$$
$$= 25$$
$$c = 5 \text{ cm}$$

d By Pythagoras' theorem
$$15^2 = d^2 + 8^2$$
$$d^2 = 15^2 - 8^2$$
$$= 161$$
$$d = 12.7 \text{ cm (3 sf)}$$

3 **a** 5 because $3^2 + 4^2 = 5^2$
    b 24 because $7^2 + 24^2 = 25^2$

c 5 because $5^2 + 12^2 = 13^2$
d 15 because $8^2 + 15^2 = 17^2$

4 $OR^2 = 4^2 + 3^2$
     $= 25$
    $OR = 5$

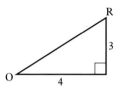

5 $PQ^2 = 5^2 + 10^2$
      $= 125$
   $PQ = 11.2 \text{ (3 sf)}$

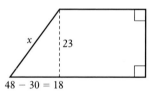

15 − 5 = 10

7 − 2 = 5

6 $x^2 = 18^2 + 23^2$
     $= 853$
    $x = 29.2 \text{ cm (3 sf)}$

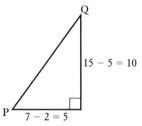

48 − 30 = 18

7 $d^2 = 62^2 + 47^2$
     $= 6053$
   $d = 77.8 \text{ nautical miles (3 sf)}$

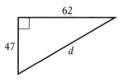

8

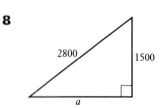

$$2800^2 = a^2 + 1500^2$$
$$a^2 = 2800^2 - 1500^2$$
$$= 5\,590\,000$$
$$a = 2364.318 \ldots$$
$$= 2360 \text{ m (3 sf)}$$

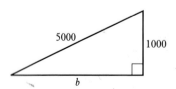

$$5000^2 = b^2 + 1000^2$$
$$b^2 = 5000^2 - 1000^2$$
$$= 24\,000\,000$$
$$b = 4898.979 \ldots$$
$$= 4900 \text{ m (3 sf)}$$

Horizontal distance $= 2360 + 4900$
$$= 7260 \text{ m (3 sf)}$$